OSMOTIC REGULATION
IN
AQUATIC ANIMALS

OSMOTIC REGULATION
IN
AQUATIC ANIMALS

by AUGUST KROGH

Late Professor of Zoo-Physiology in the University of Copenhagen

DOVER PUBLICATIONS, INC., NEW YORK

Published in Canada by General Publishing Company, Ltd., 30 Lesmill Road, Don Mills, Toronto, Ontario.

Published in the United Kingdom by Constable and Company, Ltd., 10 Orange Street, London W. C. 2.

This Dover edition, first published in 1965, is an unabridged and unaltered republication of the work first published by the Cambridge University Press in 1939. This work is reprinted by permission of the Cambridge University Press.

The publisher is grateful to the Director of The Ohio State University Libraries for making a copy of this book available for reproduction purposes.

Library of Congress Catalog Card Number: 65-25703

Manufactured in the United States of America

Dover Publications, Inc.
180 Varick Street
New York, N. Y. 10014

24884

CONTENTS

PREFACE

The first stimulus to reactivate a long dormant interest in problems of osmoregulation was given me in 1930 by a casual conversation with a man dealing in live eels who mentioned certain changes in these animals when transferred from sea water to fresh water.

When Dr A. Keys was asked to study these changes he found it necessary to work out his perfusion technique and discovered the secretion of chloride taking place in the gills.

I lectured on the general subject in the spring of 1935 and was asked to publish these lectures, but too many points seemed obscure and we have since been busy in the laboratory trying to elucidate some of these. Although new material keeps pouring in I venture to believe that a stocktaking and general review is opportune at the present moment. I have not attempted to give a complete review of the literature. Many more papers have been consulted than appear in the list of references and doubtless a number have been overlooked. My aim has been to present the essential features of the problem and to direct attention to points about which information is highly desirable. A small number of observations made in this laboratory are published here for the first time.

The scope of the book is somewhat wider than indicated by the title including as far as possible the concentration and regulation of single ions both in the organism as a whole and in cells.

I wish to record my debt of gratitude to the friends and collaborators who have helped me with suggestions and criticisms and especially to Dr K. Berg of the Laboratory for Fresh-water Biology, Hillerød, Dr Henri Koch of the University of Louvain and Mr E. Zeuthen of this laboratory.

AUGUST KROGH

COPENHAGEN
January 1939

OSMOTIC REGULATION
IN AQUATIC ANIMALS

INTRODUCTION AND DEFINITIONS

The building unit of living organisms, the cell, can as a very crude first approximation be described from the point of view of osmotic conditions as a solution contained within a membrane. Surrounding the cells in multicellular animals we have similar solutions contained within the cellular integument and constituting the "internal environment" of the cells. With insoluble constituents of the organism we are not here concerned. The "solvent" is always water which is present in very variable proportion, from over 99 to less than 50 % of the total mass of solution.

Going a step further we can distinguish between dissolved particles which are of the same order of size as the water molecules and move at similar rates and the much larger colloidal particles, in the organisms almost always of a protein nature, which are in comparison practically immobile. The small particles + the amount of water in which they are free to move is often called the "continuous phase" and distinguished from the "disperse phase" constituted by the colloidal particles and the "bound" water. The question of bound water is rather controversial, but in most cases the quantity seems to be small, so that we can consider practically all the water present as solvent water.

In the present monograph interest centres upon the relations between the concentrations of solutions, inside and outside cells and organisms. The "total concentration" is given by the number of particles present in a litre of solution or in a kilogram of water. It is expressed in moles, and 1 mole of any substance, the number of grams corresponding to the molecular weight, means 6×10^{23} ultimate particles. A solution containing 1 mole of particles, irrespective of their chemical nature, per litre is called a "molar solution", and a solution containing 1 mole per kg. water is called a "molal solution". In fairly dilute solutions like the water in nature and the body fluids of many animals there is no significant difference between concentrations expressed by molarity or molality and we shall not treat it seriously; but in more concentrated solutions, like the blood of higher animals and the content of most cells, the distinction becomes important, mainly because the colloidal particles make up a large fraction of the mass, but, on account of their relatively enormous size, only a small fraction of the number of dissolved particles. In such cases we express the concentration of substances in true solution by their molality, assuming as the solvent the quantity of water which is expressed by the difference between fresh weight and weight of dry substance. No account is taken of the possible presence of bound water.

Very important physical properties of solutions are quantitatively dependent upon their total (molal) concentration. The one in which we are mainly interested is the "osmotic pressure" which is usually defined by means of the properties of a membrane called "semi-permeable", which will allow water molecules to pass through, but will hold back all dissolved substances. If a solution is enclosed in rigid, semipermeable walls and surrounded by pure water the inside pressure will attain the value of 22·4 atmospheres per mole held in solution by 1 kg. of water. At this pressure equilibrium is established between the quantity of water "attracted" by the dissolved molecules inside and the water filtering out by reason of the "hydrostatic pressure" inside. When the outside fluid is not pure water, but a solution, the pressure developed will be proportional to the concentration difference, and when the concentrations are made equal there will be no pressure.

It is deeply significant that the conception of osmotic pressure was introduced by a physiologist studying plants (Pfeffer, 1877), who also succeeded in constructing osmometers with semi-permeable membranes and establishing experimentally the relation between concentration and osmotic pressure. The plant cells are natural osmometers having a rigid wall of cellulose supporting a protoplast which is practically semipermeable and contains in many cases one large vacuole. The concentration of the cell sap sets up by attraction of water a hydrostatic pressure generally of many atmospheres and responsible for the turgor of plant tissues. When such cells are tested by means of solutions of increasing strength, a concentration can be found which will reduce the inside pressure to 0 and cause the protoplast just visibly to recede from the cellulose wall, and this concentration is a measure of the concentration within the cell. A further increase in outside concentration brings about a definite shrinkage of the protoplast.

In animal cells there is, with few exceptions, no mechanically supporting structures, and only a very slight hydrostatic pressure, amounting to some centimetres of water, can be borne by the protoplasmic membrane. When such cells are at all permeable to water (and impermeable to solutes) it is a necessary consequence that the concentration must be the same inside as outside, and when the outside concentration is lowered water must flow in and dilute the content, until equilibrium is restored by swelling. Shrinkage must take place for the same reasons when the outside concentration is raised above the inside. A number of exceptions to this general rule will be discussed in the following.

To measure osmotic pressures of solutions, whether artificial or obtained from organisms, directly by means of semipermeable membranes in artificial osmometers is a very difficult proposition. In some cases determinations can be made by swelling or shrinkage experiments on the animal cells themselves, but in most cases indirect methods have to be applied. These take advantage of one or other of two facts.

The water in a solution freezes at a lower temperature than pure water, and the freezing-point depression Δ is at fairly low concentrations directly proportional to the total concentration, a molal solution freezing at $-1 \cdot 86^{\circ}$ C. Determinations of freezing-point depressions are theoretically very simple, but where biological fluids are concerned there are several difficulties, referred to in the Appendix on methods.

The water in a solution has a lower vapour tension than pure water. The difference in vapour tension is very small and a direct measure is generally not feasible, but comparisons can be made with known solutions according to two different principles. One utilizes the fact that when two solutions of different concentration are placed side by side the more dilute will evaporate at a more rapid rate and therefore have a lower temperature, which difference can be measured by a suitable thermocouple (Appendix, p. 211). Measurements according to this method can be carried out in a short time. In the other method changes in volume are used, since water will be transferred as vapour from a more dilute to a more concentrated solution. This transfer is so slow that ordinarily measurements will require 24 hr. or more.

While the freezing-point determinations yield absolute values, the vapour-pressure determinations are always carried out as comparisons with known solutions, and it has become customary in biology to use solutions of NaCl for the purpose and to express concentrations by the osmotically equivalent NaCl concentration.

NaCl as a reference substance has certain drawbacks. As an electrolyte it is in dilute solutions completely dissociated into the ions Na^+ and Cl^-, and each molecule should act as two separate particles, but the observed osmotic activity is somewhat lower and the reduction depends to a certain extent upon the concentration, being larger in more concentrated solutions. This will affect the recalculation of freezing-point depressions into molar concentrations. I have on the whole disregarded the concentration factor and used the relation 0·293 mole Cl (or Na) = 1·00° freezing-point depression as giving a sufficient accuracy for the problems here under discussion.

By determinations of total concentrations we can find out whether the internal medium of an organism is in osmotic equilibrium or not with the external medium and with the continuous phase within cells, and, when differences are found, we can draw certain inferences regarding the movement of water from one solution to another, but in a large number of cases we are also interested in the distribution of single dissolved substances, and the concentrations of these must be expressed also by moles when different neutral or charged particles (ions) are to be compared. As the mole unit is inconveniently large for our purposes I use throughout as unit of concentration the millimole (designated mM.). A 1 mM. solution of NaCl means a solution containing 1 mM. of $Na^+ + 1$ mM. of Cl^- per litre and a 1 mM. solution of Na_2SO_4 contains 2 mM. of Na^+ and 1 mM. of $SO_4^=$ per litre. The atomic weights by which the weight units used in many papers are converted into mM. units are Na 23·0 mg., K 39·1 mg., Ca 40·1 mg., Mg 24·3 mg., Cl 35·45 mg., S 32·1 mg. and P 31·0 mg. When no misunderstanding is possible quantities of substances are also given in molar units, and it has been found convenient generally to use the micromole (designated μM.) as the unit. 1μM. of sodium means 23 micrograms (γ).

We have to deal in the organism only with neutral solutions in which the kations and anions balance each other practically completely. It has been found convenient, though undeniably inconsistent, to denote the total concentrations of ions by the sum of either kations or anions, although of course the real concentration is double this figure and the osmotically effective concentration somewhat less than double.

Osmotic flow of water. As referred to above any difference in total concentration across a semipermeable membrane will cause a flow of water through the membrane, and it is possible and desirable in several cases to express quantitatively the permeability of such membranes. This can be done by measuring the rate at which water will penetrate under pressure, whether osmotic or hydrostatic. The rate is evidently proportional to the pressure difference between the two sides of the membrane and the area exposed, and inversely proportional to its thickness. In biology we have to disregard the term "thickness" which can in most cases not even be defined, and it has become customary for artificial membranes used in ultrafiltration experiments to express permeability by the minute number which, being inversely proportional to the rate of water penetration, is the time necessary for 1 cubic centimetre (cm.^{3}) to pass through 1 square centimetre (cm.^{2}) of membrane by a pressure difference of 1 atm. This time is for filters which will retain bacteria less than 1 min. and for collodion membranes which will filter off practically all colloids of the order of 100 min. For the animal membranes with which we have to deal the time varies from a few days (of 1440 min.) to a few years.

Absolutely semipermeable membranes in the sense defined above probably do not exist at all. Organic membranes which are found impermeable to water are somewhat permeable to gases like O_2 and CO_2, and it is the rule for membranes having "minute numbers" of a few days or weeks to be slightly permeable at least for certain ions. The permeability to organic substances is in many cases not related at all to the permeability to water. The water permeability of an organic membrane is not an invariable quantity. It usually changes with time, and it is often highly dependent upon the nature of the solutions bathing its surfaces. Many examples, illustrating this point, will be given in the following.

Diffusion of solutes. When two solutions containing the same substance in different concentrations are separated by a membrane permeable to that substance, diffusion will take place from the solution having the higher concentration towards the solution with the lower and go on until the concentrations shall have become equal.* Several substances may diffuse simultaneously and even in opposite directions, and the exchange by diffusion is also largely independent of osmotic differences in total concentration, although of course diffusion against a flow of water is retarded. For electro-neutral substances like urea or glucose the exchange by diffusion is theoretically a simple affair. For charged particles conditions are more complicated. Suppose we have on the two sides of a membrane permeable to kations, but not to anions, equal concentrations of NaCl and KCl respectively, an exchange of Na with K will take place, but the rate will be governed by that ion (Na) which diffuses most slowly, because a more rapid transfer of K ions would set up electrostatic forces sufficient to keep back the fast-moving ions until they could be exchanged in equal amounts with Na ions. Suppose again that we had KCl and $CaCl_2$ respectively, and that the membrane was permeable to K^+ but not to Ca^{++}, then no diffusion could take place. If, however, hydrogen ions or ammonium ions were produced on the side of the Ca^{++}, these would pass out in exchange with K^+. Because of the complications briefly referred to, because of difficulties in defining and reproducing the properties of living membranes and also for technical reasons, measurements of diffusion rates for ions through living membranes

* This does not hold absolutely when other substances are present which do not pass the membrane. In such a case, as for instance between a solution containing protein and an "ultrafiltrate" from the same, there will be slight differences in concentration of single ions and we speak of a "Donnan" equilibrium between the two solutions. We can, in almost all cases, afford to disregard differences caused by Donnan equilibria.

are completely lacking, and the most that can be done is to arrange ions in the order of their rate of penetration through a definite membrane.

In recent years "heavy water", D_2O, has been utilized for the study of permeability. D_2O in ordinary water on one side of a membrane will diffuse like any other dissolved substance, and it is comparatively easy to measure the rate of diffusion. It is necessary to point out, however, that it is not possible to figure out the rate of osmotic water transport from diffusion experiments with D_2O. According to Jacobs (1935, p. 79) the two processes are of a different nature. When, however, a membrane is found to be impermeable to D_2O it is legitimate to conclude that it is also water impermeable, and very large differences in the diffusion rates for D_2O will indicate at least a difference, going in the same direction, in the rate of osmosis.

Active transport of substances across membranes. In living organisms concentration differences can be maintained in spite of the permeability of membranes, such as is the case in all water-permeable organisms living in fresh water and keeping up at an approximately constant level a much higher total concentration than that of the surrounding water. This can be done only by the steady expenditure of energy in special mechanisms adapted for the purpose. In such a case there is no equilibrium between the internal and external medium, but we use the word "steady state" to characterize the situation.

The main object of this book is to describe the osmotic and ionic steady states encountered in aquatic animals, to locate the mechanisms by which they are maintained, and to describe, as far as that is found possible, their mode of working. Such description is in the present state of affairs very incomplete.

With regard to cells I have stated above the general rule that they are in osmotic equilibrium with their surroundings. The concentrations of single ions in the cell water are, however, in almost all cases widely divergent from the outside concentrations. We have in the body fluids of most animals a great excess of Na^+ and Cl^- over all other ions. K^+ makes up a few per cent, at most, of the total kations and $HPO_4^=$ an infinitesimal fraction of the anions, but the state inside the cells is often completely reversed, K^+ and $HPO_4^=$ being in excess, and generally greatly, of all other ions present. We have, therefore, an ionic steady state along with osmotic equilibrium.

The body fluids which make up the environment of most of the cells in multicellular organisms are themselves separated from the external medium by membranes which are usually cellular, and the cells of which are bathed on the inside by body fluid, on the outside by the external medium. When there is osmotic equilibrium between the external and internal medium, and when this latter follows passively concentration changes in the external, we designate the animal in question as "poikilosmotic". A very large number of marine invertebrates are not only poikilosmotic, but the ionic composition of their body fluids shows only insignificant deviations from that of the sea water surrounding them. Certain other marine animals are poikilosmotic, but the ionic composition of their body fluids shows definite deviations from that of the surrounding sea water.

When animals maintain a total concentration of their body fluids different from that of the surrounding water they can be termed "homoiosmotic", when it is remembered that there are all possible transitions between complete independence of the internal concentrations from that of the external and the poikilosmotic state. Fresh-water animals are, in this broader sense, without exception homoiosmotic.

The term "stenohaline" is used for animals which can live only within a limited range of outside concentrations, while "euryhaline" forms can live over a wide range—either by toleration, when they are poikilosmotic, or by regulation of the internal concentration.

It has been attempted to arrange the material presented on the following pages according to the physiological viewpoints sketched above, but the task proved too difficult. The solutions of osmotic problems actually encountered in nature were too diverse to fit into any "rational" scheme, and the simple plan had to be adopted of presenting results within the frame of the zoological system. This arrangement at least brings out one fact which it is important to keep in mind, viz. that our knowledge is extremely meagre and fragmentary and that it may well be possible to find animals better suited as objects for the solution of special problems than the few species hitherto experimented on.

The material is accordingly divided into chapters corresponding to the major systematic groups of the animal kingdom. A special chapter is devoted to the osmotic conditions in eggs and embryos.

In a final chapter the whole of the material is reviewed, and certain general conclusions presented, with suggestions concerning the most useful lines of future work.

In an Appendix a selection of methods used and proposed in the study of osmotic and ionic regulation are briefly described and commented on.

PROTOZOA

In the phylum Protozoa we are confronted with the major problems of osmotic regulation, but while we find that the tiny organisms have solved these problems for themselves, our task of getting an insight into the solutions is made exceedingly difficult by the very minuteness of the mechanisms concerned.

Among the Protozoa certain forms are morphologically simple and can be considered as primitive, but others possess highly complicated structures and must have been evolved from a long line of ancestors showing increasing complexity. In all the larger groups we have both marine and fresh-water forms, and genera adapted to the peculiar conditions of a parasitic existence are also quite common. The minute size involves an extremely large surface per unit volume. To illustrate this very important point let us calculate the surface per cm.^{3} of cubes of 0·001, 1 and 1000 cm. Such cubes have volumes of 10^{-9}, 1 and 10^9 cm.^{3}, and surfaces of 6×10^{-6}, 6 and 6×10^6 cm.^{2} The surface per cm.^{3} is therefore respectively 6000, 6 and 0·006 cm.^{2}, and we have generally that when linear dimensions are reduced or increased the surface areas per unit volume will change in the inverse ratio.

In the Metazoa we distinguish between the internal environment immediately in contact with the cells and the external in contact only with the body surface. In this sense there is no internal medium for the Protozoa, the cells being directly exposed to any variation in the external medium. We are concerned here primarily with variations in the molar and ionic composition of the medium, but with other variations only in so far as they result in modified reactions on the part of the organisms to the ionic or osmotic environment. Certain organisms, both among Protozoa and among Metazoa, are extremely sensitive to changes in the environment, while others will stand large variations, and in this latter case the power of endurance may lie either in a power of toleration or in a power of resistance or in both.

It is important to note that the plasma membrane of Protozoa shows very little power of resistance against hydrostatic pressure. In the case of the heterotrichous ciliate *Spirostomum ambiguum*, Picken (1936) measured the internal hydrostatic pressure to about 4 cm. water.

Even in forms possessing an exoskeleton or shell no significant internal pressure can develop because of the openings in the shell. When the plasma membrane is permeable to water the equality of external and internal hydrostatic pressure means either an identical molal concentration of solutions on both sides of the membrane or else an active transport of water from the more concentrated to the less concentrated solution to compensate the osmotic flow in the opposite direction.

MARINE PROTOZOA. Certain large groups of Protozoa, like the Radiolaria and Foraminifera, have representatives only in the sea, and several others are found mainly in sea water.

Many of the marine Protozoa have calcareous or siliceous shells or skeletons and are distinctly heavier than sea water, but naked forms are also as a rule slightly heavier than sea water and all must be assumed to be osmotically in equilibrium with the water.

At least one form, *Noctiluca miliaris*, is, however, definitely lighter than sea water, and this fact, together with its well-known power of emitting flashes of light on stimulation, has made it the object of several interesting investigations. The anatomy was carefully studied by Pratje (1921), from whom Fig. 1 is taken. The protoplasm is made up by one main mass connected by numerous strands to a thin layer of ectoplasm from which the pellicle is produced by secretion. The large spaces between the protoplasmic strands are filled with a clear colourless liquid.

An excellent study of *Noctiluca* was made in 1892 by Goethard and Heinsius and published as a report to the Dutch Minister of the Interior in the *Staatscourant*. Since this report is difficult of access I have obtained a photostatic copy through the courtesy of the "Rijksuitgeverij" and Dr J. Verwey, and a very full abstract is given below.

The authors determined the specific gravity of *Noctiluca* taken from water with a specific gravity of 1·024 and found that the animals would just float in diluted sea water at 1·014. This would only last for a short time however, and they would begin to rise again almost at once until a specific gravity of 1·008 was reached.

When *Noctilucas* were allowed to rise through successive layers of sea water of decreasing concentration the rate of rise was observed to decrease very slightly, the volume visibly increasing at the transition to each new layer until they would finally burst and begin to sink at concentrations varying between 1·007 and 1·012. The authors rightly conclude that *Noctiluca* is in osmotic equili-

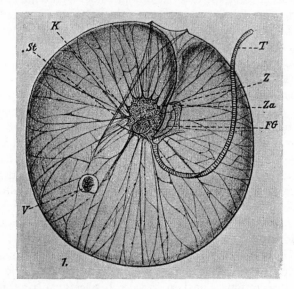

Fig. 1. *Noctiluca miliaris*, ×100. *T*, tentacle; *V*, food vacuole; *Za*, central plasmatic mass; *K*, nucleus. (Pratje.)

brium with the surrounding water and that the sap must contain an osmotically active substance of definitely lower specific gravity than NaCl. Only a small number of substances are known which could be isosmotic with sea water and possess a lower specific gravity, and of these NH_4Cl is the most likely to occur.

Noctiluca is found to sink in (isotonic) solutions of NH_4Cl, but just to float on an average in a solution containing 0·8 % NH_4Cl and 2·9 % NaCl.

By testing with Nessler reagent the authors finally proved the presence of ammonia in the cell sap which also gave the Cl reaction with silver nitrate. Tests for sulphate were negative. By sublimation of the cells they obtained typical crystals of NH_4Cl on which they could also obtain the reactions. They did not, however, succeed in preparing $(NH_4)_2PtCl_6$. The paper also contains remarks on the morphology and the statement that the outer membrane (which according to Pratje is of protein character and can be thrown off on mechanical stimulation) does not dissolve in boiling KOH and is therefore possibly chitinous.

The significance of this old paper can scarcely be overestimated. The experiments show conclusively (1) that the cell wall is water permeable, (2) that the cell will rapidly come into osmotic equilibrium with the surrounding solutions down to the point where osmotic uptake of water causes disruption of the wall, and finally, (3) that the ionic composition of the sap is entirely different from that of the surrounding water, a characteristic of living cells which is quite general, but has only in recent years become generally appreciated.

The later studies upon *Noctiluca* (E. B. Harvey, 1917; Ludwig, 1928; Gross, 1934) have confirmed the fact of the lower specific gravity of *Noctiluca* compared with the sea water, but assume erroneously that this may be due to hypotonicity of the cell sap. Gross, however, brought out the important fact that the sap is acid (pH 3 or even lower). In a neutral solution NH_3 would be present largely as free ammonia which would probably diffuse out. By the pH found by Gross ammonium ions (NH_4^+) are practically exclusively present, and this is, I believe, the reason why the ammonia can be retained. A slight loss will probably take place which is made good by the breakdown of food from which all the ammonia must ultimately be derived.

E. B. Harvey showed that lack of oxygen, brought about either directly or by poisoning with cyanide, prevents the light reactions of *Noctiluca*, but has no influence upon the specific gravity or volume. This speaks strongly against any active process being responsible for the low specific gravity, and in so far confirms the work of Goethard and Heinsius. Although the main problem can be taken as solved renewed experimentation on *Noctiluca*, using modern methods of microchemical analysis, would probably throw further light upon the osmotic behaviour of this interesting organism.

THE FRESH-WATER PROTOZOA* possess a plasma membrane which is (in all cases investigated) permeable to water, but impermeable or very slightly permeable to ions or organic substances like sugars. This can be shown by placing the organisms in more concentrated solutions which will cause them to shrink. Mast and Fowler (1935) have developed a technique allowing fairly accurate volume measurements on *Amoeba* by sucking them into a narrow capillary of known diameter and measuring their length. Repeated determinations on the same individuals of *A. proteus* in a "normal" medium of 2 mM. concentration gave results with a mean error of about 5 %. When lactose was added to the medium to a concentration of 200 mM., the volumes decreased gradually and were after 105 min. on an average only 53 ± 1 % of the original. In 50 mM. lactose the shrinkage was extremely slow and reached about 40 % in 7 days, when an even slower increase in volume began and reached about 10 % of the original in 3 days. It appears doubtful whether in this case the shrinkage was purely osmotic or partly due to lack of food. At any time during the process of shrinkage the change was reversible when the animals were returned to the original 1/60 Ringer. These experiments establish the fact of (almost exclusive) water permeability and fix the inside osmotic concentration to be lower, but only slightly lower, than 50 mM. of an undissociated substance like lactose.

In accordance with this result the animals must in pure water and in solutions of dissociated salts of lower concentration than 25 mM. take up water by osmosis, and a mechanism for eliminating this water must be present. There can be very little doubt that the contractile vacuole or vacuoles possessed by the vast majority of fresh-water Protozoa functions as such a mechanism. Morphologically the contractile vacuole shows considerable variation. Adolph (1926) gives the following description relating to *Amoeba*.

---

* It has not been found possible to restrict the following discussion to fresh-water forms or to arrange the animals in any systematic order.

Several small vacuoles form in various parts of the protoplasm. These gradually come into contact with one another as they are passively moved about in the streaming plasma sol and fuse together. Ultimately one becomes larger than the others and is finally embedded in the plasmagel at the posterior end of the body where it remains until it contracts and discharges into the surrounding medium. The contraction is generally sudden and complete, but fairly often a visible remnant is left and serves as a nucleus for the next contractile vacuole. In ciliate Infusoria the vacuole is a more permanent structure, but in some forms it is "vesicle fed" as in *Amoeba*, while in others "canals" present in the protoplasm take up fluid and discharge it into the vacuole, which communicates with the exterior through a permanent tubule and pore (King, 1928). A chance observation by Weatherby (1927) is worth recording. On injection of the caustic Nessler reagent into a *Paramaecium* the plasma was at once dissolved, but the wall of the contractile vacuole (like the nucleus) resisted for a brief period.

Mast describes in a very recent paper (1938) a definite membrane $0.5\,\mu$ thick surrounding the contractile vacuole in *Amoeba proteus*. Adjoining this on the outside there is usually a viscous layer containing numerous granules. Various functions have been ascribed to the contractile vacuole. It has often been taken to be an organ for the discharge of nitrogenous and other soluble waste products, but Weatherby (1927), while showing that urea is the main excretion product of *Paramaecium caudatum*, failed to find by very delicate tests any ammonia or urea in the fluid of the vacuole. This result does not of course exclude the possibility that in other Protozoa (marine forms especially) the vacuole may serve as an excretory organ. Ludwig (1928) is of opinion that the chief function of the contractile vacuole may be the excretion of CO_2, but this idea, although apparently accepted by R. Müller (1936), cannot be taken seriously, since CO_2 diffuses through all known organic membranes with the greatest ease.

In a small number of forms the osmoregulating function of the contractile vacuole has been studied in such detail that definite conclusions are possible.

Amoeba proteus was examined by Adolph in 1926. He showed that the simple record of the pulsation rate of vacuoles on which previous authors had mainly relied was insufficient, because a slowing of rate was often accompanied by an increase in final volume. He therefore combined measurements of rate and volume and calculated the rate of water elimination. From his own observations he concluded that there was no simple relation between outside osmotic concentration and rate of water elimination, but his results are vitiated by several errors in technique. The concentrated solutions employed were unbalanced and harmful to the organisms. The time of observation after changing the medium was too short, and generally no account was taken of the change in volume of the organism as a whole. Mast and Fowler, in the paper quoted above, did not measure vacuoles, but they state expressly that in all their definitely hypertonic solutions the contractile vacuole ceased to function—a fact which is in itself very significant.

R. Müller (1936) tested *A. proteus* in different concentrations of sea water and measured, like Adolph, the rate of water excretion in cubic micra per second. The animals were taken from a culture fluid of unknown concentration and transferred to various concentrations of sea water from 0 to $3\cdot3°/_{oo}$ (corresponding to 55 mM. NaCl), taking care to change the order in which the solutions were tested. His results, given graphically in Fig. 2 (p. 19), show an increase in excretion up to a concentration of $1\cdot4°/_{oo}$ salt (23 mM.), but above that point the decrease expected. In the experiments a period of about 10 min. was allowed to adapt the animals to each new solution, and thereupon five measurements were made and the average taken. It is doubtful whether a complete equilibrium was attained, and the measurements were almost certainly complicated by a change in volume of the animals. It is significant also that the excretions measured in the culture solution, which one would expect to be less concentrated than $1\cdot4°/_{oo}$ salt, were always lower than in distilled water. Müller himself takes his experiments to prove the osmoregulatory function of the contractile vacuole in *Amoeba*.

Zoothamnium hiketes, a peritrich ciliate belonging to the family of Vorticellidae, was obtained by Müller (1936) from brackish water of 12–18 $°/_{oo}$ salt concentration. It shows in constant conditions a very even rate of excretion through the contractile vacuole which is only $1\cdot1\ \mu^3$/sec. in $18\ ^o/_{oo}$ salt, but increases to 45 in $2\cdot4\ ^o/_{oo}$. In distilled water a decrease is observed which may well be due to a poisonous action of the water. In experiments with pure salts ($NaCl$, $MgCl_2$ and KCl) the rates, especially in KCl, were definitely lower than in sea water of the same concentration. When the total volume of an experimental animal is not determined, it is evidently very important that only harmless balanced solutions are employed for determinations of excretion rates.

Frontonia marina, a brackish water ciliate also studied by Müller, has given similar but rather irregular results.

Müller stresses the result that in very dilute solutions (below about $1\cdot4\ ^o/_{oo}$ salt) the rate of water excretion decreases in the animals experimented on, but, as stated above, it seems doubtful whether this observation is really significant.

Paramaecium caudatum was studied in two papers by Kamada (1935, 1936), who finds first that when an animal is placed in a more concentrated solution the rate of discharge of the contractile vacuole will show a steady decrease lasting some 10–20 min. and approaching a minimum which will be the lower the more concentrated the solution, but after this decrease the rate will increase again, and in the course of 2–3 hr. reach a value which is nearly the same for concentrations varying between $0\cdot2$ and 20 mM. NaCl. Kamada rightly concludes that *Paramaecium* cannot be truly homoiosmotic. The inside concentration must increase slowly with increasing concentration of the medium, a point which was also brought out in the experiments of Mast, although with *Amoeba* and sugar the reaction was much slower.

In the second paper it is concluded by a reasoning which is perhaps somewhat hypothetical that a *Paramaecium* adapted to a very dilute solution has an inside concentration corresponding to $M/40$ NaCl (25 mM.), while if the outside fluid is raised to this concentration the inside will rise to $M/32$ (31 mM.). Picken's (1936) determinations of vapour pressure on the heterotrich ciliate *Spirostomum ambiguum* gave a value of about 25 mM. NaCl.

Interesting experiments on *Paramaecium caudatum* were made by Tchakotine (1935). By means of his radiation-puncture technique he damaged one contractile vacuole in specimens containing two. He explains how this "remained extremely swollen", while the other increased its rhythm and could keep the animal almost normal. After 20–24 hr. the damaged vacuole often recovered. When both vacuoles were damaged in this way they would both remain enormously increased in size, and swelling and disintegration of the protoplasm would generally take place. In a few cases vacuoles were formed *de novo* from parts of the canals beginning to pulsate and acquiring an excretion pore. It is unfortunate that the description fails regarding the very interesting point whether the damaged vacuole goes on taking up water from the protoplasm after its power of evacuation has become abolished.

Peritrich ciliates were studied by Kitching (1934, 1936, 1938) in papers which give the most complete and clear-cut evidence so far on osmotic regulation by means of the contractile vacuole. Kitching used sessile organisms of a simple form, allowing the body volume to be calculated from a few measurements and showing also a remarkable constancy of vacuolar volume. He examined one freshwater form, *Rhabdostyla brevipes*, and also *Vorticella marina*, two species of *Zoothamnium* and three of *Cothurnia* which are all marine. While under observation the animals were kept in a continuous flow of fluid at a constant temperature and a pH varying only between 7·9 and 8·2. The fluids used were mixtures of tap water with sea water. The tap water is here taken to have a concentration of 1 mM., the sea water of 560. I reproduce in Table I a few measurements.

It is worthy of note that at a concentration of 68 mM. the vacuole of *Rhabdostyla* practically stops beating, and the concentration cannot therefore be far from that inside the cell.

In several experiments on *Cothurnia* there was a marked falling off in the rate of output after the animal had been for some time in dilute sea water, and at the same time the volume of the animal decreased as shown in Fig. 4. It is significant that such animals when returned to normal sea water had their volume reduced. A normal experiment on *Zoothamnium* is illustrated in Fig. 3.

The curve (Fig. 5) shows the relation between body volume and concentration of sea water in medium for two marine forms. The

Table I

Concentration of sea water in medium %	Concentration mM.	Mean rate of output in μ^3 per sec.	Volume of organism in $1000\,\mu^3$	Duration of treatment in min.
		Rhabdostyla brevipes (fresh water)		
0	1	$17\cdot2 \pm 0\cdot9$	—	15
4	24	$10\cdot1 \pm 0\cdot6$	—	44
0	1	$16\cdot9 \pm 1\cdot0$	—	25
0	1	$10\cdot2 \pm 0\cdot7$	—	25
12	68	$0\cdot28 \pm 0\cdot02$	—	184
0	1	$10\cdot0 \pm 0\cdot6$	—	56
		Cothurnia curvula (marine)		
100	560	$0\cdot96 \pm 0\cdot13$	$20\cdot7$	44
40	235	$18\cdot3 \pm 0\cdot4$	$33\cdot4$	34
100	—	$1\cdot14 \pm 0\cdot14$	$20\cdot0$	201
		Zoothamnium niveum (marine)		
100	560	$10\cdot4 \pm 0\cdot5$	$241\cdot5$	50
$12\frac{1}{2}$	70	$167\cdot3 \pm 12\cdot2$	$487\cdot5$	36
100	—	$10\cdot0 \pm 1\cdot5$	—	60

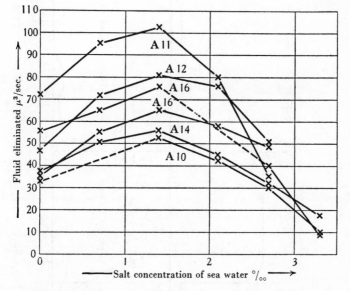

Fig. 2. Relation between excretion through contractile vacuole in μ^3/sec. and sea-water concentration in five specimens of *Amoeba proteus*. (R. Müller.)

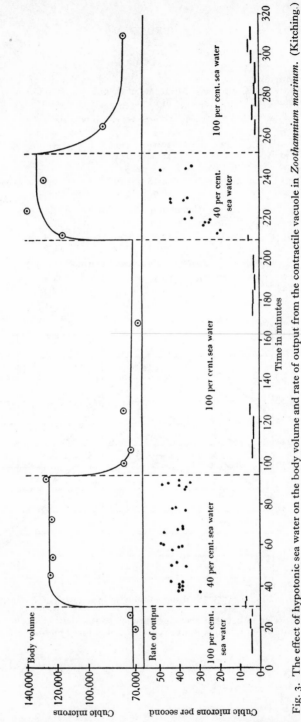

Fig. 3. The effect of hypotonic sea water on the body volume and rate of output from the contractile vacuole in *Zoothamnium marinum*. (Kitching.)

volume increases more slowly than the dilution, being about 1·5 when the concentration is reduced to ½, and from 25 % downwards the volume becomes constant. Kitching points out that all these results are consistent only with the assumption that the contractile vacuole discharges in all cases almost pure water and must there-

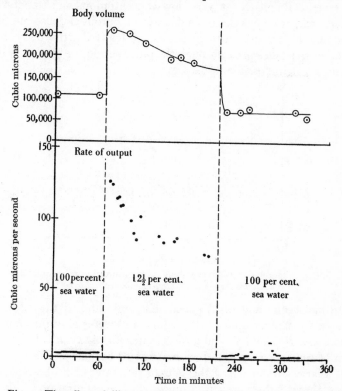

Fig. 4. The effect of dilute sea water on the body volume and rate of output from *Cothurnia curvula*. (Kitching.)

fore require the expenditure of energy to become filled up and emptied. In the marine forms the results also make it necessary to assume that the plasma membrane of the body is nearly or completely impermeable to salts, and that the osmotic concentration of the inside fluid is slightly higher than that of sea water. When transferred to dilute sea water these organisms swell by osmotic

uptake of water, and down to concentrations of about 75 % sea
water (420 mM.) such swelling is scarcely if at all counteracted by
an increased output from the vacuole, but below that the swelling is
reduced and a steady state maintained by an increase in the output.
A maximum increase of 70–80 times that in sea water has been
observed. Regularly at very low concentrations and sometimes
(*Cothurnia*) at higher there is a decrease in output and also in body
volume which must mean that salts are lost from the body, but
whether this takes place through the outer surface or by way of the
vacuole it is impossible to decide.

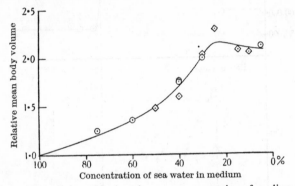

Fig. 5. The relation of body volume to concentration of medium for
Zoothamnium ⊙ and *Cothurnia* ◇. (Kitching.)

In his second and third papers Kitching studied the effect of
foreign substances upon body volume and water excretion rate in
Cothurnia, *Rhabdostyla* and a fresh-water *Zoothamnium*. The addition of cane sugar, glycerol or urea caused shrinkage of the body,
and a large proportion of the salts of sea water could be replaced
with these substances in equiosmotic concentration without
causing any change. These results confirm the relative impermeability of the surface to salts and extend the result to the substances
studied. It is specially significant that the surface is almost impermeable even to urea.

Of the experiments with "narcotics" those with cyanide are the
most instructive. Cyanide in suitable concentration (10^{-5} to
$10^{-2} M$) will reduce considerably the activity of the contractile

vacuole, and this effect is completely and almost instantaneously reversible when the organisms are returned to cyanide-free water. A marine peritrich which has been in dilute sea water for a sufficient time to establish a constant rate of water excretion and a constant body volume will begin to swell when cyanide is applied and the rate of excretion reduced, and on recovery after treatment for half an hour the excretion rate will at first be greatly increased and the body volume reduced in consequence even below that observed before.

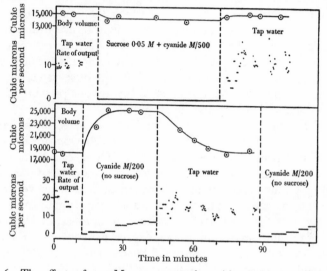

Fig. 6. The effects of 50 mM. sucrose together with cyanide (above) and of cyanide alone (below) on body volume and rate of output in *Zoothamnium* sp. from fresh water. (Kitching.)

In the fresh-water forms swelling sets in at once when cyanide is added, but can be prevented or converted into a slight shrinkage when 50 mM. sucrose is added with the cyanide. In this case the contractile vacuole stops completely, but when the body swells the vacuole will show an increasing rate of activity even in spite of a high concentration of cyanide (Fig. 6). These facts clearly demonstrate the osmoregulatory significance of the vacuole. They are consistent only with the assumption that the vacuolar fluid is practically pure water, and they show further that an increase in body volume must act as a strong stimulus for the formation and evacuation of the vacuole. Incidentally, they show that the plasma membrane must be permeable to the cyanide ion. The action of cyanide is well known to depress respiratory metabolism and thereby abolish or reduce the supply of energy. Kitching points out the desirability of experiments directly involving lack of oxygen.

The minimum amount of work theoretically necessary to separate a given volume of pure water from a solution of known concentration can easily be calculated (Kitching, 1934), but it is extremely difficult to picture a mechanism by which the separation can be effected. In the case of the vacuole one might think of the wall as being built up by the intercalation of new micellae between the first formed. If such a spherical wall is and remains permeable to water only the sphere would become filled with pure water, but the pressure on the wall would be equal to the osmotic pressure of the salt solution or about 25 atm. in sea water.

Mast and Fowler and also Kitching have calculated the permeability for water of the plasma membrane of *Amoeba*, fresh-water ciliates and marine ciliates respectively. These calculations are based upon measurements of the surface area, rates of swelling (or shrinkage), and difference in osmotic concentration between the inside and the outside solution. They cannot lay claim to any great accuracy, but their order of magnitude is significant. They are given by the authors in cubic micra of water per square micron per minute per atmosphere pressure difference. I recalculate them to minute numbers expressed in days as defined on p. 5.

$1\,\mu^3/\mu^2/\text{min.}/\text{atm.}$ corresponds to a minute number of 10,000 or 7 days. Mast and Fowler found by measuring shrinkage of *Amoeba* the permeability corresponding on an average to 270 days, and they state that swelling proceeded at an even slower rate. Kitching's results on marine ciliates correspond to minute numbers between 140 and 70 days, and for the fresh-water *Zoothamnium* the figures range from 56 to 28 days. When it is remembered that a collodion membrane just impermeable to protein has a minute number corresponding to 2 hr., the extremely low permeability of these organisms for water becomes apparent.

It is probably a significant fact that the marine ciliates studied could live for a long time in very dilute sea water and some even in fresh water as a result of the increased activity of the contractile vacuole. It would be of considerable interest to see whether over a number of generations they could become completely acclimatized.

Finley (1930) tested fifty species of fresh-water Protozoa and succeeded in adapting twenty, including *Paramaecium aurelia* and *P. caudatum*, to pure sea water, which involved a very large reduction in vacuolar pulsation rate, but Frisch (1935) did not succeed in bringing any of them above 40 % sea water.

In a paper by Herfs (1922) there are useful lists of sea-water ciliates, respectively without and with a pulsating vacuole. Several of those with a vacuole live in more or less putrid water which one would expect often to be brackish. Several of the others have a very slow rhythm, but *Cryptochilum tortum* is mentioned as having a 15 sec. rhythm.

PARASITIC PROTOZOA, living in blood or organs of higher animals, appear to be always without a contractile vacuole, while the ciliates found in the intestinal canal usually have one (or more). Herfs states that the non-ciliate Protozoa from the stomach (rumen?) of ruminants like *Entamoeba bovis, Monas communis* and others have no contractile vacuole. A special study was made by Herfs on the flagellate *Opalina ranarum* regularly found in the cloaca of frogs. This animal, which absorbs all its food through the plasma membrane, possesses no contractile vacuole. Its normal environment will usually have a fairly high osmotic pressure, but must be variable, and Herfs found that *Opalina* could be gradually transferred to fresh water and live for 8–10 days. It is therefore unlikely that no osmotic regulation should be possible, but the mechanism must differ from that of most other Protozoa. A paper by Spek (1923) confirms that *Opalina* in solutions of very different concentration can retain a constant volume. The action of different ions on the plasma membrane is discussed, but the experiments are too incomplete to allow definite conclusions with regard to osmotic regulation.

Konsuloff (1922) found in *Opalina* a richly branched system of channels or "intercommunicating vacuoles" which do not pulsate, but open to the outside through pores which are to be observed only when "excretion corpuscles" are passed out. This system appears well adapted to take care of the water elimination.

Concluding this account of the osmotic regulation in Protozoa, I feel it necessary to refer at some length to a paper by Buchthal and Péterfi (1937) who measured the electrical potential difference between the protoplasm of *Amoeba sphaeronucleus* cultivated on agar and the surrounding fluid, a solution according to Knop with a molarity of 0·05. (This solution is made up of $Ca(NO_3)_2$, KNO_3, $MgSO_4 + H_2O$ and KH_2PO_4, and contains no Na or Cl.) They introduced one unpolarizable micro-electrode into the protoplasm (in some cases into the vacuole) and put the other in contact with the medium. In about half the cases the interior of the cell was negative compared with the medium and in the other half it was positive. In both cases the average difference was about 1 mV. with variations from 0 to 1·5. The difference (in both directions) was larger in young active cells than in older ones and was clearly dependent on the metabolism since it was abolished by 0·002 M KCN.

Injections of $N/10$ KCl, which is definitely hypertonic, in a quantity corresponding to 0·05–0·2 % of the volume of the *Amoeba* increased the potential difference in the direction of positivity by 2–3 mV., with a return to the previous value in 2–3 min., and the injection of a similar quantity of distilled water brought about a negative variation of about 1 mV. lasting 1–2 min. (Figs. 7, 8). It seems probable therefore that the normal potential difference corresponds to a difference in osmotic concentration between the cell and the environment which is always very small (less than 0·05 mM.), but sometimes positive, sometimes negative. When this is taken to be the case there should be no measurable osmotic uptake of water, and the contractile vacuole when showing activity should excrete a solution also almost isotonic with the medium, but on the whole rather hypertonic, because the breakdown of food must raise the osmotic concentration. The *Amoeba* feeds on bacteria which are taken up in "food vacuoles" with a little of the medium. The potential difference between the vacuole and the medium was difficult to determine, because most often the vacuole would be destroyed by the introduction of the electrode. The authors succeeded, however, in twenty cases, and of these fourteen gave a positive difference of 0·5–2·5 mV. (average 1·5) and six a negative with an average of about 2 mV.

Other explanations of the potentials measured than concentration differences are perhaps possible, but these experiments should serve as a warning against too schematic conceptions. It seems

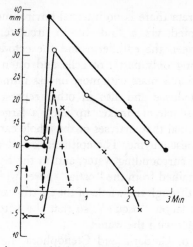

Fig. 7. Variation in potential between *Amoeba* and medium produced by injection of KCl at ↑. + - - + - - experiment on agar model. (Buchthal and Péterfi.)

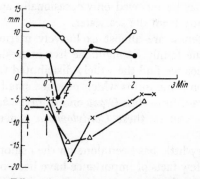

Fig. 8. Effect of water injection on potential between *Amoeba* and medium. (Buchthal and Péterfi.)

possible that the contractile vacuole may come much nearer in its function to the kidney of higher animals than is indicated by the direct studies of osmotic regulation.

COELENTERATA

In the Coelenterata there is no internal environment in the sense commonly accepted, viz. a fluid able to circulate, but there is in most cases between the entoderm and the ectoderm a "mesenchyme" consisting only partly of cells and often to a very large extent of a gelatinous mass with more or less numerous fibres. In many of the Medusae and also in other representatives of this division the mesenchyme makes up such a large proportion by weight of the animal that analyses of the whole can be taken as representing the mesenchyme. The epithelial ectoderm is directly in contact with the surrounding water, and in the Spongia a current of water is maintained from the "ostia", pores which are generally very numerous, through the whole of the gastro-vascular cavity and out through the larger "oscula", so that the entoderm is also in permanent contact with the water.

In the phyla of Cnidaria and Ctenophora the gastro-vascular cavity is open only through the mouth, and in cases where it branches into a system of canals the water contained in more remote parts may be renewed only occasionally and may possibly differ significantly from the sea water.

The Coelenterata are almost exclusively marine. Among the Spongia only the family Spongillidae live in fresh water. In the class of Hydrozoa we find the widely distributed fresh-water form *Hydra*, and even some forms which produce small free-swimming Medusae. Certain forms like *Clava* and *Cordylophora* are found in brackish water, and of these *Cordylophora* penetrates even into fresh water.

Although very little has been done on the osmotic conditions in Coelenterata a few facts of importance have been brought out. By determinations of the freezing-point depression (Fredericq, 1901; Macallum, 1903; Bottazzi, 1908) or vapour tension (Bateman, 1932) the total osmotic pressure is generally found to be equal to that of sea water, although there are occasional, rather large, discrepancies (Macallum, Bateman). These are probably due to errors.

Macallum made very careful determinations of single ionic constituents in the jelly of the Medusae *Aurelia flavidula* and *Cyanea
arctica*. He showed that the effects of varied concentrations of Na,
K and Ca in the surrounding water described by Loeb (1900) were
not due to changes in composition of the fluid within the tissues,
but to stimulation of special sense organs in the subumbrellar epithelium, and he proceeded to analyse the juices obtained in large
quantities by breaking up and kneading the specimens by hand and
straining through muslin. The solutions thus obtained were analysed together with the sea water according to Dittmar's methods,
as described in the famous memoir on sea water in the *Challenger
Reports*.

The organic material in the body of Medusae amounts to less
than 1 and most often to less than ½ %, but the ionic composition
of the solution shows definite and characteristic differences from
the outside sea water, differences which are not due to any chemical
adsorptive binding to the colloids.

The results for the water and Medusae fluids obtained at Canso
expressed in mM./litre are as follows:

Table II

	Cl^-	$SO_4^=$	Ca^{++}	Mg^{++}	K^+	Na^+	Total acid mE.	Total base mE.	Total salt g./litre
Sea water	465	23·6	8·78	45·6	8·56	400	512	517	29·8
Cyanea	474	14·1	8·68	41·95	17·62	391	502	508	29·3
Aurelia	485	15·2	9·58	45·2	12·30	404	515	526	30·0

The significant differences in these analyses are in the sulphates,
which are much less concentrated in the juice of both animals than
in the sea, and in the potassium which shows a higher concentration.
The K is highest in the form having the highest proportion of protein
and presumably the highest metabolism. It is not possible to find
out whether the differences observed are due to the salts contained
in the food (which will generally have a much higher K concentration), whether they are directly related to conditions of exchange
with the water or perhaps to some selective action on the part of the
epithelium. It is significant that in all living cells so far analysed
K is accumulated, and the accumulation appears to bear some re-

lation to the intensity of the metabolism. This point will be discussed in more detail below.

K. Hosoi (1935) studied three species of sea anemones, viz. *Cribrina* sp., *Metridium dianthus* and *Diadumene* sp., and determined the concentration of Ca^{++}. These forms have a high proportion of dry substance: *Cribrina* 24–23, average 23·7 %; *Metridium* 20·2 %; and *Diadumene* 21·3 %. When the Ca concentration is calculated in relation to the water content he finds per litre water for *Cribrina* 9·97 mM., *Metridium* 9·10 mM. and *Diadumene* 8·40 mM., while in the sea water the concentration is about 10 mM.

When put in sea water diluted to one-half the water content increases, and in 10–24 hr. reaches a constant value of a little over 140 % of the initial. After 24 hr. the Ca content is reduced to 6·63 or slightly more than corresponding to the increase in water content, but it goes on decreasing and reaches 5·03 or just about one-half the original value in 5 days. When the animals were returned to normal sea water the Ca content slowly returned to normal. Further experiments with concentrated sea water and with sea water to which an isotonic solution of $CaCl_2$ was added confirmed the conclusion that the body wall is permeable both to water and to Ca ions which, however, penetrate only slowly. This conclusion can probably be extended to other ions and to the majority of marine Coelenterata.

In certain Siphonophora special zooids (bracts or hydrophyllia) are developed which are definitely lighter than sea water and serve as floats for the whole colony. W. Jacobs (1937), who studied the problem of floating in Siphonophora, found such bracts among the Physophora in the genera *Agalma* and *Forskålia*. The bracts are gelatinous and much lighter than sea water. They break off easily and will then float at the surface. Both *Agalma* and *Forskålia* have small pneumatophores which are, however, insufficient to float the whole colony. Among the Calycophora Jacobs examined *Galeolaria quadrivalvis*, *Diphyes appendiculata* and *Hippopodius hippopus*. These are able to float without any pneumatophore, and both *Diphyes* and *Hippopodius* are able to change their weight slowly in the water so as to become in the course of $\frac{1}{2}$–1 hr. either lighter or heavier. *Galeolaria* and *Diphyes* have two very large and gelatinous nectocalyces (swimming bells). In *Galeolaria* the lower and in *Diphyes* the upper of these is lighter than sea water, and in *Galeolaria* the hydrophyllia covering each group of zooids are also definitely lighter so that the whole colony will float in a horizontal position. In *Hippopodius* all the swimming bells are gelatinous and lighter than sea water. It is obvious that all these zooids must possess special osmotic properties, but whether they possess the same molar concentration as sea water and contain salts of lower specific gravity (ammonium salts) or perhaps have a lower salt content is unknown so far, but should not be very difficult to find out.

H. W. Palmhert (1933) made some experiments and observations on the fresh-water polyps *Pelmatohydra* and *Chlorohydra* and compared them with *Clava* from brackish water. He finds that the fresh-water forms will stand addition of sea water to the medium up to concentrations of 2–2·5 $^{\circ}/_{\circ\circ}$ salt, while distilled water will kill them. *Clava* could live in sea water of 10–30 $^{\circ}/_{\circ\circ}$ concentrations. There are reasons to believe that the distilled water employed by him was directly poisonous (as is often the case (Krogh, 1937)). In the brackish water the weight of *Hydra* after 24 hr. was definitely reduced when the concentration exceeded 1·5 $^{\circ}/_{\circ\circ}$. It appears, therefore, that the osmotic concentration inside these animals must be very low (not higher than 1 $^{\circ}/_{\circ\circ}$ salt or 17 mM.). Determinations of the respiratory exchange showed no influence whatever of the concentration of the outside medium within the limits which the animals are able to stand. It is not possible to decide from these experiments whether any active regulation of osmotic pressure is in operation.

The tissues of the fresh-water Coelenterata undoubtedly have a higher osmotic concentration than the surrounding water (which corresponds generally to 2 mM. or less), and being permeable to water they must possess some mechanism for getting rid of the water entering osmotically. No organs have become known so far which could perform this necessary function.

ECHINODERMA

In the echinoderms we find a coelomic cavity of ample dimensions, at least in many echinids and Holothuria. In the textbooks I have found no reference to propulsing organs of circulation, but Kawamoto (1927) describes a fairly complete circulation in *Caudina chilensis*. The coelomic fluid contains more or less amoeboid blood corpuscles which in *Caudina* are present in numbers between 0·1 and 0·2 million per mm.³ (Kawamoto).

A separate system of vessels, the "ambulacral", is in most forms (Holothuroidea excepted) in open connection with the sea water through the pores in the madreporite. The narrow vessels connecting these pores with the rest of the system are provided with cilia beating inwards and maintaining a certain hydrostatic pressure in the whole of the ambulacral system. By means of this pressure (helped by local contractile mechanisms) the ambulacral feet and the tentacles in some forms can be filled up and become turgescent. By the movements of the animals a considerable renewal of ambulacral fluid with outside sea water must take place. The coelomic fluid (which in most Holothuroidea comprises also the ambulacral) is shut off from the sea water, but through fairly large thin-walled surfaces, serving respiratory and other functions, an exchange of substances can take place. The body wall itself is made up generally of calcareous plates which are probably practically impermeable. In the Holothuroidea the body wall is muscular. In these animals a pair of special thin-walled, richly branched internal organs, the "respiratory" trees, are filled with outside water which is renewed at irregular intervals. The intestine is well developed and, especially in the forms which feed on bottom material, sea water must be passing through it in considerable quantity, but it is unknown whether any exchange of ions takes place through its walls. Special excreting organs have not been observed.

All the Echinoderma are marine and only a few can live in brackish water. From the older experiments by Enriques (1902) and Henri and Lalou (1904) the conclusion was drawn that the body wall and intestine of echinoderms (*Holothuria*, *Stichopus*, *Strongylocentrotus*, *Sphaerechinus*, *Spatangus*) is permeable only to water, but the experiments were of too short duration to prove the point, and more recent work has demonstrated conclusively the permeability to the ions normally present in sea water. Okazaki and Koizumi (1926), Koizumi (1932) analysed carefully the mineral composition of the coelomic fluid (freed from corpuscles) of a sea cucumber, *Caudina chilensis*. They found the specific gravity slightly higher than that of the sea water in which the animals were living, 1·0250 as against 1·0241. The freezing-point depression was identical with that of sea water and the ions analysed, Cl^-, $SO_4^=$, Na^+, K^+, Ca^{++} and Mg^{++}, showed the same concentrations within the limits of error. For K^+ the tendency for the body fluid to give higher values than the corresponding sea water is, however, unmistakable, the average value for the water being 10·3 mM. and for the body fluid of eight animals 11·0 mM.

Bethe and Berger (1931 *a*) analysed *Echinus esculentus* from Helgoland and *Holothuria stellata* from Naples. The variations found are larger and the equilibration with a definite sea water uncertain, but large deviations from the sea water are certainly absent.

In a second paper (1931 *b*) the absorption of iodine into the ambulacral and coelomic fluids of *Echinus* was studied. The animals, *E. esculentus* of 300–400 g. weight, were placed in 1–1½ l. sea water to which 5 %, almost isotonic, $\frac{1}{2}M$ NaJ had been added. The initial outside concentration was therefore 25 mM. of I^-. After 14–42 hr. I^- was determined in the coelomic and ambulacral fluids.

In some of these experiments the mouth was closed, and in others both mouth, anus and madreporite. This apparently did not make any difference in the rate of uptake, and it is concluded that iodide diffuses in through the general epithelium and mainly through the ambulacral feet. The results are somewhat irregular. It is stated in the paper that a diffusion equilibrium was only attained in one case, but apparently no allowance was made for the dilution of the outside fluid by the diffusion which is far from negligible. When the animals are put back into normal sea water the iodide diffuses out again, and very low concentrations are reached within 24 hr.

There can be no doubt therefore that iodides can pass by diffusion both into and out of the animals studied, but rates of diffusion cannot be calculated.

Koizumi (1932, 1935 c) studied very carefully on *Caudina chilensis* both the osmotic passage of water and the rates of diffusion of single ions, and experiments were made both on animals in normal condition and on such in which the anterior and posterior ends were out of water so that diffusion could only take place through the muscular body wall. Osmotic equilibrium by the passage of water is reached more rapidly when inner surfaces are also exposed than through the muscular body wall. Shrinking takes place more rapidly than swelling, but it is not concluded that any irreciprocal permeability is present, but only that the elastic tension of the body plays a part, and this is borne out by the fact that an animal previously shrunken in concentrated sea water will show the same velocity constant for swelling as for shrinking.

When placed in sea water modified as to the relative concentrations of Na^+, K^+, Ca^{++}, Mg^{++}, Cl^- and $SO_4^=$, but of normal total concentration, the rates of diffusion of the single ions could be measured. Again, it was found that the rates were much higher for the total body than for the isolated outer surface. For the former the relative rates were $K^+ > Ca^{++}$, Mg^{++}, Na^+ and $Cl^- > SO_4^=$, and for the body wall definitely $K^+ > Na^+ > Ca^{++} > Mg^{++}$ and $Cl^- > SO_4^=$.

Koizumi (1935 d, e) studied the inorganic composition of the blood corpuscles and muscles of *Caudina* and found the ionic concentrations very different from those of the coelomic fluid.

The corpuscles were concentrated by centrifugation until making up about one-half of the volume (determined as accurately as possible by centrifuging in a haematocrit), and both the pure fluid and the fluid + corpuscles were analysed. The possible error from admixture of fluid in the haematocrit is probably quite small. The muscles were dissected out and lightly pressed between filter paper. They must have contained an unknown quantity of "extracellular fluid" of the same composition as the plasma. According to experiments with other marine animals to be discussed below (p. 59), this contamination is probably of the order of 10–20 %. Calculated per litre of water content the millimolar and milliequivalent concentrations, given as averages of several determinations showing satisfactory agreement, are as follows:

Table III

	K	Na	Ca	Mg	Sum of cations mE.
Plasma	12·0	467	10·9	51·5	604
Corpuscles	236	273	9·3	19·5	567
Muscle	178	245	114	50·5	752
Skin	99	382	342	114	1390

	Cl	SO_4	Sum of anions mE.	Water content %
Plasma	531	29·3	590	98·5
Corpuscles	169	176	521	75·2
Muscle	156·5	84	324	77·4
Skin	348	120	580	79·3

These results, published by Koizumi without comment, are very interesting and of importance from the general point of view of ionic regulation in cells as against whole organisms. It is a well-known fact, studied both on plant cells (Osterhout, 1933; Collander, 1936) and on many animal cells, that K is taken up in excess of the concentration in the surrounding medium. Collander finds for instance on *Nitella*, in fresh water, that corresponding to a K concentration of 0·04 mM. in the water the concentration in the cell sap is 100 (ratio 2500 : 1). This is put in relation by several authors to the metabolic processes and explained as an exchange with the H^+ ions produced in the cells and diffusing out. The explanation involves the assumption, which is probably correct, that the protoplasmic membrane may be permeable to H^+ ions and K^+ ions which are only slightly hydrated, but much less permeable or practically impermeable to Na^+ ions. Since the accumulation of K^+ in living cells is of such general occurrence it seems very likely that the cause is general and the uptake not determined by any selective activity on the part of the membrane, but this argument will scarcely hold for the other ions accumulated, and I would point especially to the very high concentration of SO_4^- in the corpuscles of *Caudina*. SO_4^- passes only with great difficulty through living membranes, and several such membranes would seem to be absolutely sulphate impermeable. When therefore sulphate is six times more concentrated in the corpuscles it must be taken up by some selective activity probably requiring the expenditure of energy.

In the corpuscles the total concentration of cations is slightly and of anions definitely lower than in the coelomic fluid. The deficit in anions is probably made up largely by HCO_3 and perhaps to some extent by phosphate, and the cation deficit may be made up by organic cations. Fredericq found as early as 1901 that the tissues of sea-water invertebrates, while in osmotic equilibrium with the blood and therefore also with the surrounding water, might show a considerable deficit in soluble salts, and he gives as one example the ovaries of *Sphaerechinus granularis* in which he found only 1·51 % soluble salt. The deficit in osmotically active substances must be made up by organic molecules of low molecular weight, and we shall find that in higher groups of marine invertebrates such molecules are present in tissues in high concentrations.

There is reason to believe that all the ions found in *Caudina* corpuscles are present in the free state and dissolved in the water phase. In the skin a large proportion of the Ca and Mg is present in the solid state in the calcareous spicules, and the large excess of cations is thereby easily explained. Solid compounds of Ca and Mg are probably also present in the muscles, but the large deficit in anions is remarkable. Phosphate determinations would have been desirable.

SCOLECIDA

The lower worms are probably not a natural group. Most of the classes and orders are represented both in the sea and in fresh water, and a considerable number of forms are parasitic. The osmotic reactions have been studied only in very few forms, but in the biological literature several hints can be found which would be well worth following up.

Turbellaria. Except for the fact that they are larger and multicellular the Turbellaria show a great deal of resemblance to Infusoria. There is no body cavity. The surface is covered with cilia. The digestive system has only one opening, the mouth, and is generally richly branched, but in the marine suborder of Acoela it is represented by a mass of cells without any digestive cavity. In this suborder no excretory system is found, but in the other suborders it consists of more or less richly branched vessels ending proximally inside special cells and opening to the outside through one or more pores. This system is slightly developed only in the marine forms, more richly branched in fresh-water Turbellaria, and in some of these there is a contractile bladder near the opening. It was shown by Westblad (1922) that the excretion of metabolic end-products takes place mainly through the gut, and the chief function of the protonephridial system appears to be analogous to that of the contractile vacuole in Protozoa.

The only turbellarian which has been at all carefully studied from the point of view of osmotic regulation is the small triclad *Gunda ulvae*, which lives in estuaries between tide marks and is there surrounded by a medium which normally varies twice a day from completely fresh water to undiluted sea water. The locality in which it was specially studied by Pantin (1931 *a–c*) is presented in Fig. 9 and shows how this variation seems to be a necessary condition of existence for *Gunda*. When transferred from pure sea water to dilutions with distilled water the animal's body will swell (Weil and Pantin, 1931). The volume can be measured by compressing the animal slightly in a chamber of known height and determining the area. Fig. 10 shows the actual increase in volume in different dilutions of sea water measured after 75 min. and compared with the theoretical curve, *b*, which should be followed if the exposed surfaces were permeable only to water. When the increase is less than the theoretical at concentrations below about 70 % it means that salt is lost from the body. In Plymouth tap water or distilled water the animals will die and disintegrate, and it is shown that this is due to lack of Ca. In the natural stream water (con-

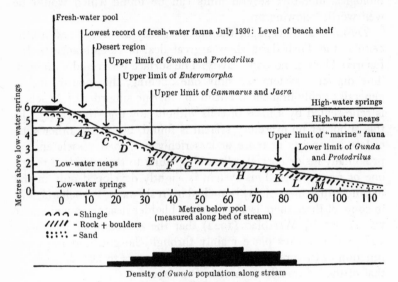

Fig. 9. Vertical section along estuary of stream, showing substratum and limits of organisms. (Pantin.)

taining 1·6 mM. of Ca) or in corresponding solutions of $CaCl_2$ the animals will survive, swelling rapidly at first and then decreasing slowly in volume (Fig. 11). It is suggested that the Ca ion acts primarily by lowering the permeability of the worms to water.

In a third paper Pantin confirms the loss of salt to dilute solutions by measuring the gradual increase in conductivity of the solution in a vessel containing a small number of *Gunda*. On cytolysis of a single worm of 1·2 mm.³ volume an increase in conductivity is measured corresponding to 0·6 mm.³ of sea water, and it is con-

cluded that the worm was originally in osmotic equilibrium with
the sea water.

In 2 mM. Ca solutions the loss of salts is greatly reduced, while
other ions and non-electrolytes gave only a slight effect or none at
all. When Ca is present in the outside fluid the worms are able to
retain 10–15 % of the salts originally present, corresponding, when
the increase in volume to 160 % is allowed for, to a salt concentration of 6–10 % of the original (34–56 mM.).

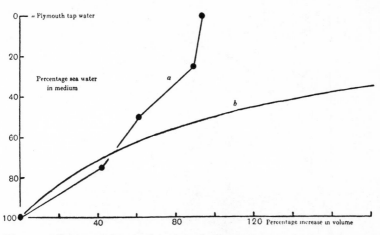

Fig. 10. a, Percentage increase in volume in *Gunda* after 75 min. in mixtures of
sea water and Plymouth tap water. b, Theoretical curve for organism bounded
by ideal semipermeable membrane. (Pantin.)

With this concentration a steady state is attained which the
worms can maintain for a very long time. The inside concentration
being much higher than the outside, water must enter osmotically
and energy must be expended to keep up the concentration. This
is brought out clearly in a paper by Beadle (1931), who measured
the relative ratio of oxygen consumption of *Gunda* (both normal and
narcotized with chloretone) in mixtures of sea water with distilled
water. He found an increase in metabolism in diluted media in
which the animals had reached a steady state, insignificant or
absent in dilutions down to 60 % sea water, but very definite at
greater dilutions, where the worms actively oppose the osmotic

inflow of water. Experiments were also done in which the volumes of worms after attainment of the steady state in 100, 25 and 10 % sea water were measured after exposure to O_2 lack. In normal sea water no influence could be observed. In the dilute sea water the animals would swell further when deprived of O_2 and shrink again when O_2 was admitted.

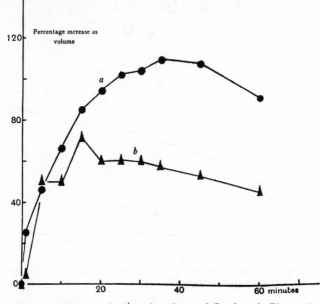

Fig. 11. Percentage increase in volume of *Gunda*, *a* in Plymouth tap water, *b* in natural stream water. (Pantin.)

Finally, it was shown that cyanide in millimolar concentration in dilute sea water would also cause swelling, followed by shrinkage, when the animals were transferred to the same solution without cyanide. The action of cyanide showed a time lag of 20 min., and respiration experiments with cyanide added confirmed that it took 30 min. before the cyanide would stop the O_2 absorption. This of course corresponds to the rate at which cyanide will penetrate into the worms.

While the determinations of O_2 absorption rate are not by themselves conclusive, the experiments with O_2 lack and cyanide furnish strong evidence for an active process by which a steady state is maintained, and an important element in this process must be the separation and excretion of the water entering by osmosis.

Some information regarding the excretion of this water is furnished in a second paper by Beadle (1934). Here it is shown that a large part of the water causing the swelling of *Gunda* in 10 % sea water is stored in the entoderm in which it forms large vacuoles. These continue to increase in size for at least 24 hr. after the maximum volume of the worm has been attained in 2–3 hr.

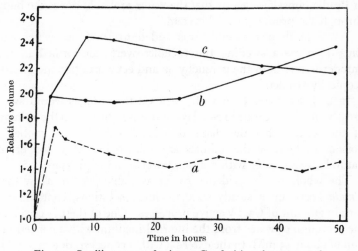

Fig. 12. Swelling curves for intact *Gunda* (*a*) and regenerated hind ends (*b* and *c*) in 10 % sea water. (Beadle.)

A typical volume curve is shown in Fig. 12(*a*). One would expect the vacuoles to be discharged into the gut, but microscopic observation of three or four vacuolated cells in a living worm for 30 min. failed to reveal the discharge of any vacuole. More conclusive evidence is furnished by the following experiment. A number of worms were operated on by cutting just behind the pharynx. The hind ends were kept in sea water for a fortnight, when it was found that the ectoderm had completely closed the wound, thus excluding the gut lumen from any direct communication with the exterior. Such specimens swelled in 10 % sea water at the same rate as whole worms. The average for twelve ends in 1 hr. was 56 %, for eleven whole animals 57 %, showing that water enters through the ectoderm only, at least when no food is taken. After 2 hr. two hind ends (Fig. 12 b, c) had increased more than a normal worm, but even these reached an almost constant or even decreasing volume and showed, when fixed and sectioned after 50 hr., a normal appearance of the tissues. As water must continue to be taken up osmotically the attainment of a steady state by the operated worms shows that water must be excreted and (contrary to the conclusions of Beadle himself) suggests that the water probably leaves the body through the protonephridial system.

When millimolar cyanide was added to 10 % sea water and caused an extra swelling the vacuoles were not formed in the entoderm, and both the parenchyma and ectoderm became microscopically swollen.

In 2 % sea water even with extra Ca the animals would swell greatly and disintegrate in 2–3 days, but this indicates (in the opinion of the writer) that the distilled water employed was probably poisonous, because the animals are able to live even longer in natural stream water with a much lower osmotic pressure.

The whole of the evidence so far available goes to show that *Gunda* keeps up a steady state in dilute solutions, containing a certain amount of Ca, by active processes. One of these is certainly the excretion of water from the internal medium with a concentration of about 45 mM. to the external with a concentration of 4 mM. or less. The role of the Ca^{++} seems to be to reduce permeability sufficiently to allow the regulating mechanism or mechanisms to cope with the incoming water and probably also to prevent an undue loss of salt. If the water excreted is practically salt free, and if the ectodermal surface is practically semipermeable this may be the whole story, but if salts are being lost by diffusion all the time some mechanism must be assumed to make good this loss.

Oesting and Allee (1935), working on the nearly related *Procerodes* (= *Gunda*) *wheatlandi*, confirm the result that Ca ions are specifically protective in delaying cytolysis in hypotonic water.

A few experiments by Kepner and Yoe (1933) on the fresh-water Rhabdocoele *Stenostomum* seem to indicate that this organism also requires a certain amount of salt (calcium?), since it will swell in distilled water with increased excretion through the proto-nephridial system.

Trematoda. The trematodes are parasitic, some ectoparasites on marine or fresh-water fishes, others entoparasites, but they all possess a well-developed excretory system, proximally closed and with ciliary mechanisms to further the flow in the canals. At a certain stage the larvae are free-swimming organisms of less than 1 mm. length, and these Cercariae in fresh water have regularly contracting bladders near the openings of their protonephridia. Herfs (1922) has shown that the rhythm of such a bladder depends on the osmotic concentration of the outside medium. In an un-determined species he observed in Ringer an average rhythm of 13·1 sec., in half-Ringer of 8·3 sec. and in fresh water of 6·3 sec., and noted that the bladder in the latter case was filled to a definitely larger volume. Westblad (1922, p. 199) gives the rhythm of *Cercaria microcotyle* in the blood of *Paludina* (with which it may probably be in osmotic equilibrium) as one contraction in 1–3 min.

Cestoda. Those living in the intestine of vertebrates must be exposed to violent variations in the osmotic concentration and ionic composition of the environment. They take up their food through the outer surface which one would expect therefore to be per-meable also to ions. They may well need the highly developed excretory system which they possess, but nothing is known about their osmotic regulation.

Rotatoria. In this group of very small forms the protonephridia are well developed and provided with a contractile bladder. The majority live in fresh water, a considerable number in brackish water, and a small number in the sea. On account of their small size a relatively large amount of water must penetrate the surface by osmosis, and the contractile bladder is observed to evacuate in $\frac{1}{2}$–1 hr. a volume of fluid equal to the total volume of the animal (Westblad, 1922).

Experiments with varying salinity on these animals and cyanide experiments would be sure to produce valuable results, the more so as in many forms the volume can be calculated from simple measurements. A comparison of the activity of the excretory bladder in sea-water, brackish-water and fresh-water forms would be interesting, and also for experiments on the electrical potential certain Rotatoria would be eminently suitable.

Gastrotricha. In this small group of very small forms protonephridia are present in the fresh-water species, but absent in the marine.

Nematoda. The Nematoda possess a very thick cuticle. In spite of the small size of many fresh-water forms the excretory apparatus is often poorly developed. It is natural in such cases to suppose that the permeability of the cuticle for water is exceptionally low; but no observations are available.

Bryozoa. The subclass of Ectoprocta, although mainly marine, has a number of representatives in fresh water. They are very delicate and present a relatively enormous surface. Nevertheless, mechanisms for elimination of water are entirely unknown. In the subclass Endoprocta, which is almost exclusively marine, nephridia are present. These facts seem to be at variance with all our conceptions of osmotic regulation, even if we take the two groups to be only remotely related systematically.

ANNELIDA

The phylum of higher worms is a fairly natural group for which the
characteristics, important from our point of view, are the following,
viz. a coelomic cavity is present, occupying in many cases a very
considerable fraction of the total body volume, with a fairly well-
developed circulatory system by which the coelomic fluid or
"haemolymph" is kept in motion and variations in its composition
in different parts reduced to a minimum. In many of the larger
forms metabolism is sufficiently intense to require the development
of "gills" presenting a large surface along which the haemolymph
is kept flowing and through which at least gases (O_2 and CO_2) are
exchanged. From our point of view it is of importance that the gill
surfaces must be responsible for a considerable osmotic uptake of
water whenever the haemolymph is hypertonic to the external environment, and that dissolved substances may also sometimes pass
through.

Nephridia are regularly present. They are long narrow tubes—
often intracellular—and in many cases they open directly into the
coelomic cavity. This does not mean that coelomic fluid flows off
through them, whenever the internal pressure is increased, but that
such flow *can* take place. There can be little doubt that the nephridia play a part in osmotic regulation, but experimental evidence
is almost completely lacking.

Among the Archiannelida and Polychaeta a few are fresh-water
forms and some interesting forms live in brackish water, but all the
rest are marine. The large majority of the Oligochaeta and Hirudinea are fresh-water (or land) forms, but the aberrant groups
Echiuroidea and Sipunculoidea are exclusively marine.

The osmotic conditions have been studied in a few species only,
and it will be convenient to deal with them from the ecological
point of view without further regard to their systematic position.
The majority of the Polychaeta are more or less stenohaline in the
sense that they do not seem to possess any osmoregulatory
mechanisms and are able to stand only limited variations in salinity.

Others, while essentially marine, are euryhaline and can penetrate far into brackish water. These may or may not possess special osmoregulatory mechanisms. The fresh-water forms are able to maintain an osmotic pressure in their haemolymph higher than that of the environment.

Adolph (1936) studied the sipunculid *Phascolosoma gouldi*, a smooth worm of a few grams weight without any respiratory organs. He finds by exposing these worms to various dilutions and concentrations of sea water that they behave as osmometers, gaining weight by water uptake in dilute solutions and losing weight correspondingly in concentrated (a conclusion also arrived at by Dekhuyzen, 1921). When they are brought back into normal sea water the original weight is completely restored after experiments of a few hours' duration. He accordingly describes the animals as being semipermeable. His experiments do not furnish any proof of this contention, because over longer periods there is a definite tendency for the animals to return toward the original weight even in the changed medium. In one set of experiments he injected a definite amount (12 % of the body weight) of variously concentrated and diluted sea water into these animals. After, say, an injection of doubly concentrated sea water an animal would take 4 hr. to gain weight up to 123 % of the original, but the curves show that the weight then begins to drop at the rate of about 1 % in 4 hr. Probably, therefore, the animal is slightly permeable to salts, as Bethe (1934) found for *Sipunculus nudus*.

Adolph lays much stress upon the fact, which he has proved beyond doubt, that the gain in weight by swelling is in *Phascolosoma* a much more rapid process than the loss in weight by shrinking, and he uses the term "differential permeability" to describe the phenomenon. Differential permeability may be characteristic for the epidermis of this worm, but to prove this experiments should have been made in which the gut and nephridia were excluded. Adolph seems to think that some active resistance to the passage outward of water is offered by the integument, but the idea is not supported by evidence.

The blood of *Sipunculus nudus* was analysed by Bethe and Berger (1931), who found the concentrations of K and Ca to be very nearly the same as in sea water, but the Mg to be definitely lower in the blood. This may be the result of some kind of regulation. Fredericq (1901) found only 1·29 % soluble salt in the muscular body wall of *Sipunculus*.

Schlieper (1929) made very instructive comparative experiments with *Nereis pelagica*, which is in a sense stenohaline, and the two more euryhaline forms *Arenicola* and *Nereis diversicolor*.

In a preliminary experiment a number of both species of *Nereis* from 32 °/$_{oo}$ sea water were exposed to dilution, first to 15 °/$_{oo}$ for 48 hr. and then to 8 °/$_{oo}$ salt concentration. This killed the specimens of *N. pelagica* by swelling, while *N. diversicolor* stood the treatment well and showed only moderate swelling. Similar experiments in which the osmotic concentration of the body fluids (haemolymph + intracellular fluid) was measured by freezing-point determinations showed for *N. pelagica* that at all concentrations of the outside medium between 32 and 8 °/$_{oo}$ salt the body fluids of the animals after 24 hr. were practically isotonic with the surrounding water. *N. diversicolor*, on the other hand, while being in equilibrium with the normal 32 °/$_{oo}$ sea water, would develop hypertonicity in more dilute media. In 17 °/$_{oo}$ sea water (237 mM.) the inside concentration corresponded to 296 mM. When the outside concentration was reduced to 121 mM. the inside was 232, and after the animals had been 14 days in fresh water (concentration probably about 2 mM.) they were still alive and the inside concentration was 135 mM.

A number of animals of this species living normally in brackish water of 4 °/$_{oo}$ (55 mM.) showed a concentration of 188 which increased to 306 when they were brought into water of 255 mM. This is the picture of typical osmoregulation, but does not reveal the mechanism by which the regulation is accomplished.

Arenicola, like *Nereis diversicolor*, will stand low salt concentrations and is found living in nature at concentrations between ocean water and 8 °/$_{oo}$. At all concentrations down to 78 mM. Schlieper found the haemolymph isotonic with the outside medium. There is no osmoregulation, but the animal is able to tolerate widely varying salt concentrations in its blood and tissues.

The difference in type of reaction to brackish water between

Arenicola and *Nereis diversicolor* is of deep significance. The development of passive tolerance towards low salt concentrations in a medium which remains essentially balanced may carry the animal far into brackish-water regions like the Baltic, but will never allow it to pass into fresh water, whereas the power to maintain hypertonicity of the blood needs only to be developed beyond a certain point to enable its possessor to overcome *the* main difficulty of life in fresh water.

Schlieper rightly concluded that the osmotic regulation in *N. diversicolor* must involve the expenditure of energy, and compared therefore the respiratory metabolism of the worms in normal sea water, where no osmotic work is being done, and in dilutions. He found in two series of experiments each on eight groups of three animals a small increase in oxygen consumption during the first hours in dilute sea water or in fresh water, but a calculation shows that it does not exceed the limits of error, and experiments after the animals had become acclimatized to the low concentrations, at a time when the osmotic regulation should be active, showed a decrease which is, however, also without statistical significance. Similar experiments by Beadle (1931, 1937), in which *N. diversicolor* was compared with the more stenohaline and non-regulating *N. cultrifera*, also failed to show any significant increase in metabolism when osmotic work was being done. This does not mean of course that no energy is expended for osmotic work, but only that the amount is not large enough for demonstration in view of the large variability of the animals, and Beadle's experiments with addition of cyanide were conclusive in showing that oxidative energy is necessary to maintain a higher inside concentration in *N. diversicolor* when exposed to a dilute medium. Beadle also confirmed the experiments of Ellis (1933) showing that in Ca-free dilute sea water the osmotic regulation breaks down and the animal goes on increasing in weight. This is well shown in Fig. 13, which illustrates the reaction of three *N. diversicolor* transferred to 17 % dilutions of sea water: *a*, in natural 17 % water, shows a sharper initial rise in weight which then decreases towards a constant value of about 125 %; *b*, in Ca-free water, shows a continued increase until at *X* it is transferred to natural sea water; and *c* begins to gain weight when at *Y* it is transferred to Ca-free water.

The results obtained in a recent paper by Ellis (1937) are very difficult to reconcile with the work of Schlieper, which is the more unfortunate because Ellis does not seem to be acquainted with

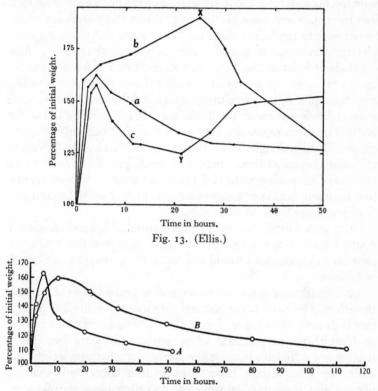

Fig. 13. (Ellis.)

Fig. 14. Weight regulation of *N. diversicolor*, *A* from Roscoff, *B* from Bangor in 20 % sea water. (Ellis.)

Schlieper's papers. Ellis finds first a very pronounced difference between Roscoff worms and such from Plymouth or Bangor in the weight curve obtained on transference of *N. diversicolor* from normal to 20 % sea water (Fig. 14). While the French worms completed their weight regulation in 50 hr. the English took over 100.

This is ascribed, as I think rightly, to a difference in race. In further experiments it is shown that the (English) worms lose chloride when transferred to 20 % water and that this Cl loss is completed in about 10 hr. when the volume is at its maximum. The Cl loss is determined by titration, in 2 hr. periods, of 20 ml. of water in which four worms weighing about 1·5 g. in all have been kept. The total loss for 1 g. worm amounts to 6 mg. When the worms are transferred back to 100 % sea water the loss is made good, but not completely, because the weight of a worm is reduced about 20 %. Ellis concludes from this and other experiments that there is a passive uptake of water and loss of salt in diluted sea water lasting 10 hr., and thereupon an active volume regulation by which fluid with the same chloride content as the dilute sea water is pumped out of the body. The experiments are very suggestive, but certainly not conclusive. If Ellis is right and if the worms studied by him belong to the same species as those studied by Schlieper, there must be an extremely interesting racial difference in power of osmotic regulation between Schlieper's animals from the bay of Helgoland and Kiel and those from Atlantic water.

Until such a difference shall be demonstrated beyond reasonable doubt I think Schlieper's result must be accepted for *N. diversicolor*, as a species, and I would look upon the Ca experiments about as follows.

The significance of Ca for the regulation process and the fact that the effect is immediate suggest strongly that the general body surface is directly involved in the regulation. The effect of Ca may be to diminish the permeability of the surface for water, but this in itself is not sufficient, because the animal actually loses weight and builds up a hypertonic haemolymph. It is conceivable that the permeability is diminished sufficiently to allow the nephridia to do the real concentration work by secreting a hypotonic urine in sufficient amount, but there is another possibility, namely, that cells in the body surface can take up salts directly from the medium. This possibility is realized in certain fresh-water Annelida.

Hirudinea. It is well known that leeches can live very long in fresh water without food, and it is even stated that *Hirudo medicinalis* will take a year and a half to digest completely the blood taken up in one meal. During all that time water must be entering osmotically through the integument and be removed through the nephridia. According to Fredericq (1905) the freezing-point depression of tissue juice is 0·40° (106 mM.). The urine may be very dilute, but it seems unlikely that it can be made absolutely salt free, and it is also improbable that the integument can be absolutely impermeable to ions. It is therefore very difficult to understand how the animal can avoid losing practically all its salt in the course of time, unless it can absorb salts from the surrounding medium. Consideration of these problems—valid for a number of freshwater animals—induced the writer to undertake experiments in which the animals were first exposed during a suitable period to a slow flow of distilled water and then in small vessels to a measured volume of ordinary fresh water, very dilute Ringer or very dilute (millimolar or double millimolar) solutions of single salts.

Experiments were made on the horse-leech, *Haemopis sanguisuga*. About twenty leeches with an aggregate weight of 18 g. were treated for about a fortnight with a flow of distilled water and were then transferred to 55 ml. of frog's Ringer diluted to 1/100. A Cl determination of this solution gave 1·067 mM. This was reduced in 1·5 hr. to 0·852, showing that the leeches had absorbed 11·8 μM. Cl or 0·48 μM./g./hr.

This and other similar experiments show that salt can be actively absorbed, but leave the question open whether the Cl$^-$ or the Na$^+$, or possibly both, are the ions actively absorbed. Electrostatically it is practically impossible, in view of the forces involved, for ions to become absorbed without being either accompanied by ions of the opposite sign or exchanged against ions of the same sign. To test these possibilities experiments were made on the same leeches with NaHCO$_3$ and with NH$_4$Cl. It is extremely unlikely, *a priori*, that the ions HCO$_3^-$ or NH$_4^+$ can be absorbed actively, and an uptake of Na$^+$ from NaHCO$_3$ would therefore indicate that Na was actively absorbed, while an absorption of Cl$^-$ from NH$_4$Cl would indicate active chloride absorption. Both sets of experiments gave positive results.

From 50 ml. 2 mM. NaHCO$_3$, Na was reduced in 5·9 hr. from 1·97 to 1·25 corresponding to an uptake of 36 μM. or 0·35 μM./g./hr.

During the same period 24 μM. of NH_3 were excreted and the combined HCO_3 of the solution was reduced by 14 μM. In the subsequent experiment Cl was absorbed, but at a slower rate, from NH_4Cl. NH_3 continued to be excreted, but the rate was reduced. The Cl in this experiment must have been exchanged against the CO_2 of the respiratory exchange.

From these experiments it must be concluded that there exists in the integument of leeches (or perhaps in the gut which was not excluded) two separate mechanisms of which one absorbs Na and perhaps other cations and one absorbs Cl and possibly other anions. In succeeding chapters a more elaborate analysis and discussion of these mechanisms will be attempted.

Oligochaeta. Lumbricus terrestris. According to Adolph (1925, 1927) earthworms which are able to live indefinitely in fresh water have a freezing-point depression corresponding to 80 mM. When transferred to 50–100 mM. solutions of indifferent substances in distilled water they lose water, but remain hypertonic, losing only very little Cl. Adolph's experiments do not allow definite conclusions, but it seems probable that earthworms, like leeches, can absorb salt.

MOLLUSCA

From the point of view of osmotic conditions and behaviour there is no essential difference between the molluscs and the invertebrates so far studied, although the general level of organization is higher in the molluscs. The molluscs possess a body cavity of varying volume and a fairly efficient circulatory system maintaining always a flow of haemolymph along the respiratory surfaces. These are in the larger forms often highly developed, which means that the ratio surface/volume is not a simple function of size, but that even in larger forms the surface area per unit volume may be considerable. The kidneys represent an advanced stage compared with the Annelida. The coelomic cavity into which they open by a ciliated nephrostome is reduced to comprise only the pericardial sac which is shut off entirely by thin walls from the body cavity proper. The powerful cilia in the proximal part of the kidney tubule reduce the pressure in the pericardial cavity and cause filtration into it from the haemolymph. The urine formed in this way is modified during its passage down the tubule by the action of cells, but details regarding the function are not available. The kidneys are usually well developed both in marine and in fresh-water forms. It is evident therefore that their general function is not osmoregulatory, but by reabsorption of ions from the walls they *may* produce a dilute urine in the fresh-water molluscs.

The large majority of molluscs are provided with an external shell consisting mainly of $CaCO_3$. They are generally able also to resist lack of O_2 for long periods, and by virtue of this faculty they can shut themselves off from the surrounding medium for periods of days and in some cases even months. In the snails the shell permanently protects a large part of the surface against diffusion and osmotic inflow of water. "No molluscs without an external shell are found in fresh water" (Ellis, 1926).

The molluscs are mainly marine and only two classes, the Pelecypoda or bivalves and the Gastropoda are represented in fresh water. Within these classes the migration of forms from the sea through estuaries into rivers has been going on from the earliest geological periods and is still in progress, so that a study of the adaptive modifications ought to be feasible. Ellis, who gives a number of examples, refers especially to the small snails of the genus *Hydrobia*, common in brackish water and with representatives also in fresh water. One species, *H. jenkinsii*, was confined entirely to brackish water until near the end of the nineteenth century. In 1893 it was first observed in an inland locality in England, and subsequently it has become abundant in rivers, streams and canals over most of England, Wales and Ireland. In continental Europe the species appears to be mainly confined to brackish water, but is reported recently from a few fresh-water habitats. In this species there must be an active regulation, and it would be interesting to see if the fresh-water individuals represent a physiological race with a more highly developed power of osmotic regulation.

MARINE MOLLUSCS

Like other marine invertebrates these are generally in osmotic equilibrium with the surrounding sea water (Fredericq, 1901; Bottazzi, 1908) and remain so when the concentration of this is slowly varied, at least within certain limits compatible with their normal life. Because rapid changes in concentration of the outside medium are followed by corresponding changes in weight of the animals exposed, the osmotic adaptation was, until the work of Bethe, taken to be due to semipermeability of the surfaces concerned. Dilution of the medium causes swelling and concentration shrinkage, and a new equilibrium, which is due mainly to osmotic gain or loss of water, is established generally in a few hours. Quinton (1904) maintained strongly that marine invertebrates (*Aplysia* especially) were permeable to chlorides, but his analyses were not sufficiently convincing. Bethe (1929), experimenting on the sea hare *Aplysia*, varied the concentration of single ions in artificial sea water, while maintaining isotonicity, and observed variations in the same direction in the blood. These variations were completely reversible, and it is significant that both increases and decreases in Ca concentration could be obtained, so that there can be no reason to assume the production of any abnormal permeability.

When transferred to an isotonic mixture of sea water with cane sugar *Aplysia* will shrink at a fairly rapid rate, because salt leaves the body and sugar does not enter in any appreciable amount (Bethe, 1930), and when such an animal is brought back in time into normal sea water it will swell, and in some cases it is noted that the original weight is even exceeded (Fig. 15). This permits the assumption that the skin is not quite impermeable to cane sugar.

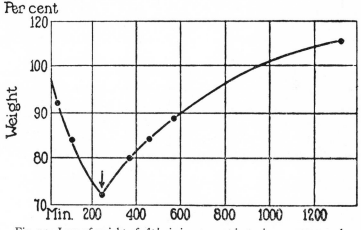

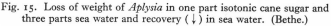

Fig. 15. Loss of weight of *Aplysia* in one part isotonic cane sugar and three parts sea water and recovery (↓) in sea water. (Bethe.)

In later experiments (1934) Bethe, replying to an objection raised by Schlieper (1929), made experiments on *Aplysia* after ligaturing the mouth, and again found a definite passage of ions (Cl⁻, SO₄⁼, Ca⁺⁺ and Mg⁺⁺) through the integument. A few experiments made on the nudibranch gastropod *Doris* in three-quarters sea water showed an increase in weight beyond what would be expected if it was semipermeable, while in all other forms studied the increase was much smaller, due to the simultaneous exchange of salt. The abnormal behaviour of this animal, which Bethe does not attempt to explain, ought to be investigated further. It shows other peculiarities to be referred to below.

In spite of the permeability of integuments the ionic composition of the blood need not be identical with that of the sea water with which molluscs are in osmotic equilibrium, but shows differences which may in some higher forms become pronounced. Duval (1925) compared the Cl content of the blood in several species with the Cl concentration of the sea water with which they were in equilibrium, and I can supplement his figures with a few more. Calculated in mM./litre we find:

Table IV

			Blood Cl	Water Cl	Blood Cl / Water Cl
Bivalves	Ostrea edulis	Krogh	423	424	0·997
	Mytilus edulis	Krogh	526	532	0·99
Gastropoda	Buccinum undatum	Duval	543	569	0·96
	Patella vulgata	Krogh	348	363	0·96
Cephalopoda	Sepia officinalis	Duval	550	599	0·92
		Duval	536	591	0·91
		Duval	536	585	0·92

Bethe and Berger (1931) give figures for some other ions calculated on the basis of Cl = 100. They find:

Table V

	Na	K	Ca	Mg
Sea water	87	1·8	2·1	9·3
Aplysia	91	1·9	2·2	8·8
Mytilus	83	1·7	2·2	9·0*
Doris	98	2·9	2·4	10·6

* This figure is taken from a determination by Krogh and Wernstedt (1938).

While some of the differences found may be accidental there can be little doubt, especially with regard to the Cl concentrations, that they express the beginning of regulation processes for which the kidneys are probably responsible. Bottazzi (1908) found the urine of *Octopus vulgaris* slightly hypotonic (Δ 2·24° C.) compared with the blood (Δ 2·296° C.).

In the molluscs ionic concentrations within tissue cells are definitely different from those in the blood and often much lower.

The first to emphasize this fact was L. Fredericq (1901), who determined the content of soluble salt in the tissues of marine animals and found it generally much lower than in sea water, while the osmotic concentrations were identical. Fredericq's actual figures are probably in many cases too low. He gives, for instance, the salt content of the adductor muscle of *Ostrea* as 1 %, while recent determinations of alkali and chloride on oysters from water of the same salinity indicate a content of alkali chloride of 1·5 %. In principle, however, Fredericq was right, and analyses on different molluscs have revealed the presence of considerable quantities of small organic molecules in tissue extracts. Thus Kelly (1904) found 5 % taurin in *Mytilus* muscles and 4·8 % in those of *Pecten opercularis*. The taurin formula is $H_2NCH_2CH_2SO_3H$, and the molecular weight 125. 5 % corresponds osmotically to 200 mM. of a soluble salt. These results were qualitatively confirmed by Mendel (1904) for gastropod muscles and by Henze (1905) for *Sepia*. Kelly also demonstrated the presence of glycin in the muscles of *Pecten irradians*.

In several tissues in molluscs the salt concentration exceeds that of sea water which is possible only if salts are present as indiffusible (probably solid) compounds. Examples are given in the adjoined Table VI recalculated from the figures of McCance and Shackleton (1937). They are included here because in some of the organs the sum of K and Na alone exceeds the total base in sea water, so that a definite fraction of these bases must be present in an unionized state:

Table VI. *Concentration mM./kg. water*

Name	Organ	Water g./kg.	Na	K	Ca	Mg	Total mE.
Littorina littorea	Foot and gut	695	428	156	294	270	1712
,,	Gonad and liver	640	475	170	356	334	2025
Patella vulgata	Whole animal	747	270	152	111	37	718
Buccinum undatum	Foot and gut	732	255	145	26	64	580
,,	Gonad and liver	738	454	280	68	56	982
Aplysia punctata	Whole animal	860	320	71	34	55	569
Sea water			967	462	10·0	10·9	54·3	603

Very comprehensive analyses were made on the nudibranch *Archidoris britannica* by McCance and Masters (1937). In this animal an enormous excess of Ca and Mg was found, and this was located as solid concrements in the body wall (along with strontium and fluorine) which are of no further interest from our point of view. When the animals were prepared for analysis the viscera were removed and thereafter the body wall was allowed to secrete mucus. On one occasion 80 g. body wall secreted 24·1 g. mucus in about $1\frac{1}{2}$ hr. As first secreted the mucus is very viscous, but after 2 hr. or so becomes much more fluid. Viscera, body wall and mucus were separately analysed, and I give the results for the major constituents recalculated as mM./kg. water:

Table VII

	Na+	K+	Ca++	Mg++	Total base mE.
Viscera	209	179	65	65	648
Body wall	293	42	—	—	—
Mucus	442	13·6	13·7	58·5	600
Sea water	462	10·0	10·9	54·3	602

	Cl⁻	F⁻	HPO₄⁼	SO₄⁼	CO₃	Total acid mE.
Viscera	391	—	13·0	27	—	635
Body wall	405	300	24	5·3	—	—
Mucus	512	—	—	—	56	568
Sea water	545	—	—	29	2	605

Regarding the body wall total concentrations cannot be given, because unknown amounts both of cations and anions are present in a non-diffusible state. The composition of the viscera shows a normal preponderance of K^+ and $HPO_4^=$, and the total concentrations are so close to those of sea water that it can safely be concluded that only a few per cent of the ions can be indiffusible. The mucus finally, which has been elaborated and excreted from the body wall without circulation or any addition of fluid, is in its inorganic composition almost identical with sea water, showing only a slight excess of K^+, Ca^{++} and Mg^{++} and a corresponding deficit in Na^+. There is also a Cl^- deficit which is mainly made up by bicarbonate. Is it conceivable that we have to do mainly with intercellular fluid pressed out by muscular contractions and to which is added a small amount of secretion, or is the mucus in its totality a secretion product from cells which one would expect to have a very different composition?

From the point of view with which we are here concerned, viz. the distribution of diffusible ions, the analyses so far given are clearly insufficient. In the whole organism or in a piece of tissue there is a certain amount of fluid which is outside the living cells and which is in the molluscs identical with the haemolymph. Inside the cells there is a certain amount of water holding certain ions in solution, and it is the concentrations of these ions which we desire to know. In addition there may be, both outside and inside cells, certain structures holding salts in indiffusible combinations which tend to complicate the analytical problems.

A preliminary attempt has been made to determine total osmotic concentrations by the vapour-pressure method as well as concentrations of single diffusible ions both in the haemolymph and in the intracellular fluid of mussels (*Mytilus edulis*) in equilibrium with varied concentrations of sea water. In order to determine the total volume of haemolymph a known quantity of a substance which was supposed not to penetrate into cells was injected and its concentration determined after a suitable interval for its distribution. The first experiments were made with thiocyanate which has been found suitable in higher animals (Lavietes, Bourdillon and Klinghoffer, 1936; Krogh, 1938), but the volume thus determined turned out in *Mytilus* to be the total amount of water in the body. It is probable therefore that thiocyanate penetrates into all cells in *Mytilus*. Experiments with thiosulphate gave results which were consistent and probable, but there is no proof that the volume so determined corresponds really to the extracellular fluid. Assuming that it does the concentration of thiosulphate in haemolymph and in press juice from *Mytilus* muscles was compared and gave the result that 12 % (11–13) of the juice was extracellular and 88 % intracellular.

Analyses were made of chloride, sulphate, total alkali and potassium in sea water, haemolymph and press juice from muscles from three animals which had been kept for many days, respectively, in about 10, 25 and 33 °/$_{\circ\circ}$ sea water. The results obtained on the muscle juice were recalculated on the assumption that 12 % of the juice was haemolymph, and all concentrations are given in mM./kg. of water:

Table VIII

Dry substance g./l.			Cl			SO$_4$		
W	Bl	M	W	Bl	M	W	Bl	M
10	26	192	152	158	55	—	—	—
25	29	246	432	419	110	22·5	19·4	13·4
33	38	234	590	554	284	30	26·2	42

Na			K			Osmolar concentration		
W	Bl	M	W	Bl	M	W	Bl	M
135	126	27	3·4	16·6	90	189	230	232
390	367	84	8·8	14·2	115	—	410	410
508	504	120·5	11·6	20·3	136·5	585	592	585

W = sea water; Bl = blood water; M = muscle water.

The results given in Table VIII show that the total concentrations and single ions in the haemolymph follow with only small differences the sea water in which the animal lives. The water content of muscle is practically the same in 25 and 33 °/$_{oo}$ sea water, but definitely higher in 10 °/$_{oo}$. In 25 °/$_{oo}$ sea water the sum of Na and K in the muscles is 199. Separate determinations of Ca and Mg have given the quantities per kg. water as 4·1 mM. Ca and 16·5 mM. Mg as against 11·2 and 44·3 in the corresponding sea water. The total base is therefore 240 mE. in the muscle as against 510 in the water, so that more than half of the osmotic concentration must be made up probably by organic molecules. The variations in the single ions, observed when the outside concentrations are changed, are very remarkable; but the material is insufficient for a discussion.

The chemical analyses give a slight and the vapour-pressure determinations a definite indication of an active osmotic regulation of haemolymph and tissues in *Mytilus* in 10 °/$_{oo}$ sea water, but we have not succeeded in confirming this by direct experimentation (Conklin and Krogh, 1938).

FRESH-WATER MOLLUSCS

Determinations of the ionic composition of the blood in *Limnaea stagnalis* from an Hungarian pond near the Balaton lake containing at the time 3·5 mM. Cl/litre were made by Huf (1934), who found that narcosis with ether would cause a loss of salts. This loss affected the different ions to a very different extent, and the concentration of K was even increased. I am inclined to look upon this as a kind of regulation by which K was given off from the tissues. The figures, recalculated into mM./litre, are given in Table IX:

Table IX

	Cl	Na	K	Ca	Mg	Total kation mE.
Fresh animals	42·6	47·5	2·8	3·05	4·8	66
Narcotized animals	31·3	39	3·0	2·35	3·95	54·4

Florkin (1938) finds that *Anodonta* preserves a constant weight in media which are hypotonic or isotonic to its own blood and loses weight rather rapidly in hypertonic media, from which he draws the tentative conclusion that the animal's surface is impermeable for water in one direction, but freely permeable from inside out!

Picken (1937) made very interesting and valuable experiments on *Anodonta cygnea* and *Limnaea peregra*.* He determined by means of the vapour-pressure method the molar concentration of blood, pericardial fluid (a filtrate from the blood) and urine. In the bivalve the blood concentration is very low, 16·2 mM. on an average, with variations between 10 and 20, while in the snail it is much higher (73 mM.). The pericardial fluid is stated to have the same molar concentration as the blood. The actual figures are lower, especially in *Limnaea*, but it must be admitted that the difference is not statistically significant. Florkin (1935), who took samples of urine close to the pericardium, found the concentration equal to that of the blood. The concentration of the final urine is definitely lower in both species, viz. 10 as the average for *Anodonta* and 54 in *Limnaea*. A reabsorption of osmotically active substances must therefore take place during the passage of the urine along the nephridial tube.

In special experiments Picken measured the rate of filtration from the haemolymph into the pericardium of *Anodonta*. He found rather large variations, but for animals of an average weight of

---

* *L. peregra* is a form which penetrates into brackish water.

50 g. (without the shell) the average filtration was about 1 ml. in 5 min. or six times the animal's weight per day. This must correspond roughly to the osmotic uptake of water, and the animal should therefore lose $0·300 \times 10$ mM. = 3 mM. of osmotically active substances per day through the urine. Picken makes calculations (admittedly rough) of the possible intake of food and comes to the conclusion that it is improbable that the salts of the food can cover the loss. He points out moreover that *Anodonta* is able to live for months in aquaria with running tap water, containing very little in the way of micro-organisms,* and finds the conclusion inevitable that *Anodonta* must be able to absorb salt through the outer surface from fresh water, in spite of the extremely low concentrations normally found there.

This conclusion is verified by work done about the same time in my laboratory, but not yet published in a paper. We tested *Limnaea stagnalis*, *Paludina vivipara*, *Dreissena*, *Anodonta* and *Unio* with about millimolar salt solutions after treatment with distilled water for periods of a few days up to 1 month.

Six *Limnaea stagnalis* with an aggregate weight of 26 g. reduced the Cl concentration of 45 ml. $0·01$ Ringer solution in 8 hr. from $1·16$ to $0·56$, taking up Cl at a maximum rate of $4·3 \mu M/hr$. In subsequent experiments Cl was absorbed from $CaCl_2$, but at a slower rate, and the concentration was never reduced below $0·9$ mM. There is reason to believe that calcium was not absorbed at all.

Eight *Paludina*, washed out only 3 days and weighing 33 g., at first failed to absorb Cl from $0·01$ Ringer, but after 11 hr. took up a little. Washed out for 4 days more they reduced the Ringer from $1·1$ to $0·105$ mM. Cl and absorbed at a maximum rate of $5·7 \mu M./hr$. The Cl concentration in the blood of two animals after the experiment was $17·3$ and $17·4$ mM., while in two animals from tap water it was 22 and $27·6$ mM.

Ten *Dreissena*,† washed out for 3 days and weighing 23 g., reduced 40 ml. NaCl solution from $0·74$ to $0·15$ in 9 hr., but this was clearly the limit to which they could attain, since the concentration rose

* Florkin (1938) observed that *Anodonta* in running tap water would keep up a normal concentration for nearly a year, but later it would drop slowly to about 18 mM. after 20 months.

† *Dreissena* is a form which has invaded fresh water from the Caspian Sea.

during the next 8 hr. to 0·22. In some later experiments *Dreissena* took up Cl from NH_4Cl, but the total amount was small only.

The first specimens of *Anodonta* tested were very large, weighing from 250 to 300 g. After washing for 6 days they failed to absorb. Nine days later a slight and doubtful absorption from mM. NaCl was noticed in single periods, but sometimes the concentration would rise again. A test with mM.$CaCl_2$ made after about 1 month's treatment with distilled water was entirely negative. It was thought at the time that the animals might be too old. The Cl concentration in the blood was determined and found to be 9·1 mM. Later experiments show that *Anodonta* can absorb Cl from millimolar solutions, but that the concentration cannot be reduced very far. Small individuals absorb with more energy than large ones and resist the distilled-water treatment better. In a small number of experiments some absorption of Cl^- from NH_4Cl with excretion of NH_3 was observed and also absorption of Na^+ from $NaHCO_3$.

Unio pictorum. From one fresh *Unio* weighing 54 g. of which the shells made up 15·4 g., 22 g. haemolymph was obtained showing a Cl concentration of 31 mM. The dry substance of the body was only 4·4 %. Four individuals with an aggregate weight of 70 g. reduced 200 ml. 1·11 mM. NaCl to 0·15 in 50 hr. with a maximum uptake of 21 μM./hr. In experiments with mM. $CaCl_2$ they took up Cl slowly, but lost Ca at the same time.

It is to be concluded from these experiments, carried out in collaboration with Agnes Wernstedt, that the fresh-water molluscs studied are able to absorb Cl^- and Na^+ from dilute solutions, but are probably unable to reduce the concentration below 0·1 mM. If this holds for all individuals they should be unable to live in water with Cl contents below 3 mg./l.

According to the experiments on fresh-water molluscs now described we find actively absorbing cells, both in the external surface and in the kidney tubule, able to take up salts from dilute solutions. As they stand Picken's experiments would place the kidney tubules as being much less effective than the cells in the surface, but I venture to predict that this is only because they were not put to a crucial test. When animals are prevented from absorbing salts from outside, the kidneys will probably be able to produce a urine which is almost salt free. Otherwise the process of washing out with distilled water would be much more rapid than is actually the case.

Philippson, Hannevart and Thieren (1910) and later Duval (1925) studied the behaviour of *Anodonta* in balanced salt solutions. Below 67 mM. the molar concentration of the blood is higher than that of the surrounding solution, but at higher concentrations there will be a complete equilibrium as shown in the curve, Fig. 28, p. 95. No regulation is possible by which the osmotic pressure of the blood can be kept below that of the external medium.

Although the problems of shell formation in molluscs do not, strictly speaking, come within the scope of the present monograph it may be appropriate briefly to draw attention to them. The $CaCO_3$, forming almost the whole of the inorganic material of the shell, must come from the water either directly or through the food. The Ca concentration in sea water is 10·9 mM. In fresh waters it is generally much lower, and, for instance, in the Danish lake Furesö about 1·1 mM. There are soft waters with Ca contents of 0·1 mM. and below. Molluscs are found in all these waters, and certain bivalves like *Margaritana margaritifera* can accumulate very large amounts of $CaCO_3$ in their shells in very soft water. In a suggestive study by Galtsoff (1934) it is shown that an oyster, showing at the beginning of May a "meat" weight of 5 g. with a 60 g. shell, grows until the middle of November, during a period when the temperature is always above 10° and food is regularly absorbed, to 15 g. "meat", while the shell reaches 100 g. Until the next May no food is taken and the weight drops to about 13 g., while the shell continues to grow at the same rate and reaches 135 g. This shows that Ca is taken up only to a slight extent with the food and mainly through the integument. The 75 g. $CaCO_3$ absorbed corresponds to 750 mM. Ca or the quantity present in 70 l. sea water or 7000 times the mean weight of the animal. It is almost inconceivable that such a quantity can be obtained from the water without a special mechanism for absorbing Ca.

CRUSTACEA

One of the essential characters of the Crustacea from the point of view of exchange with the surrounding water is the possession of a chitinous exoskeleton covering the whole of the body and all appendages including the gills. This allows only restricted volume changes, and while thin chitin membranes are in some cases fairly permeable to water and salts thick chitin and especially the lime-encrusted chitin shells of higher Malacostraca have a very low permeability. Exchanges can therefore in many forms take place through the gills only. The permeability of gills shows very wide variations which are probably due to differences in the living hypoderm membranes and only to a slight extent or not at all to differences in the chitinous covering.

Renal organs are usually well developed. In most of the higher forms one pair of kidneys is present opening towards the outside on the first segment of the second antennae where the pores are covered by a movable valve. The proximal end of each kidney is a closed "coelomic" sac richly supplied with haemolymph through a number of small vessels and lacunae.

A complicated canal made up of histologically different sections connects the coelomic sac with the bladder in which urine is stored for some time. The structure of the kidney in certain forms in which the urine has been studied from the point of view of ionic or osmotic regulation will be mentioned in some detail below.

Crustaceans undergo repeated processes of moulting. A moulting is preceded by an absorption into the body of a considerable proportion of the substances present in the exoskeleton, while certain zones in the endophragmal skeleton disappear completely. At the moult the exoskeleton is cast off, and immediately afterwards the soft body generally increases considerably in size by absorption of water before a new exoskeleton is formed by secretion from the hypodermis.

The Crustacea are no doubt primarily a marine group of animals, but several interesting forms show osmoregulatory adaptations which allow them to live in more or less dilute sea water or even to penetrate into fresh water. A number of forms are permanently adapted to a fresh-water existence and some live on land.

Without regard to the systematic divisions it will be convenient to discuss first the purely marine and comparatively stenohaline forms, then the euryhaline which can stand more or less wide variations in salinity, and finally the fresh-water Crustacea.

STENOHALINE CRUSTACEA

The blood or "haemolymph" is normally in osmotic equilibrium with the surrounding sea water. This was well shown by Duval (1925) who discusses the older determinations and shows further that in the species *Palinurus vulgaris, Platycarcinus pagurus* and *Maia squinado* the Δ of the blood follows closely that of the sea water when this is varied between 2·5° and 1·5°. At still lower salinities there is a slight, but unmistakable, tendency for *Platycarcinus* to show a higher concentration than the medium (Fig. 16). This tendency was also noted by Schlieper (1929) for *P.* (= *Cancer*) *pagurus*. At an external concentration of 220 mM. he found the internal to be 280 mM. Several other and more pronounced deviations from the general rule of isotonicity have been observed. Thus Bateman (1933) found that the isopod *Ligia oceanica*, living between tide marks and forming perhaps a link between marine and terrestrial forms, will show hypertonicity when exposed to 3/4 ocean water (550 as against 450 mM.), but die in an oedematous condition in 1/2 sea water.

In certain, mainly grapsoid, crabs, the blood is normally hypotonic in comparison with the surrounding sea water. Thus Baumberger and Olmsted (1928) found on the press juices of a large number of *Pachygrapsus crassipes* a concentration of 388 ± 6 mM., while the sea water was 575 mM. Schwabe (1933) also observed a definite hypotonicity for *Pachygrapsus marmoratus* amounting to 57 mM., while he confirmed the absolute isotonicity for *Portunus corrugatus, Herbstia condyliata, Dromia vulgaris* and *Maia verrucosa*. Enid Edmonds (1935), who studied the marine rock crab *Leptograptus variegatus* occurring abundantly on the Australian coast around Sidney, found a slight but definite hypotonicity, viz. ocean water 622 mM., blood of the crab 577 mM. This crab shows in dilute sea water, to which it is apparently never exposed in nature, a pronounced hypertonicity.

It will be shown below (p. 80) that certain euryhaline crabs have the power to maintain hypotonicity in concentrated sea water, while becoming definitely hypertonic in dilute.

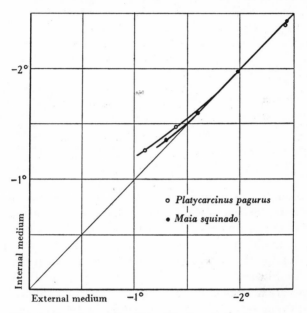

Fig. 16. Freezing points of blood (ordinate) of two crabs as a function of the external medium. (Duval.)

The normal isotonicity of blood and sea water does not necessarily mean an identical ionic composition although ions penetrate fairly rapidly (Bethe, 1927). Duval compared the Cl content in the blood of a number of crustaceans with that of the water with which they were in equilibrium and obtained the results shown in Table X.

The lower Cl concentrations in the blood are partly accounted for by the fact that the amount of dry substance is higher in blood than in sea water, and they would become reduced, but not abolished, when calculated per kg. of water.

Table X

| Crustacea | NaCl in g./litre | | NaCl blood |
	Blood	Sea water	NaCl water
Palinurus vulgaris	30·4	35·0	0·87
Homarus vulgaris	30·2	31·3	0·96
Atelecyclus cruentatus	31·8	32·7	0·97
Maia squinado	31·5	33·3	0·94
,,	31·5	33·3	0·94
Platycarcinus pagurus	27·5	33·0	0·83
,,	30·1	32·1	0·93
,,	29·8	32·1	0·92
,,	32·7	34·4	0·95
Pagurus bernhardus	28·1	33·0	0·85
,,	25·8	32·7	0·79
Portunus puber	30·2	33·0	0·92
,,	30·7	32·4	0·95
,,	31·0	33·3	0·93
,,	32·1	34·4	0·93
Carcinus maenas	29·2	33·0	0·88
,,	29·5	32·4	0·91
,,	31·5	34·4	0·91

According to Bethe and Berger (1931), who analysed the blood from several specimens of the crabs *Maia*, *Hyas*, *Portunus*, *Cancer*, and the lobster, *Homarus*, there is in relation to the Cl^- relatively more Na in the blood of these animals (97–102 %) than in sea water (87 %). The values for K are generally much higher and those for Mg lower, while Ca shows irregular variations. These relations are illustrated by the diagrams (Figs. 17, 18), and can be taken as expressions of a regulation brought about mainly by the kidneys. The actual figures should not be taken too seriously however, because the past history of the specimens is in the main unknown and considerable variations, due for instance to the intake of food, are likely to occur.

The kidneys of marine Malacostraca have a coelomic sac only moderately developed and with no excessive supply of blood. While the next kidney section, the "labyrinth", is often very large there is no "nephridial canal", and the bladder is connected directly with the labyrinth as shown in Fig. 26 (p. 90).

It is believed, mainly on anatomical and histological grounds, that a blood filtrate, consisting mainly of water and crystalloids, is

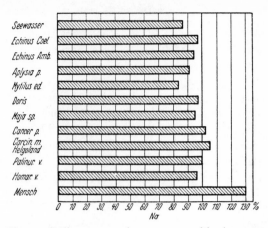

Fig. 17. Sodium content in sea water and in the serum of some animals. (Bethe and Berger.)

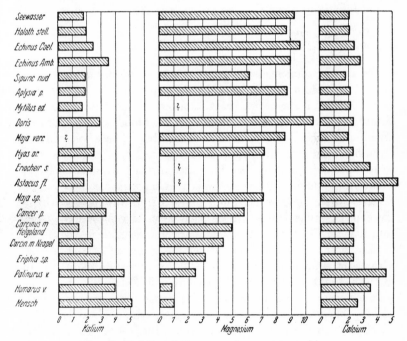

Fig. 18. K, Mg and Ca content in sea water and in the serum of some animals. (Bethe and Berger.)

poured into the coelomic sac, and that substances individually secreted are added in the labyrinth. It is, however, quite possible that some reabsorption may also take place.

Bialaszewicz (1932) studied the rate of urine formation and the composition of urine in large specimens of *Maia squinado* weighing 2 kg. or more. Urine was produced at a rate of about 2–2·5 ml./hr. or not more than 3 % of the weight in 24 hr. The normal urine contained more Ca, Mg and sulphuric acid than the blood, but definitely less K.

Typical results are given in Table XI. (The values are recalculated into mM./litre):

Table XI

	Sea water	Blood ultrafiltrate	Urine	$\dfrac{\text{Urine}}{\text{Blood}}$
Cl	636	626	626	1·00
SO_4	33·4	26·2	38·2	1·46
K	13·6	16·4	13·5	0·82
Ca	12·9	11·5	14·0	1·23
Mg	70·0	51·1	71·0	1·38

On the filtration reabsorption theory these results might be explained by assuming a reabsorption of water and K. In other experiments by Bialaszewicz the Cl concentration of the urine was found to be so much lower than that of the blood or sea water that this ion can also probably become reabsorbed. The whole conception, however, is highly hypothetical.

It is pertinent to ask where the water and salts excreted by *Maia* come from when complete isotonicity exists with the surrounding water. Partly they are no doubt derived from the metabolism of food, or of tissues if the animals have been starved for some time, and it is possible that the whole may come from this source.

The permeability to salts of the integuments of the marine Crustacea studied is fairly high. This was first brought out in Bethe's (1929) experiments on the shore crab *Carcinus* in which the animals were placed in artificial sea water with one ion either lacking or present in excess. The haemolymph always showed changes in the corresponding direction. In Ca-free sea water the normal Ca content was reduced to one-half in 140 hr., which did not appear to have any effect upon the animal. In 300 hr. it was reduced to about one-fifth, which greatly reduced the tonus and reflexes. Brought back into water with a surplus of Ca (32 mM.) an animal recovered in 6 hr., while the Ca rose to about 10. Similar experiments with Mg gave corresponding results and also the chlorine could be greatly reduced when about one-half was replaced by SO_4 in the water. K-free sea water would kill the animals in 36–48 hr. without greatly reducing the K content of the blood. It seems practically certain that the blood concentration was kept up by the tissues and that it was the loss of K in these which was fatal.

Berger and Bethe (1931) experimented with iodide which can be easily determined and demonstrated the permeability for this ion in *Hyas aranea*, *Portunus depurator*, *Cancer pagurus* and *Carcinus maenas*. In several of these experiments the intestine was shut off which made no difference. While the main exchange took place through the gills it was shown in special experiments that iodide would penetrate at a slow rate even through the carapace in crabs.

Nagel (1934), experimenting also with iodide, could show that the comparatively stenohaline Brachyura, *Portunus* and *Hyas*, were much more permeable to iodide than the more euryhaline *Cancer* and *Carcinus*. When placed in sea water containing a small amount of NaI the two first-named species would reach in $2\frac{1}{2}$ hr. a steady state at which the blood of *Portunus* showed about 96 % of the outside concentration and *Hyas* about 80 %. At the same time the blood of *Carcinus* would only contain 13 % and go on increasing for at least 80 hr. The experiments of Nagel make it probable that a similar difference exists with regard to the permeability of the gills for water, but the experiments made by Huf (1936) in continuation of preliminary work by Bethe (1934) and Bethe, v. Holst and Huf (1935) do not bear this out. In these experiments the hydrostatic pressure of the haemolymph was measured by inserting a vertical tube in the carapace. The normal pressure when the animals are in sea water is quite low, viz. 1–3 cm. water, but when they (*Hyas* and *Cancer*) are brought into 1/2 sea water, causing osmotic uptake of water, it rises abruptly and reaches 15–20 cm. in a couple of

hours. This corresponds to an increase in weight of about 6 %.
When the gut and antennary glands are closed much higher pressures and increases in weight are obtained, but it appears to me
doubtful whether loss of fluid was really prevented. In *Carcinus*
with open antennary glands there is no increase in weight and pressure, but it becomes apparent as soon as the antennary glands are
closed and there is no clear difference between the rate of increase
in the three genera.

The osmotic changes connected with moulting were carefully
studied by Baumberger and Olmsted (1928) on *Pachygrapsus
crassipes*, and the results were confirmed by Baumberger and Dill
on the apparently euryhaline blue crab *Callinectes sapidus*. Before
the moult there is a large increase in osmotic concentration, confirmed also by Robertson (1937) for *Carcinus*. In *Pachygrapsus* the
concentration rises from 388 to 760 and in *Callinectes* from about
400 to above 550. Just before the moult the shrunken animal is
partly withdrawn from the shell. Just after the moult water is
absorbed osmotically and the concentration becomes substantially
equal to that of the sea water. Baumberger and Olmsted calculate
for *Pachygrapsus* that pure water is absorbed, but Robertson finds
in *Carcinus* that chloride and Ca are taken up with the water.

The most interesting point is the mechanism of the large increase
in concentration just before the moult which has not so far been the
object of study. A hypotonic solution would seem to be eliminated. Salt may be taken up, but there is also the possibility that
organic substances produced within the body are responsible.
Baumberger and Dill failed to find in *Callinectes* any significant increase in the sugar concentration, and the increase observed by
Drilhon (1933) in *Maia* just before the moult, viz. from 6 to 18
mg. %, is also much too small.

We seem to find in some strictly marine "stenohaline" higher
Crustacea osmoregulatory and ionoregulatory mechanisms which
by further development might make the animals much more independent of the surrounding medium. Such development has taken
place in several forms and a study of these will be specially instructive.

EURYHALINE CRUSTACEA

The form which has probably been the object of the largest number of experiments is the common shore crab, *Carcinus maenas*.

Fredericq (1904) already observed a freezing-point depression of 1·68° for the blood of a crab acclimatized in dilute sea water ($\Delta = 1·19°$). Duval (1925) showed that the blood of *Carcinus* is isotonic with the sea water only at high concentrations (above

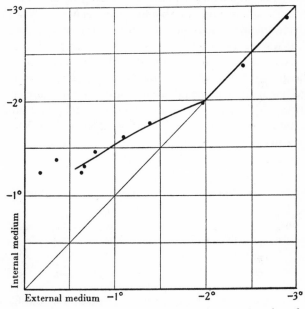

Fig. 19. Freezing points of blood of *Carcinus* as a function of the external medium. (Duval.)

530 mM.), while below that point it becomes hypertonic as shown in Fig. 19. Down to an outside concentration of 160 mM. the crabs would live indefinitely and maintain an inside concentration of 330 mM., but lower concentrations were lethal. Schlieper (1929a) found *Carcinus* thriving in Kieler Förde with a concentration of 200 mM., while their own concentration was maintained at 400 mM. The mechanism of this hypertonicity was investigated repeatedly by Bateman (1933), Nagel (1934), Huf (1936) and Picken (1936).

Bateman planned his experiments from a physicochemical viewpoint and achieved very little in the way of elucidating the problem. He found, however, that cyanide in a non-lethal concentration of $M/20,000$ to $M/15,000$ would only slightly reduce the power of crabs to maintain hypertonicity in dilute sea water. The animals would seem to be in a stupor, but continued stimulation would awaken them and they would then remain active for an hour or two. Bateman's conclusion that "it is very probable that the gill membrane is almost impermeable to water" is not really supported by his experiments and is easily shown to be erroneous. As a matter of fact, it was deduced almost simultaneously by Margaria (1931), working in Hill's laboratory, from the dilution curves of the blood that the gills of *Carcinus* are permeable both to water and salts.

Nagel compared the osmotic concentrations of *Carcinus* blood and urine with the sea water in which the crabs had attained a steady state, and obtained the following results (Table XII) which I express in millimolarity:

Table XII

	Sea water		Blood		Urine	
Salinity	Total	Cl	Total	Cl	Total	Cl
32·4	488	520	507	485	514	530
18·9	280	285	396	347	396	396
17·0	261	268	385	345	339	342
13·3	196	212	350	302	325	302
12·0	178	184	318	243	294	252

Although the figures are somewhat irregular and the Cl values probably too high, the table shows clearly enough that the urine is at all concentrations practically isotonic with the blood and in dilute sea water definitely hypertonic to the water.

The osmotic regulation is therefore not brought about by the kidney function which is, on the contrary, acting all the time to reduce the surplus of salt present in the blood.

This is accentuated by the fact that the urine production is increased in dilute sea water. The urine on which the above analyses were made was collected in 10 hr. periods, during which the antennary glands were kept closed, and measured by weighing the animals. On account of the resistance thus produced the values found, especially in dilute sea water, may possibly—nay, even probably—be too low. The urine production thus measured gives a minimum value for the osmotic uptake of water. Calculated for a 50 g. crab over 24 hr. at 15° C. Nagel found in 31–34 $^{\circ}/_{\circ\circ}$ sea water an average of 5·1 ml., in 16–17·3 $^{\circ}/_{\circ\circ}$ 6·3 ml. and in 15·7 $^{\circ}/_{\circ\circ}$ 8·5 ml. The water absorption was not measurably affected by keeping the intestine completely closed, and it is thus shown that the water comes in through the gills.

In experiments referred to above Nagel showed that the permeability for iodide was much lower in *Carcinus* than in the more stenohaline crabs *Portunus* and *Hyas*, and further evidence is adduced to show that generally the gills of *Carcinus* are much less permeable for ions in both directions than those of *Hyas*. This lower permeability is of importance in diminishing the amount of work necessary to maintain hypertonicity, but cannot of course explain away the hard fact that such work must be done, and Nagel finally made experiments showing that the work was performed by an active transport of salt (chloride) across the gill membrane from the outside towards the blood. These experiments were done by transferring crabs from one dilute medium to another somewhat more concentrated, but still more dilute than the blood. After such a transfer the Cl concentration of the blood would rise as shown by the following example: a crab with closed intestine was transferred from water with a Cl concentration of 240 mM. to water with 320 mM. which brought about a rise from 370 to 410 mM. The total concentrations measured by freezing-point determinations showed corresponding increases. The only objection which could be raised against this and a series of similar experiments seems to be that salt could be given off from the tissues under the stimulus of the action of the higher concentration upon the gills, but this would not explain how a permanently higher concentration is kept up against the constant loss through the kidneys.

Picken (1936) studied in some detail the urine formation in *Carcinus*. By means of vapour-pressure determination accurate to about 5 mM./litre he compared the concentrations of sea water, blood and urine in *Carcinus*. As an average of complete determinations on fourteen animals the sea water was 605 mM., the blood 602 mM. and the urine 600 mM., but the variations in both directions were so large that there can be no doubt that the urine can be both hypertonic and hypotonic to the blood. The hydrostatic pressure of the blood was measured in the sternal sinus and found to average 13 cm. water pressure. In the vessels of the antennary gland the pressure must be higher. In the pericardium there are pulsations with a maximum pressure of 40 cm. water. The difference in colloid osmotic pressure between the blood and the urine averages 9·6 cm. water. Picken concludes that there is a sufficient surplus pressure to produce filtration into the coelomic sac of the kidney. This is supported by the finding of Huf (1936) that an artificial increase in hydrostatic pressure within the body causes a considerable increase in the flow of urine.

The studies on *Carcinus* can be summarized as follows. The main mechanism for the maintenance of a higher osmotic pressure when the crab lives in dilute sea water is represented by the power (resident probably in certain cells in the gills) to absorb salt from more dilute solutions. This power becomes insufficient and breaks down when the crabs are exposed to very low salinities. It is helped by a low degree of gill permeability compared with the stenohaline forms, and by a kidney structure allowing urine production at a greater rate.

The mechanism for absorbing salt (Cl) against a concentration gradient performs thermodynamic work and must use up energy. An increased metabolism in *Carcinus* in dilute sea water has been demonstrated repeatedly and taken to be an expression of the secretion work performed by the gills.

Schlieper made the first experiments in 1929, and a careful comprehensive study was undertaken by Schwabe (1933). There can be no doubt that in *Carcinus* there is a considerable and permanent increase in metabolism when the animals are living in a dilute medium, about as shown in the diagram, Fig. 20, taken from Schwabe's paper. In view of the results obtained on *Eriocheir sinensis* and *Potamobius fluviatilis* (pp. 86 and 92), it appears very doubtful whether this increase is due exclusively or even mainly to the activity of the salt-absorbing mechanism. The gills make up only a small fraction (probably less than 1 %) of the total weight of a crab, and only part of the gill tissue can be active. An increase in metabolism of the active cells, not of 50 %, but of at least a hundred-fold, would therefore be required to explain the metabolisms observed.

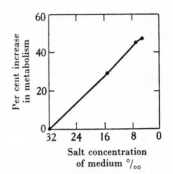

Experiments on isolated gills of *Carcinus* and also of *Mytilus edulis* and *Eriocheir sinensis* by Sylvia Pieh (1936) seem to demonstrate a relation between the degree of swelling brought about in different solutions and the respiration of the tissue. The gills of *Mytilus* and *Carcinus* were found to swell in hypotonic sea water and also in isotonic NaCl and showed a definite increase in

Fig. 20. Percentage increase in metabolism of *Carcinus* by dilution of sea water. (Schwabe.)

metabolism as measured with the Winkler and Warburg techniques. The gills of *Eriocheir* from fresh-water animals did not contain more water than those from sea-water animals.

The problem concerning the energy necessary for osmotic work cannot be studied by simply isolating the gills in different solutions. It will be necessary to do perfusion experiments with simultaneous determinations of salt uptake and metabolism.

Heloecius cordiformis is a small Australian crab living in mangrove swamps uncovered at low tide. It is found along the Hawkesbury river where the salinity varies from 100 mM. to almost pure ocean water and was studied by Dakin and Edmonds (1931) and especially Edmonds (1935). In ocean water it is slightly but definitely hypotonic, but in dilute water it becomes hypertonic and maintains an almost constant osmotic concentration of a little over 400 mM. down to outside concentrations of 50 mM. as shown in Fig. 21. In fresh water the concentration falls slowly and death supervenes in 48 hr. or less, but 2 % sea water will be enough to keep it alive for a long time. The active regulation of the osmotic pressure is therefore almost sufficient to allow this crab to penetrate into fresh water, but the mechanism is unknown. In highly concentrated sea water (900 mM.) the concentration of the blood of *Heloecius* will rise very slowly, but even after 21 days it is hypotonic to the extent of 150 mM.

Two other brackish-water crabs, *Sesarma erythrodactyla* and a species of *Macrophthalmus*, examined by Enid Edmonds, also show a permanent hypertonicity in dilute sea water.

E. Widmann (1935) observed *Gammarus marinus* in brackish water (160 mM.) and found the freezing-point depression of the blood corresponding to 460 mM.

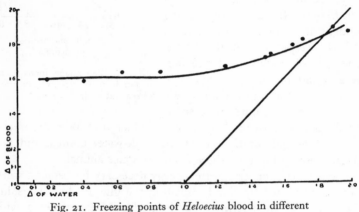

Fig. 21. Freezing points of *Heloecius* blood in different concentrations of sea water. (Edmonds.)

A small number of marine species belonging to different groups of Crustacea are able to penetrate into fresh water, but very little is known about the mechanism or mechanisms in most of them. Two examples are mentioned here and one, *Eriocheir sinensis*, is dealt with at some length.

Among the prawns of the marine genus *Leander* the species *longirostris* penetrates, according to Gurney (1923), many miles up rivers and can live in pure fresh water, but the egg-bearing females return to the sea and the eggs never hatch in fresh water. The young return to fresh water when they have reached a length of about 20 mm.

Chiridotea (= *Mesidotea*) *entomon*, which is derived from the arctic marine form *Chiridotea sibirica* (Wesenberg-Lund, 1937,

p. 553), is common in a large part of the Baltic, but is found also in several fresh-water lakes. Bogucki (1932) studied the Baltic form and found it by Cl determinations distinctly hypertonic in the brackish water, but approaching isotonicity in pure sea water (Fig. 22). The Baltic race could live only a few days in fresh water.

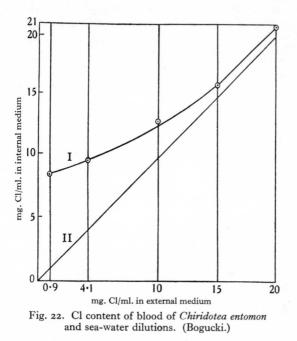

Fig. 22. Cl content of blood of *Chiridotea entomon* and sea-water dilutions. (Bogucki.)

Bogucki gives the following figures (Table XIII, recalculated into millimoles) for the different ions of the blood of *Chiridotea* compared with the Baltic water in which it lives:

Table XIII

	Na	K	Ca	Mg	Cl	P	S
Serum	202	6·1	12·5	11·6	206	1·3	7·2
Water	82	1·8	2·6	10·0	102	0·0	6·0

Eriocheir sinensis. The animal most remarkable for its penetration into fresh water is the Chinese "wool-handed" crab which was first encountered in Europe in 1912 and has since spread over large areas. The young crabs ascend the rivers in early spring and reach in the Elbe a distance of 700 km. (400 miles). They grow up to maturity in fresh water, but in the autumn the mature animals emigrate to the sea to breed.

When in sea water *Eriocheir* is slightly hypotonic to the surrounding water as seen in Table XVI (p. 82), and recent experiments by Conklin and Krogh (1938) have confirmed and extended this observation. We found by gradually acclimatizing young *Eriocheir* to sea water of increasing salinity that they became in normal sea water and higher concentrations definitely hypotonic (by vapour-pressure determinations) and showed a lower Cl content. In one series of experiments the crabs were kept in sea water which became concentrated by evaporation and was sometimes filled up with more dilute sea water. The following values were obtained (Table XIV):

Table XIV

Day ...	15		26		8	
	Cl	Total	Cl	Total	Cl	Total
Blood (mM./l.)	536	541	590	600	639	679
Water ,,	635	659	660	667	718	744
Diff. ,,	99	118	70	67	79	65

In a second series a crab was kept for 14 days in 45 $^o/_{oo}$ sea water of constant concentration. The hypotonicity which was pronounced at first showed a definite decrease. The figures are here corrected for the solids (Table XV):

Table XV

	mM./kg. water	
	Cl	Total
Crab 9 days	602	—
Crab 14 days	741	800
Water	774	802

When *Eriocheir* is transferred to fresh water or distilled water it loses salt (Cl) at first rapidly and then more slowly (Berger, 1931).

In fresh water a constant value is reached, but in distilled water the loss is continuous although at a decreasing rate (Fig. 23).

Scholles (1933) showed that the urine of *Eriocheir* produced at the rate of about 2·5 ml./day in a 60 g. crab, is approximately isotonic with the blood both in fresh water and in sea water. His

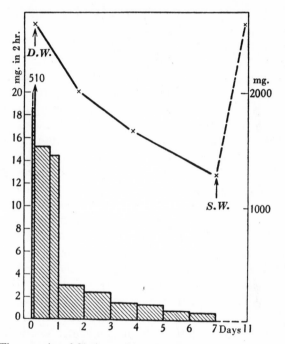

Fig. 23. The quantity of Cl given off in 2 hr. periods to the surrounding water by an *Eriocheir* of 151 g. transferred at *D.W.* to distilled water, frequently changed. The upper curve (right ordinate) shows the change in Cl content of the crab (calculated from the blood concentration). (Berger.)

figures for single ions recalculated in mM. are given in Table XVI (p. 82).

On the whole the urine is isotonic with the blood, but the ional composition shows very significant differences. It is very characteristic, for instance, that in sea water the kidneys tend to reduce the Mg content of the blood while in fresh water Mg is actively

retained. It is evident that there must be an extrarenal mechanism
which actively maintains the hypertonicity in fresh water.

Table XVI. *Eriocheir*

		No. analysed	Cl	K	Ca	Mg	Total from Δ
In fresh water	Blood	24	280	5·1	10·0	3·4	318
	Urine	19	264	7·0	4·7	0·7	330
In sea water	Blood	20	440	8·7	11·5	15·8	470
	Urine	18	500	10·0	10·7	35·0	486
	Water	—	494	10·3	7·6	39·8	503

The ion-absorbing mechanism located in the gills was studied by
Krogh (1938 *a*). A crab of 144 g. taken directly from fresh water
and placed in 500 ml. distilled water, changed at $2\frac{1}{2}$ hr. intervals,
lost Cl^- at the rate of 200–400 μM./hr. and Na^+ at about the same
rate, while NH_3 was given off at rates increasing from 24 to 110 μM.
The losses were determined by accurate analyses of the fluid in
which the animal was placed. After being washed for 24 hr. the
crab was subjected to a series of 2 hr. experiments in which the
openings of the antennary glands were alternately open and closed.
NH_3 was now lost at a constant rate of 85 μM./hr., independent
of the kidneys, while the rate for Cl showed regular alternations
between 108 and 82 μM./hr. The gills are therefore highly
permeable both to Cl and to NH_3, and only about 14 % of the Cl
loss takes place through the kidneys. It is therefore easy to wash
out *Eriocheir* with distilled water.

When a crab, washed out previously with distilled water, is
placed in ordinary fresh water or in millimolar solutions of pure
salts it will absorb at a great, but very variable rate, the maximum
recorded being about 200 μM. Cl/hr. from an average concentration slightly below millimolar into a crab of only 44 g. weight. The
outside concentration is never reduced to anything near 0, but the
absorption apparently stops when the concentration is between 0·2
and 0·4 mM., and when a crab is placed in distilled water which is
not changed the final concentration of Cl^- reaches the same level
at which active absorption just covers the loss through the gills and
kidneys.

By testing *Eriocheir*, after washing out, on a number of different mM. or 2 mM. solutions it was found that Cl^- is taken up actively from NaCl, KCl, $CaCl_2$ and NH_4Cl. From the last two solutions Cl is exchanged against HCO_3 without being accompanied by any cation, and absorption stops at higher concentrations than in the two first. Cl^- is also taken up at a normal rate from millimolar NaCl in 100 mM. Na_2SO_4, which is nearly isotonic with the haemolymph of the crab. The absorption is therefore independent of the simultaneous osmotic inflow of water.

A number of other anions were tested in a similar manner. When, however, an ion is absorbed which is not present beforehand in the haemolymph the initial decrease in outside concentration may be due to diffusion, and a proof of active absorption can be obtained only when the uptake continues after the inside concentration has become higher than the outside.

By experiments of this type it was found that iodide, nitrate and sulphate are not absorbed. Nitrate will diffuse in at a rapid rate, iodide slowly and sulphate apparently not at all.

Bromide, thiocyanate, cyanate and azid from NaBr, NaCNS, NaCNO and $Na-N{=}N{\equiv}N$ are all actively absorbed. The three first-named ions are almost non-poisonous and can be raised to much higher concentrations inside than outside, while azid is very poisonous, and experiments have to be discontinued after less than half an hour when the animal is still able to recover in ordinary fresh water.*

The anions which can be absorbed are all nearly related chemically. It will be shown below (pp. 137, 160) that the anion-absorbing mechanism of the vertebrates studied is much more selective, absorbing only Cl^- and Br^-, while rejecting CNS^- and CNO^-. On the other hand, Lundegårdh (1937) describes for plant roots an anion-absorbing mechanism transporting salts from the very dilute solutions present in the soil and concentrating them in the sap rising through the stems, a mechanism which does not distinguish between any of the anions tested and will especially absorb nitrate even more easily than chloride.

Lundegardh uses the term "Anionenatmung", because he was

* The experiments with azid, undertaken with the collaboration of Mr E. Zeuthen, are published here for the first time.

able to show that the amount of anion absorbed stands in a definite relation to the CO_2 liberated by the absorbing roots, and in his case cations appear to enter mainly by the electrostatic forces without any further expenditure of energy. In the gills of *Eriocheir* and in the absorbing systems of the animals studied so far the existence of separate mechanisms for cation absorption can be demonstrated when the cation is taken up from a salt the anion of which cannot or does not get in.

Na is thus absorbed from Na_2SO_4 and $NaHCO_3$, being exchanged against NH_3, while it is absorbed in the main with the anions from NaCl, NaBr and NaCNS.

The independence of the anion and cation absorptions respectively is well brought out if for instance NaCl is presented after a period with $NaHCO_3$. In the NaCl period the Cl^- absorption will be greatly in excess of the Na^+ absorption. When, on the other hand, NaCl is given after NH_4Cl the Na^+ absorption will prevail. It is very significant and distinguishes the absorption mechanisms of *Eriocheir* from those found in vertebrates that K is absorbed at a rate almost equal to that of Na. Absorption of NH_4^+ or Ca^{++} has not been observed.

We must look upon the ion-absorbing mechanisms in *Eriocheir* as being rather primitive in character and being developed independently of similar mechanisms in other animals. The cells responsible for the absorptions have not so far been located in the gills.

Considered from an oecological point of view the ion-absorbing mechanisms now described will allow the wool-handed crab to penetrate far into fresh water and secure a supply of Na, K and Cl even when no food is taken. In waters with salt contents below about 0·3 mM. the absorption will be insufficient to cover the large loss taking place by diffusion. The balance between the different ions must be maintained by the function of the kidneys which are supposed to act in a more selective way. It would appear that in the moulting periods an active absorption of Ca might be required and it may very possibly exist.

Scholles found that the female *Eriocheir* carrying eggs and normally living in sea water of 30 °/$_{oo}$ concentration cannot stand transference into fresh water, but will die in 2 or at most 5 days. It is a very curious fact, well worth a close investigation, that in these animals, which are supposed never to return to fresh water, the absorption mechanism has lost its functional power.

Scholles made some analyses on muscles and other tissues to study the "internal regulation", but as he could not be aware of the salt uptake through the gills and because the conditions were, also in other respects, not sufficiently well defined a discussion of the results is scarcely called for.

In my laboratory we have made a preliminary study of the concentration of a few ions inside the muscle cells of *Eriocheir*, comparing animals which had been for 3 days in distilled water with others taken simultaneously from fresh water and from 33 $^{\circ}/_{\circ\circ}$ sea water. All the animals had been without food for over 2 months. The animals in sea water and in fresh water were in equilibrium or in a steady state respectively, but those in distilled water could not of course be in a stable condition and would have died from loss of salts in a few days.

Table XVII. *Eriocheir*

Dry substance g./litre			Cl, mM./kg. water			Na, mM./kg. water		
W	Bl	M	W	Bl	M	W	Bl	M
o	—	15·3	o	154	23	o	184	13
—	—	14·3	1·5	269	53	1·1	307	21
3·3	—	19·9	594	446	139	528	462	33

K, mM./kg. water			Molar concentration		
W	Bl	M	W	Bl	M
o	6·0	95	o	222	245
0·09	8·6	103	7	350	355
12	7·4	136	597	560	—

W = water, Bl = blood, M = muscle.

The alkali concentration of the muscles is so low in all cases that there must be a very large deficit in total concentration to be made good by organic substances, and this probably holds for all higher Crustacea, but the organic substances have not so far been determined. The deficit is greatly reduced in fresh water and distilled water, but nothing definite can be said because alkaline earths were not determined.

The results show at least how tenaciously the K is held by the muscles. The variations in Na and chloride are also quite small absolutely, but large when calculated on a percentage basis. The really interesting experiment will be to follow the uptake of ions into cells from the blood after depletion in distilled water. There can be very little doubt, even now, that certain ions are taken up against the concentration gradient.

A series of experiments by Schwabe (1933) failed to show any significant difference in respiratory metabolism in *Eriocheir*, whether the animals were in approximately isotonic sea water (15 $°/_{oo}$), in normal sea water (32 $°/_{oo}$), or in fresh water. There is some reason to believe that a transport of ions is kept up all the time.

FRESH-WATER CRUSTACEA

Potamobius (*Astacus*) and *Cambarus*. The crayfishes are a small natural group of decapod Crustacea living exclusively in fresh water in Europe and North America.

The blood of these animals has a fairly high and almost constant osmotic concentration as observed by freezing-point determinations. This was shown by Duval (1925, p. 342) and for the American *Cambarus* by Lienemann (1938). The average value for *Potamobius fluviatilis* is 235 mM. and for *Cambarus* 189 mM.

The urine is very dilute. For *Potamobius fluviatilis* Herrmann (1931) gives the average value 47 mM. and for *P. leptodactylus* 82 mM., while Scholles found 26 mM. for *P. fluviatilis*. Scholles doubts the values of Herrmann, but large individual variations are likely to occur for reasons to be given below. Such variations were found by Picken (1936), who made simultaneous freezing-point determinations on the blood and the urine from both kidneys on individual crayfishes. He finds occasional large differences, and he finds that the urine from animals kept in hard water is definitely more concentrated than from animals in very soft water. In *Cambarus* Lienemann found on an average 53 mM. According to Duval about 90 % of the osmotic concentration of the blood is due to chlorides. For *Potamobius fluviatilis* Scholles gives the following average figures (Table XVIII) for the ions in blood and urine (recalculated). Bogucki (1934) and Huf (1934) found somewhat different figures for blood which I include for the sake of comparison:

Table XVIII

		mM./litre				
		Cl	K	Ca	Mg	Na
Blood	Bogucki	175	3·1	12·0	2·5	152
	Huf	199	10·1	7·8	1·6	184
	Scholles	195	5·2	10·4	2·6	—
Urine	Scholles	10	0·6	2·7	1·2	—

For *Cambarus* the figures given in mM./litre by Lienemann are as shown in Table XIX:

Table XIX

	Cl	Na	K	Ca	Mg
Blood	117	381	11·8	9·9	2·5
Urine	9·6	176	1·6	2·2	1·2
Tap water	0·2	6	Trace	1·1	0·5

The figures for Na in *Cambarus* are obviously erroneous, as they are for the blood about 100 % and for the urine over 200 % higher than the total concentrations. The variations recorded are absolutely inconsistent with the constancy of total concentration as observed by freezing-point determinations. Apart from this the figures in both tables show that the urine plays an essential part in the ionic regulation. The average urine production given by Herrmann for *Potamobius* is 3·8 % of the live weight in 24 hr., while Lienemann found 5·2 % for *Cambarus*, which is much smaller. In both cases the determinations were made by weighing the animals after closing the nephropores.

More detailed studies of the kidney function, important from the point of view of osmotic regulation, were made by Peters (1935) and Picken (1936). Peters points out the morphological difference between the kidneys in the marine *Homarus* and the fresh-water *Potamobius*. In the latter there is between the labyrinth and the urinary bladder a long nephridial canal with a considerable surface development (Figs. 24–26). The supply of blood as judged from the number of blood vessels and lacunae is much larger in the fresh-water form than in the marine. Peters drew out samples of urine with capillary pipettes from different parts of the kidney and compared their Cl content by micro-analyses with that of the blood.

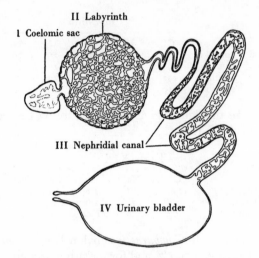

Fig. 24. Diagram of the antennal gland of *Potamobius*. (Peters.)

His results, which are averages of six separate samples, are given in Table XX:

Table XX

		Urine from			
	Blood	Coelomic sac	Main labyrinth	End of labyrinth	Nephridial canal	Bladder
Cl	196±3	198±2	209±7	212±7	90±6	10·6±0·6

I have recalculated his figures into mM./litre and added the mean errors on the averages to show the excellent agreement between single determinations, which is not, however, sufficient to establish a concentration of the urine within the labyrinth. According to these analyses the urine produced in the coelomic sac is in equilibrium with the blood. Substances are very probably added in the labyrinth, but the results establish almost beyond doubt that chlorides are reabsorbed in the nephridial canal. The alternative possibility of a large excretion of pure water in the nephridial canal is extremely unlikely.

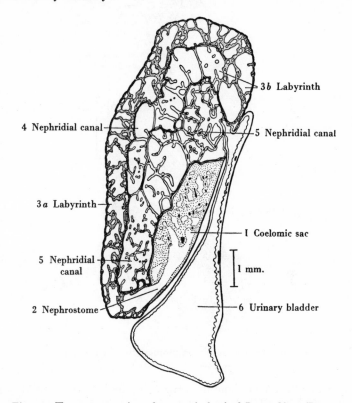

Fig. 25. Transverse section of antennal gland of *Potamobius*. (Peters.)

Peters's results furnish a strong argument for the assumption that urine is formed by filtration from the blood into the coelomic sac, and Picken, who determined hydrostatic and colloid osmotic pressures of blood and urine, finds values which are compatible with

such a filtration. It is evident from the studies of the urine that
the kidney function is an essential factor in the maintenance
of hypertonicity in the blood of crayfishes.

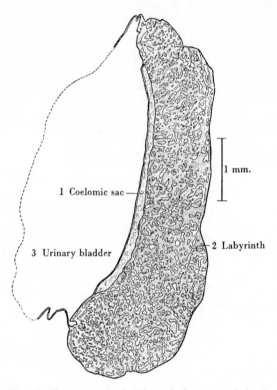

Fig. 26. Transverse section through the antennal gland
of *Homarus*. (Peters.)

A further factor of some importance is the low permeability of
the integument. Maloeuf (1937), testing the soft abdominal integument as a membrane in an osmometer, found it absolutely impermeable both to water and salts. This does not mean very much
since the main exchange takes place through the gills, but Huf
(1933), who measured the total osmotic uptake of water, obtained
figures which were very low compared with those found in marine

forms at a similar concentration difference, and Nagel showed that iodine diffuses in at a much slower rate.

However, there is a continuous osmotic uptake of water, amounting to about 4 % of the body weight per day, and this water is again excreted as urine containing some 30 μM. per ml. (Scholles, 1933). A crayfish of 50 g. will therefore lose every day about 60 μM. of osmotically active substances of which about one-third is chloride. Such a loss can probably be made good easily through the food, but like so many other animals the crayfish can starve for weeks without apparently losing much salt. The experiments of Berger (1931), Herrmann (1931) and Huf (1933) indicated that in sea-water mixtures hypotonic to the blood the osmotic pressure of the blood would rise and the blood would remain hypertonic up to a concentration somewhat higher than the normal, but these conditions are of course artificial. In unpublished experiments made in January 1936 the writer found that a crayfish of 40 g. weight would lose salt in distilled water at an initial rate of 22 μM. chloride in 24 hr. Washed out for 3 days in distilled water it took up Cl from Ringer/50 at the rate of 2·3 μM. Cl/hr. over 3 hr. and bromide from a corresponding concentration (2 mM.) at the same rate. The maximum rate observed was 6 μM./hr. over 11 hr. from a NaCl solution which was reduced from 1·2 to 0·26 mM. and at a slower rate down to 0. From 2 mM. $CaCl_2$ the uptake was somewhat slower, viz. 1·4 μM. Cl/hr. over 10 hr. in spite of the higher Cl concentration, and Ca was, in the few experiments made, not taken up at all. It is therefore evident that there is a special anion-absorbing mechanism which cannot distinguish between Cl⁻ and Br⁻. The cation absorption was not studied. It is significant that the rate at which Cl can be absorbed is much lower than in an *Eriocheir* of the same size, but that, on the other hand, the Cl concentration in the water surrounding a crayfish can be reduced practically to 0 which will enable the crayfish to live in natural waters very poor in chlorides. In such a case the low rate of loss is of paramount importance. Huf (1934) found that narcotized crayfish would lose salt (Cl) in ordinary fresh water, but the mechanism of this loss is uncertain.

Huf (1933) determined the Cl concentration in the blood of *Potamobius leptodactylus* (one specimen living in spring water with a Cl content of 0·5 mM.) over the moulting period. It is interesting to note the large fall in Cl preceding the moult and the rapid increase afterwards (Fig. 27) which Huf does not attempt to explain. It is noteworthy, further, that an increase in weight did not take place.

In 15 °/$_{oo}$ sea water the production of urine in *Potamobius fluviatilis* practically ceases, while the inside concentration corresponds to 20 °/$_{oo}$ salt. Schwabe (1933) and, later, Peters examined the respiratory metabolism of crayfishes acclimatized in fresh water and in 15 °/$_{oo}$ sea water respectively and found the metabolism lowered 40 % in the sea water.

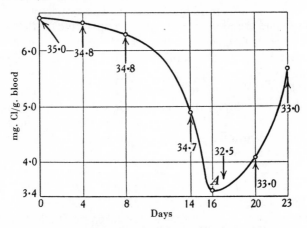

Fig. 27. Chloride content in blood of *Potamobius* in moulting period. The figures marked with arrows along the curve give the weight. At *A* the moulting was just finished. (Huf.)

Peters attempted further to determine by means of the Warburg technique the respiration of tissue pieces in solutions with 14 and 20 °/$_{oo}$ salt in the approximate combination of sea salt. 14 °/$_{oo}$ corresponds to the haemolymph of the animals in fresh water. He found the metabolism of all the tissues studied, including muscles, liver and kidneys, much higher in 14 than in 20 °/$_{oo}$ salt. The increase of the metabolism of the whole animal in fresh water is therefore a complicated affair which cannot be due exclusively to absorption and reabsorption processes and may be due in its entirety to something else. Although he finds that the metabolism of the nephridial canal in which the reabsorption processes take place increases more in the less concentrated medium than that of the labyrinth or other parts, it seems to me very doubtful whether this can be accepted as a measure of the energy utilized for absorption activity.

Bogucki (1934) transferred specimens of *Potamobius fluviatilis* to different concentrations of sea water and found that they would survive in 66 % sea water for 1 month and in 50 % for 3 months. In the higher concentrations of sea water their blood becomes isotonic with the water, but he finds a definite regulation of the mineral composition, the Mg being much lower than in the water and the alkalies correspondingly higher. I have recalculated his analytical results in Table XXI:

Table XXI

mM./litre

	Cl	K	Ca	Mg	Na	Cations mE.
Fresh water	0·48	0·075	1·5	0·25	0·65	4·2
Blood	175	3·1	12·0	2·5	152	184
20 % sea water	113	—	2·25	7·0	—	—
Blood	220	—	9·7	3·7	—	—
50 % sea water	292	5·1	5·5	17·6	247	298
Blood	312	6·5	12·5	4·9	258	299
66 % sea water	372	6·7	7·2	23·4	—	—
Blood	399	14·3	24·0	11·5	—	—

Bogucki finds further that the water content of muscles becomes reduced by increasing concentration of the blood, as shown in Table XXII:

Table XXII

Medium	Water in muscles %
Fresh water	84
20 % sea water	83·6
50 % ,,	79·3
66 % ,,	76·2

The mechanisms of these regulatory processes will require further study.

Other fresh-water Crustacea. It seems to be a general rule that the nephridial organs are better developed and have a relatively longer nephridial canal in fresh-water Crustacea than in related forms living in the sea. According to Schwabe (1933) this was first noticed by Grobben (1880) for the nauplii of *Cyclops* and *Cetochilus* respectively. Later it was confirmed on other copepods and found in phyllopods, ostracods and decapods. Rogenhofer (1909) made actual measurements of the organs in isopods, amphipods and decapods and Schwabe himself confirmed the facts in a detailed comparison of the nephridial organs in *Gammarus pulex* (fresh water) and *Gammarus locusta* (15–17 °/$_{oo}$ sea water).

In some forms, however, there is little or no difference, and it was noticed by Schlieper (1929) that in the fresh-water crab *Telphusa* (= *Potamon*) the kidneys are of the same type as in the marine crabs. Determinations of the urine concentration in this fresh-water animal showed practical isotonicity with the blood (Schlieper and Herrmann, 1930). *Telphusa* is, like *Eriocheir*, highly hypertonic in fresh water (Duval, Fig. 28), and there can be very little doubt that the mechanism is closely analogous to that of *Eriocheir*.

It may be noted here that Erna Widmann (1935) and Otto (1937) have observed an annual cycle in the osmotic concentration of the blood in a number of Crustacea, including *Eriocheir*, *Potamobius* and several amphipods and isopods which show higher values in winter. This is shown in some cases to be directly related to the temperature of the water, but the oecological significance is unknown.

Daphnia magna. In a paper finished in 1914 and published in 1916 Fritsche made a large number of very careful determinations of the freezing-point depression of the blood of *Daphnia* utilizing almost exclusively *D. magna* from which he could obtain enough blood by cutting one of the antennae. He used the micromethod of Drucker and Schreiner (1913), and it is evident that he mastered the many difficulties inherent in this technique. It is unfortunate that he gives his results very often in atmospheres and speaks about the internal pressure as if a hydrostatic pressure was meant. This has led several zoologists into grave misunderstandings, but should not detract from the value of the work. Fritsche finds the osmotic concentration, here expressed by the molarity of an equivalent NaCl solution, consistently higher than that of the surrounding solution. In normal well-fed animals it is about 68 mM. It seems to vary slightly with temperature showing a maximum about 20° C., but this is not statistically significant, and higher values have been found both at lower and at somewhat higher temperatures. The sexual cycle, the age and especially the state of nutrition have a definite influence. In cultures deprived of food the concentration of the blood became reduced in one experiment from 67 to 47 mM.

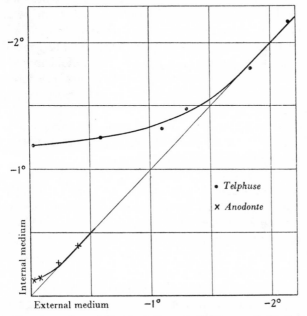

Fig. 28. Freezing points of blood of the crab *Telphusa* and the fresh-water bivalve *Anodonta* as a function of the external medium. (Duval.)

From our point of view the most interesting factor is the concentration of the surrounding medium. There are many observations in which this has been altered more or less accidentally and presumably slowly, and these show with increased concentration of the outside medium from 4 to 60 mM., a slight increase in the blood concentration reducing the difference to 20 mM., a difference

which can be maintained and even increased up to outside concentrations of 150 mM. In one series of experiments Fritsche himself varied purposely the saline content of the medium and obtained
by slow variation the results illustrated in Fig. 29. The points give
the individual determinations on animals and the short horizontal
lines the depression of the water to which they were acclimatized.
Fig. 30 illustrates a very instructive experiment. To the left are
given determinations on acclimatized animals, to the right the results obtained in a series of determinations on animals transferred
at zero time from 6 to 132 mM. water. After 3 hr. some of the
animals show a concentration in excess of that of the water. Isotonicity with the water might be attained by osmotic loss of water,
but in that case the animals would have lost their turgor completely
which they did not, and the increase beyond isotonicity requires the
assumption made by Fritsche "that the excess pressure is made
possible by uptake of salts from the water", an assumption which
I also find it difficult to avoid.

Hydrostatic pressure or turgor is certainly a factor of importance
in the life of *Daphnia*. The hydrostatic pressure is, however, only
a small fraction of the osmotic pressure.

In a series of papers Naumann (1933) studied the influence of
toxic substances upon *Daphnia magna* and found that the traces of
heavy metals usually present in ordinary distilled water are highly
toxic. It is a very remarkable fact, however, abundantly verified by
Naumann and also in other laboratories, that in the purest glass-
distilled water *D. magna* will live without food for 10 days or more.
Such experiments are made generally on three to eight individuals
in 100 ml. water. It seems almost inconceivable that animals with
an aggregate weight of (at most) 25 mg. can avoid losing the salts of
their blood during such a long period.

Experiments made by Ussing in this laboratory with heavy water
show that there is an 80 % exchange in less than 2 min., while a
complete equilibrium is reached within 5 min. Water therefore
enters fairly easily, and we must conclude from Naumann's observations either that a loss of salt through the integument and kidneys
can be *completely* avoided or else that the animals can stand some
loss (say a total of 1 μM.) and absorb salts to a steady state from the

resulting solution in which the concentration can scarcely be higher than 0·01 mM. Experiments to solve this question would not be

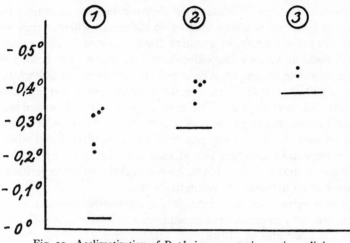

Fig. 29. Acclimatization of *Daphnia magna* to increasing salinity of the surrounding water. (Fritsche.)

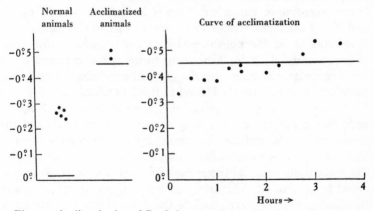

Fig. 30. Acclimatization of *Daphnia magna* by uptake of salt. (Fritsche.)

difficult when the vapour-tension technique and Wigglesworth's Cl determinations are applied.

The Euphyllopoda. A small number of experiments on *Branchipus*

(*Grubii?*) and *Apus* (*Lepidurus productus*) were made by the author in 1938 In spite of the systematic relationship with the Daphniae these animals behave in a very different manner in pure water and dilute salt solutions. Without food they can be kept alive only for a day or two, and it makes little or no difference whether they are kept in distilled water, in ordinary fresh water or in Ringer/100. In all these fluids they lose chloride at a decreasing rate from 3 to 0·7 μM./g. live weight/hr. The initial content found in *Branchipus* was 30 μM./g., but at the time of determination they had probably already lost considerably. The percentage of dry substance was about 8 decreasing to 7 in an experiment of 6 hr. duration. We seem to have animals without any power of active regulation and which can make good a constant loss of salts only by taking up food in sufficient amount. It is evident, however, that further experimentation will be necessary to settle the point.

Closely related to *Branchipus* is the interesting *Artemia salina* living normally in permanent or temporary salt lakes containing up to 220 $^{\circ}/_{\circ\circ}$ salt and in "Rockpools" in dry climates where the sea water becomes highly concentrated. According to Medwedewa (1927) the animals maintain a much lower internal concentration, found according to Barger's method to lie between 12 and 14 $^{\circ}/_{\circ\circ}$ and giving the highest value in the most concentrated saline.

In order to see whether the animals might perhaps be impermeable to water, which in these small forms was considered to be possible without endangering the gas exchange, the following experiment was made by Dr Ussing in this laboratory.

Twenty *Artemia** were placed in 280 mm.^{3} of molar NaCl in 20 % heavy water. Samples were drawn out at intervals and the concentration was reduced in 55 min. from 20·06 to 19·46 %. The D_2O lost from the water diffused into the animals, and after $1\frac{1}{2}$ hr. the concentration in the tissue fluid of these was determined and found to be 4·50 %. This is an exchange of less than 25 %, and considering the very large surface the permeability of *Artemia* to water is extremely low. It *is* permeable, however, and the animals must possess some osmoregulatory mechanism, the nature of which is at present unknown.

---

* These were kindly supplied by Prof. Baas Becking from Leiden.

ARACHNOMORPHA

The Arachnomorpha are perhaps systematically a natural group, but biologically and especially from the point of view of osmotic conditions we must distinguish between the marine Xiphosura, comprising only the genus *Limulus* which behaves like the marine stenohaline Crustacea, and the Arachnoidea of which the majority are land animals leading osmotically the same life as the terrestrial insects, while a single genus of Araneae, *Argyroneta*, and a large number of mites have penetrated into fresh water.

Next to nothing is known concerning osmotic conditions or osmoregulation.

The osmotic concentration of *Limulus* (*polyphemus*) was studied by Garrey (1905), who found the freezing point of the blood to be identical with that of the sea water within 0·02°. He made experiments with *Limulus* in diluted sea water, $\Delta = 1·02°$, and found after 25 hr. that the freezing point of the blood was reduced to $-1·43$, while after 52 hr. it was $-1·12$. The initial effect was probably largely due to osmotic transfer of water, but to obtain the final adjustment in the 50 hr. experiment permeability also to salts must be postulated, and Garrey showed further that *Limulus* gills dipping rhythmically into a small volume of fresh water lowered the freezing point of this to $-0·20$ in 8 hr., a change which was due mainly to chlorides.

Limulus was studied again by Dayley, Fremont-Smith and Carroll (1931), who confirmed the complete agreement in freezing-point depression between the "serum" of the haemolymph and the sea water. The chloride concentration was slightly lower, viz. 501 as against 517 mM. in the water and Na slightly higher (441 as against 437 mM.). The Cl difference is accounted for by the Donnan equilibrium due to the indiffusible serum protein which amounts to 2·5 %.

Argyroneta aquatica, the water spider, is virtually a terrestrial animal which carries a supply of air below the surface of the water like divers or caisson workers and does not enter into any exchange with the water. The exoskeleton is probably both water- and air-tight.

The Acarina, living in fresh water, have that only in common that they are very small. In some of the forms a low rate of metabolism is probable, and possibly the chitinous exoskeleton may be water impermeable without preventing the necessary oxygen uptake. In many other forms this appears unlikely *a priori*, and if so osmoregulatory mechanisms must be present, but nothing is known about them.

INSECTA

The insects form a very large and (on the whole) homogeneous group, adapted since very early geological periods to a life on land. Representatives of several orders have become secondarily adapted to live in fresh water, and a few of these have penetrated, at least as larvae, into brackish or salt water. Within each order, and in several cases within families, the adaptation to an aquatic life is an independent development, and we must expect that the problems of osmotic regulation have been solved in different ways, as is so conspicuously the case with the respiratory problems.

For a very large number of insects living on land the main osmoregulatory problem is the conservation of water by reduction of evaporation, and in such forms the chitinous exoskeleton is practically impermeable even to water vapour; evaporation takes place only from the tracheal system, and mechanisms have been described (Hazelhoff, 1926) by which the loss of water through spiracles is reduced to the minimum unavoidably bound up with the necessary exchange of respiratory gases.

In all the insects the excretory system is made up mainly of the Malpighian tubes opening into the intestine. The end-product of protein metabolism is usually uric acid which is generally excreted in solid form, and it is the rule for the excretion in insects that water is retained as far as possible.

Experimentally the osmotic adaptation of insects to a life in water has been studied only in very few forms, but something can be inferred from the structure, and there is a definite correlation between the need for osmoregulation and the mode of respiration.

Many aquatic insects are air-breathing, and such forms can be osmotically independent of the water by possessing, like the majority of their terrestrial relations, a water-impermeable exoskeleton. This is almost certainly the case with the imagines of water beetles belonging to the families of Dytiscidae, Hydrophilidae and Gyrinidae. Claus (1937) has published experiments to be discussed below which demonstrate an osmotic exchange with the water in Corixidae, although these animals are air-breathing.

When aquatic insects obtain their oxygen from the water it is possible for small forms to do without respiratory organs, and eggs and first-instar larvae may have a metabolism low enough to allow them to obtain the necessary amount of oxygen through an outer surface impermeable to water, but generally respiratory surfaces are permeable also to water and the animals have to solve the same osmoregulatory problems as other inhabitants of fresh water.

Alexandrov (1935) describes an ingenious method of studying the permeability of the chitinous exoskeleton on certain suitable forms. After cutting off both ends of a more or less cylindrical animal he removes the hypoderm by rolling pressure, washes the skin with distilled water, puts in a number of micro-organisms (*Paramaecium*) from a culture, ties off both ends of the skin and puts the closed sac in the solution to be studied. Alexandrov showed in this way by observation of the behaviour of the organisms in the sac that the chitin of *Chironomus* larvae is very permeable and the chitin of *Corethra* only slightly permeable to such substances as alcohol, $HgCl_2$, acetic acid and NH_3. Utilizing concentrated heavy water and suitable organisms it would even be possible to measure the permeability of the chitin for water. As far as can be seen Alexandrov does not consider the possibility of holes in the chitin exoskeleton.

The total osmotic concentration of the blood in insects seems to be fairly high. Florkin (1937), who summarizes some of the older determinations, gives values varying from $\Delta = 0\cdot5°$ to $\Delta = 1\cdot0°$, but some of the highest values do not inspire confidence. The values of $1-1\cdot2$ % NaCl given by Harnisch for *Chironomus thummi* are certainly too high. Backmann (1911), using the haematocrit and comparing with known NaCl solution, found for the larvae of the dragon flies *Libellula* and *Aeschna* $0\cdot63°$ and $0\cdot56° = 184$ mM. and 163 mM. respectively. Munro Fox and Baldes (1935) compared by accurate vapour-pressure measurements the concentration of the blood in aquatic insect larvae having a low and high metabolism respectively. They found no significant differences and their values are for the ephemerid nymphs *Ecdyonorus venosus* 159 mM., *Ephe-*

mera danica 128 mM. and *E. vulgata* 128 mM. For the trichopterid
larvae *Hydropsyche* sp. and *Limnophilus vittatus* they found averages
of 135 and 132 mM. respectively, with rather large individual variations. Wigglesworth (1938) found for mosquito larvae (*Culex* and
Aëdes) by the vapour-pressure method values from 128 to 154 mM.
It is a significant fact, brought out first by Portier and Duval (1927),
confirmed by Duval, Portier and Courtois (1928) and by Florkin
(1937), that a considerable proportion of the osmotic pressure of
the blood of insects is due to organic substances, especially amino
acids. In *Culex* and *Aëdes* Wigglesworth (1938) found that only
about 35–40 % of the osmotic pressure was due to chlorides.

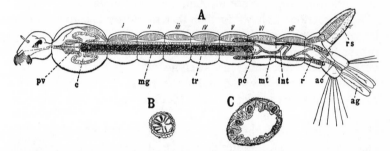

Fig. 31. A, anatomy of larva (semidiagrammatic): *ac*, anal canal; *ag*, anal gills;
c, caeca; *int*, intestine (hindgut); *mg*, midgut; *mt*, Malpighian tubes; *pc*, pyloric
chamber (hindgut); *pv*, proventriculus; *r*, rectum; *rs*, respiratory siphon;
tr, one of the main tracheal trunks. The figures i, ii, etc., indicate the respective
abdominal segments. B and C show cross-sections of the hindgut, B through
the intestine (*int*), C through the rectum (*r*). (Wigglesworth.)

The first investigation of osmoregulation in an insect was undertaken by Wigglesworth (1933 *b*) on *Aëdes argenteus*, an air-breathing
mosquito larva (Fig. 31) provided with fairly large anal papillae
which were up to then taken to be gills. Wigglesworth showed that
their gill function was negligibly slight, in good agreement with the
two facts that both their tracheae and their blood circulation are
very poorly developed, while he could show that they were far more
permeable to water than the rest of the body. This he did by placing
ligatures round the body of such larvae in different positions and
plunging them in various solutions. A larva placed in hypertonic
(2 *M*) glucose would shrink rapidly, but when a ligature was placed

round the body in front of the Malpighian tubes only the hindpart would shrink, showing that the permeability is in the main confined to this part. When a larva was ligatured between the fifth and sixth abdominal segments no fluid could be discharged by the Malpighian tubes into the hind gut (cp. Fig. 31), and when ligatured also round the neck the larva could not swallow water. When such a larva is placed in fresh water the hindmost part of the body gradually swells and the Malpighian tubes in this part become enormously distended. The segments of the body between the ligatures show no change or swell only slightly. Since the general body surface can take up or give off very little water it follows that absorption must take place through the anal papillae.

The experiment shows further that the water absorbed is to a large extent transferred to the Malpighian tubes, and when a ligature is placed in front of the forward loop of these, so as not to obstruct their discharge, no swelling takes place in tap water. Watching a larva in water under the microscope Wigglesworth could see fluid accumulate in the pyloric chamber of the intestine (cp. Fig. 31) and be carried down to the rectum at intervals of 2–3 min. From the rectum it is evacuated either in small quantities every few minutes or in a larger quantity at intervals of 15–20 min.

So far we seem to have the arrangement common to the large majority of fresh-water animals, viz. water is absorbed osmotically and eliminated through the renal system, but in this case there are interesting complications. The uptake of water takes place almost exclusively through the anal papillae, and Wigglesworth assumed this water uptake to be their chief *function*. He found, however, that by immersing larvae for 2–3 min. in 5 % NaCl the papillae could be damaged so that in many cases they would afterwards blacken and slough away, leaving only four little scars. Such larvae could live and become adult, but seemed to grow more slowly than normal larvae in the same culture. When such larvae are ligatured at the sixth segment there is no swelling in tap water, no distension of the Malpighian tubes, and normally very little fluid passes from the Malpighian tubes down the hindgut, and that which passes is reabsorbed from the rectum. Even in the larvae with intact papillae

Wigglesworth could observe some reabsorption taking place in the hindgut. We shall return to these observations later.

An attempt to study osmotic regulation on the larva of the Harlequin fly, *Chironomus thummi* (Fig. 32), was made by Harnisch (1935), who unfortunately was not acquainted with the work of Wigglesworth. These bright red larvae live in mud and utilize haemoglobin to combine with O_2 taken up through the whole of the body surface at extremely low pressure. It is therefore probable *a priori* that the surface is also permeable for water.

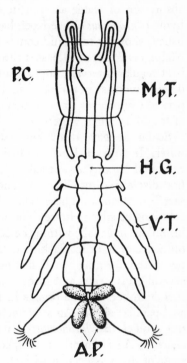

Harnisch demonstrated the osmotic uptake of water through the whole of the body by ligaturing either the posterior or both ends of the larva which caused a very distinct swelling and increase in weight. Ten larvae weighing initially 95 mg. increased in 43 hr. in water to 129 mg. or 36 %. In corresponding experiments in which the larvae were kept in 0·9 % NaCl no increase in weight was observed.

Fig. 32. Diagram of hindpart of *Chironomus* larva. *A.P.* anal papillae; *V.T.* ventral tubules; *H.G.* hindgut; *Mp.T.* Malpighian tubes; *P.C.* pyloric chamber. (Original.)

When the normal larvae do not swell in water there must be a water-eliminating mechanism, and Harnisch tried to locate this by placing ligatures at different distances from the posterior end. He thought he could observe that a ligature in front of the pre-anal tubuli behind the openings of the Malpighian tubes would prevent swelling of the anal part, and he tried accordingly to find evidence of a water-eliminating mechanism in the hindgut. Studying the epithelium on serial sections he observed a characteristic vacuolation made up of large basal and smaller distal vacuoles. Harnisch assumes an accumulation of water in the basal vacuoles and a transport of the water through the distal vacuoles towards the lumen of the gut. The observations might be interpreted just as well by absorption of water as seen in *Aëdes* by Wigglesworth. On the living *Chironomus* larvae Koch has made observations (not yet published) showing that fluid comes in considerable quantity from the Malpighian tubes. It passes through a "pyloric chamber" which is at regular intervals emptied into the hindgut. Koch observed a definite increase in turgor, equivalent to swelling, also of the hindpart of *Chironomus* larvae, when a ligature prevented the emptying of the Malpighian vessels.

So far we have dealt only with the uptake and elimination of water. In 1934 H. Koch studied the curious affinity for silver salts exhibited by certain special cells in a number of arthropods and first discovered by Gicklhorn and Keller (1925) in the "branchial sacs" of *Daphnia*. These cells will absorb silver from very dilute solutions of silver nitrate. The metal becomes precipitated (as an insoluble silver salt) within the cells and is later reduced under the influence of light to black metallic silver. Cells showing this property and forming small distinct organs had been observed in several crustaceans and insects, and Koch added considerably to their number. All the organs in Diptera larvae called anal gills or anal papillae absorb Ag selectively (Fig. 33), but the so-called ventral tubules in *Chironomus* do not. In the Anisoptera (*Libellula*, *Aeschna*) Ag is absorbed by special tissue patches in the rectum, some of them associated with the rectal gills (Fig. 34), but also by three epithelial plaques in the prerectal ampoule where urine collects. Wigglesworth (1933) thought that these special organs like the anal papillae of many Diptera larvae were water absorbing, but Koch suggests an explanation of their function which is much more likely, namely, that they absorb salts. This suggestion was put to the test on *Culex* and *Chironomus* larvae in a series of experiments on which a preliminary note was published by Koch and Krogh (1936), while a detailed account is given by Koch (1938) who planned and did all the experimental work. As in similar experiments on other forms the larvae were treated with distilled water during a

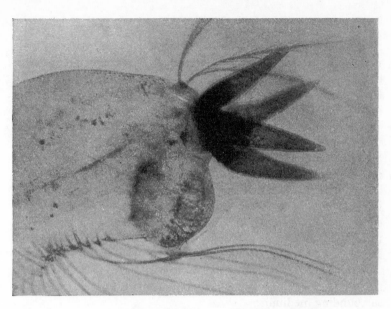

Fig. 33. Microphotograph of silver-stained anal papillae
of *Chironomus*. (Koch.)

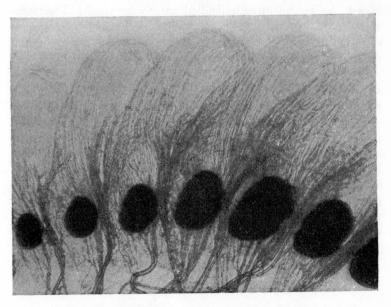

Fig. 34. Microphotograph of rectal gills in *Libellula*
stained with silver. (Koch.)

suitable period, and chloride determinations were made on 100–150 mg. larvae (four to six individuals of *Chironomus*, ten to twelve of *Culex*) before and after such treatment. A batch of the treated larvae were then exposed to a salt solution—usually frog's Ringer diluted to 1/100—and afterwards analysed to study the uptake of Cl.

Such experiments invariably showed a loss of Cl in distilled water and a return to normal values or even slightly beyond in the very dilute salt solutions. Experiments in which a ligature was placed just behind the head showed that the gut was not involved in this salt absorption. That the general body surface, including the ventral tubuli, was not responsible for the Cl uptake was shown by experiments in which a ligature was made round the last body segment. This completely prevented the uptake of Cl from Ringer/100. In special experiments in which the anal papillae alone were ligatured and put out of action by heat it was finally shown that these organs are alone responsible for the salt uptake from the dilute surrounding medium.

A single set of experiments was made in which the uptake of NaBr was compared with that of NaCl. The initial Cl concentration after 65 hr. treatment with distilled water was 7·9 mM. Treatment for 48 hr. with 1·11 mM. of NaBr raised the concentration (Cl + Br) to 11·8 or by 0·081 μM./g./hr., and in the corresponding experiment with NaCl the concentration rose to 18·0 (by 0·21 μM./g./hr.). Cl$^-$ seems therefore to be taken up at a much faster rate than Br$^-$. The difference is larger than what we find in animals with a definite anion-absorbing mechanism and might suggest either that Cl$^-$ can be distinguished by these organs from Br$^-$ or that Na is perhaps the ion absorbed actively while the anion follows suit by electrostatic forces. The latter alternative is the more likely, because Cl$^-$ is the more mobile of the two. Observations by Pagast (1936) are in favour of such a suggestion, as is also the fact that the cells take up Ag$^+$ with such avidity, the Na and Ag ions being somewhat related, but to settle the point by experiments on these small animals will be quite a difficult task.

The demonstration in this case that the organs which take up and are stained by Ag are indeed salt absorbing adds greatly to the significance of their detection in other organisms and also to the interest of their histology and microchemistry. They have been observed in many aquatic arthropods, but so far as I am aware not outside this group. This suggests an essential similarity within arthropods, as distinct from all other animals, in the cellular machinery for salt uptake which is the more remarkable because, as stated above, the power to absorb salts from dilute solutions must have been independently developed within many subdivisions of arthropods. I feel incompetent to discuss this conception further and prefer to point out as a caution that the Ag-absorbing cells are conspicuous in species of phyllopods (*Branchipus*) in which I did not succeed in finding evidence of any chloride absorption.

Koch draws attention to several cytological characteristics of the Ag-absorbing cells of which the most conspicuous seems to be the numerous fibrils connecting the outer and inner surfaces of the cells, a point of structure also emphasized by Wigglesworth (1933 *a, c*) in the case of the anal papillae of *Aëdes*.

From the biochemical point of view the reduction of Ag and permanganate was emphasized by Gicklhorn, but Koch points out that this is a secondary process, taking place even after the cells have been killed, while for the rapid and selective absorption and accumulation from very dilute solutions life is essential.

Koch's result on *Chironomus* is confirmed and amplified by Wigglesworth (1938) for *Culex* and *Aëdes*. Wigglesworth determined on the blood of single larvae both Cl by his new ultra-micro-technique and total osmotic concentration by the vapour-pressure method. The normal osmotic pressure in both *Culex* and *Aëdes* larvae varies between 130 and 150 mM. and the Cl concentration of the larvae in tap water is only about 50 mM. The higher values are given by animals which are abundantly fed, and starvation will reduce both the total concentration and the Cl content of the haemolymph. The main point is that the non-chloride—presumably organic—part of the osmotic pressure is definitely regulated by the larvae and made to compensate unavoidable variations in chloride content—a regulation which is apparently purely internal and independent of the surrounding medium. In an experiment in which larvae were starved in distilled water and tap water respectively Wigglesworth found on the seventh day:

Table XXIII

In distilled water total concentration 112 mM., Cl 8·5 = 7·7 %
In tap water   120 mM., Cl 43 = 36·0 %

The lowest Cl concentration in distilled water was reached in 6 days, and no further loss took place in 6 days more before the animals died. This final retention is very difficult to understand and should be studied on similar lines as the resistance of *Daphnia* to distilled water.

Wigglesworth discovered that the larvae possess a very definite power to resist the uptake of Cl when the outside concentration becomes higher than the inside. Fig. 35 shows the determinations of total osmotic pressure and Cl content of larvae brought into balanced solutions, made up only of chlorides in increasing concentration as marked along the abscissae. The higher concentrations were obtained by rearing the larvae at 0·9–1·0 % NaCl and then allowing the medium to evaporate slowly. The straight lines show where the points would fall if the outside and inside medium had the same composition. The curves for total osmotic concentration are very similar to those published by Duval for other fresh-water organisms. The Cl concentrations beyond 0·3 % (51 mM.) are consistently lower in the blood than in the medium. In the interval from 0·8 to 1·3 % NaCl there are large individual variations in the power of resisting a Cl uptake, and the much smaller variations in total concentration over this range show that an increase in Cl can be successfully compensated by a decrease in the non-chloride concentration. In special experiments Wigglesworth tested the power to keep chloride out by suddenly transferring larvae from dilute media to 0·95 % salt (162 mM.). Many died, but in those which survived the Cl rose to about 125 mM. at first, but dropped after 1–3 days to 110 mM. or lower.

Wigglesworth does not discuss the possible mechanism of this power of resistance to Cl uptake. The general body surface must be practically impermeable to chloride ions, but there can be little doubt that Cl penetrates fairly easily through the anal papillae and that the main work of resistance must fall upon the Malpighian tubes. Koch found in experiments (so far unpublished) on

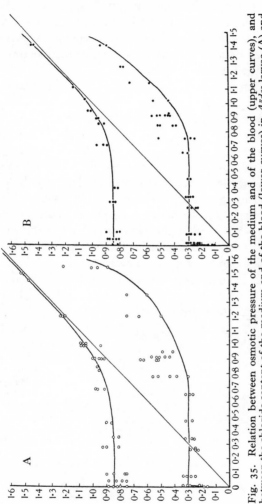

Fig. 35. Relation between osmotic pressure of the medium and of the blood (upper curves), and between the chloride content of the medium and of the blood (lower curves) in *Aëdes* larvae (A) and *Culex* larvae (B). Ordinates: values in the blood; abscissae: values in the medium, both expressed as equivalent concentrations of NaCl in g./100 c.c. The straight line shows where the points would fall if blood and medium had the same composition. (Wigglesworth.)

Chironomus larvae that the urine on entering the gut is hypertonic with regard to Cl, showing up to three times the Cl concentration of the blood, but that the concentration may be reduced in the hindgut.* By the excretion of a Cl-rich urine the blood concentration can be kept down, and there will be enough water for such excretion, because the total osmotic pressure of the blood is always above that of the medium.

The regulation processes in salt solutions are of special interest, because several species of Nematocera in the genera *Chironomus* and *Aëdes* either normally or occasionally live in brackish or salt water. There is a close correlation, as first noted by Martini (1923), between the size of the anal papillae and the salt content of the medium, and Martini found experimentally on *Aëdes meigeanus* and *A. nemorosus* that during the larval development the papillae would respond by growth to variations in salt concentration, becoming very large in distilled water, smaller in tap water and smaller still in 0·45 % NaCl. Wigglesworth (1938) gives the following experimental results for the larvae of *Culex pipiens* (Fig. 36, upper row) and *Aëdes aegypti* (Fig. 36, lower row) reared in different balanced chloride solutions. On six larvae in each medium the lengths of the papillae were measured and the individual variation as well as the mean length is recorded as follows:

Table XXIV

		Culex mm.	*Aëdes* mm.
A	distilled water	0·82 (66–92)	0·89 (65–93)
B	tap water (1 mM.)	0·36 (32–55)	0·60 (55–77)
C	,, (13 mM.)	0·33 (27–36)	0·60 (57–75)
D	,, (58 mM.)	0·22 (20–26)	0·53 (45–58)
E	,, (112 mM.)	0·20 (15–21)	0·71 (52–82)
F	,, (154 mM.)	0·20 (15–21)	0·50 (38–73)

The main reduction takes place in quite low concentrations as

---

* Koch's observation suggests a possible mechanism for the excretion of water by Malpighian tubes which, compared with the excretory organs of Crustacea, must be considered as aglomerular. If ions are transported into them by active secretion, water may be attracted osmotically and dilution brought about by reabsorption of ions at a lower level. This would be a complicated and apparently wasteful mechanism, to be understood only on the basis of an evolution from land-living and water-conserving ancestors.

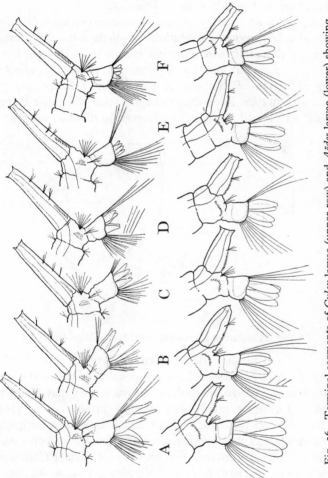

Fig. 36. Terminal segments of *Culex* larvae (upper row) and *Aëdes* larvae (lower) showing anal papillae in different media (see text). (Wigglesworth.)

observed also by Pagast (1936), and the largest difference is between distilled water (in which minute quantities of salt dissolve out from the food) and tap water, from which the larvae can absorb a sufficient amount of salt without difficulty.

Pagast (1936), who made comparative measurements on the anal papillae of *Aëdes aegypti* in solutions of single salts complicated, however, by the addition of *Paramaecium* cultures as food, found that the Na ion, but not the Cl ion, has a specific effect in causing reduction of the size of papillae. His figures are not convincing, however. According to Pagast acids will cause elongation, but not beyond the lengths observed in distilled water.

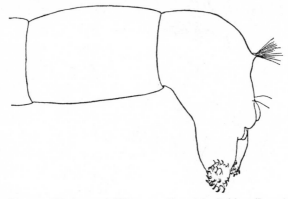

Fig. 37. Hindpart of *Chironomus* from lake Bahiro. (Lenz.)

Also in the Chironomidae a relation between the development of the anal papillae and the composition of the surrounding medium is observed. In brackish or salt water they may be greatly reduced and in moor ponds they increase in size. Lenz (1930) gives the adjoined pictures. Fig. 37 shows the almost completely reduced papillae in a chironomid from the Bahiro lake in Tunis which has a fairly high salt content. Fig. 38 shows a normal *Chironomus thummi* and Fig. 39 a larva from an "Almtümpel", an alpine pond in Austria used as a drinking place by cattle and strongly fouled by their droppings. In a very acid solfatara pond in Sumatra (pH 2·8) the anal papillae were also abnormally large. It seems unlikely that the water of the "Almtümpel" should be exceptionally poor in

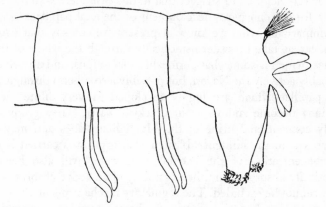

Fig. 38. Hindpart of normal *Chironomus thummi*. (Lenz.)

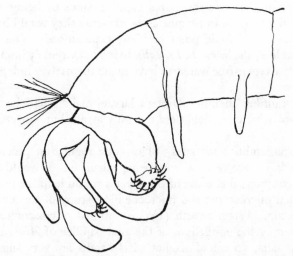

Fig. 39. Hindpart of *Chironomus* from "Almtümpel". (Lenz.)

salts or very acid, and I suspect that in this case there is some other reason for the enormous development of the anal papillae.

Summarizing what we know at present we can say that *Chironomus* larvae take up water osmotically through the whole of their surface, which is somewhat permeable also to ions, and absorb salt (probably actively the Na ion, but possibly also others) through the anal papillae which are highly developed in very dilute media and may become rudiments in brackish water. They produce a highly concentrated urine in the Malpighian tubes and may re-absorb salt in the hindgut. If such reabsorption is carried below the concentration of the haemolymph water will also become osmotically absorbed, and the possibility of an active absorption of water cannot be excluded. The regulatory mechanisms of Culicidae are very similar, but the body cuticle shows a very low permeability (air is breathed through spiracles). Salt and water are taken up simultaneously through the anal papillae, water always osmotically, salt in dilute media by an active process. It is at present difficult to see why the air-breathing larvae of *Culex*, *Aëdes* and many other genera should possess these anal papillae, since by being without them and having an impermeable exoskeleton they would be, from the osmotic and ionic point of view, land animals. One would expect at least the larvae of *Eristalis*, living in extremely impure and regularly oxygen-free water, to have made themselves independent in this way.

In a number of other Diptera larvae anal "gills" have been described which are doubtless not gills at all, but salt-absorbing organs.

The possibilities for study of osmotic regulation processes in Diptera larvae are very far from being exhausted. It would appear, on the contrary, that some of the species would lend themselves to a detailed microscopic and microchemical study of the active up-take of ions. Wigglesworth (1933 *a*) studied microscopically the behaviour of the epithelium of the anal papillae of *Aëdes* in solutions of salts, acids and alkalies. His results are very suggestive, but cannot now be utilized, because the power to absorb ions actively was not recognized at the time.

In almost all the other orders of insects aquatic larvae are met with which, possessing tracheal or so-called blood gills, must be assumed to enter regularly into osmotic exchange with the water, but experiments to decide the point have only been made on *Libellula*, on which I have found by experiments with heavy water that they are water permeable, and on larvae which had been treated for 3 days with distilled water that they would take up chloride from Ringer/100, ten larvae with an aggregate weight of 5·3 g. ab-

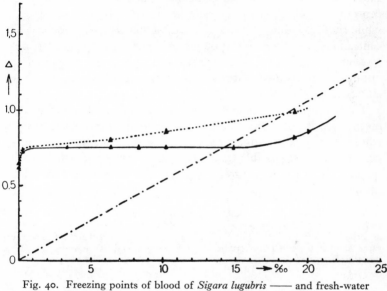

Fig. 40. Freezing points of blood of *Sigara lugubris* ——— and fresh-water *Sigara* - - - - as a function of external medium. (Claus.)

sorbing at a rate of about 2 μM./hr. over 10 hr. The absorbing organs I take to be the plaques in the hindgut staining with $AgNO_3$ (Fig. 34, p. 107).*

* In supplementary experiments made in November and December 1938 the selectivity of the ion-absorbing mechanisms of *Libellula* and *Aeschna* larvae has been studied. There are in these animals two distinct mechanisms. The one for anions absorbs Cl and Br (no other anions have been tested) from 2 mM. solutions of NaCl, NaBr, KCl and NH_4Cl, from the two last-named solutions without any accompanying cation. The rates are variable and tend to slow down when no cation is absorbed simultaneously. The maximum observed for Cl is nearly the same as that given in the text, while for Br it is slightly lower (0·29 μM./g./hr.) from a 2 mM. solution. Of cations only Na and K have been

In a recent paper Claus (1937) describes experiments on *Sigara* (*Corixa*) comparing the brackish-water species *S. lugubris* with the fresh-water forms *S. distincta* and *S. fossarum* under exposure to varied concentrations of sea water. Relevant from our point of view are, especially, determinations of total concentrations in the blood, and the curve (Fig. 40) illustrates the results which are essentially similar to those obtained by Duval on several invertebrates. It is interesting that *S. lugubris* maintains a constant concentration in the blood over salinities ranging from 1 to 14 $°/_{oo}$, while the fresh-water species show a gradual rise. At higher concentrations *S. lugubris* is hypotonic to the surrounding water, but it seems doubtful whether the experiments were of sufficient duration. In distilled water the animals gain in weight and lose chloride.

There can be no doubt of an active osmotic regulation, but the mechanism is not clear. The Corixidae are air breathing, and one would expect their integuments to be practically water impermeable. Is it possible that they take up water and salt in such quantity with the food (green algae?) that an osmotic regulation becomes necessary?

tested. Na is taken up from NaCl and $NaHCO_3$ at rates definitely higher than those found for Cl reaching $0.67 \mu M./g./hr.$ from 2 mM. NaCl, while K is not absorbed at all from $KHCO_3$ or KCl. The selectivity appears therefore to be the same as that observed in vertebrates, but experiments with more ions are desirable.

CYCLOSTOMATA

Nothing seems to be known about the osmotic conditions in the Tunicata or in *Amphioxus*, but these purely marine animals probably do not differ essentially from the marine invertebrates.

The Cyclostomata are a small group of rather primitive (or degenerate) vertebrates only remotely related to the remaining classes. From the point of view of osmoregulation the Cyclostomata show essentially vertebrate characters. There is a closed system of blood vessels and a separate lymphatic system. The fluids in the two systems must, however, be in osmotic equilibrium and the ionic differences can be small only in view of the permeability of the separating membranes. All the blood passes directly from the heart through the gills and is distributed through the dorsal aorta to the organs. The kidneys are simple in character and possess a few large Malpighian bodies in which urine is produced by ultrafiltration from arterial blood. It is assumed that this urine is modified by reabsorption and possibly secretion in the proximal convoluted tubules which are supplied with blood from the Malpighian bodies and also with venous blood from the tail (cp. discussion in the chapter on Teleostomi, pp. 130–132, and Fig. 41, p. 131). The skin is almost certainly permeable to water and perhaps to some extent to salts. The gills are placed in a branchial chamber through which water is passed by muscular movements.

The information available for the marine Cyclostomata belonging to the families Myxinidae and Bdellostomatidae is somewhat conflicting, but the analyses which I think most likely to be correct indicate that the blood of these animals is in almost complete osmotic and approximate ionic equilibrium with the sea water. Homer Smith (1932) found in *Myxine glutinosa* that the Δ of the blood was slightly higher than that of the water, 1·92 as against 1·88° C., and quotes older determinations by Dekhuyzen (1904) on *Myxine* and by Greene (1904) on *Polistotrema* (*Bdellostoma*) *stouti* to the same effect. Signe and Sigval Schmidt-Nielsen (1923), experimenting on *Myxine* in different sea-water concentrations between Δ 2·32 and 1·85, found a complete agreement between the concentration of the water and that of the blood. When the animals were transferred from one concentration to another the new equilibrium was reached in a few hours and mainly by changes in the water content. The osmotic concentration is made up largely by salts, and in *Myxine* the chlorides make up according to Schmidt-Nielsen and Homer Smith about 82 % of the total concentration (= 84 % of the isotonic sea water), while in *Polistotrema* Bond, Cary and Hutchinson (1932), who also exposed the animals to varied concentrations of sea water, found a relation between Cl in the blood and Cl in the medium of 0·89.

Against these results, which show a satisfactory agreement, must be put the analyses of Borei (1935) giving much lower values for the Cl content of blood and lymph in *Myxine*, viz. in water, containing 520 mM. Cl, only 325 mM. in the blood and 370 mM. in the lymph. In the same specimens Borei found urea concentrations amounting to 3500 mg./l. while Homer Smith found only 70–130 mg./l. Borei's urea determinations are certainly erroneous and the chloride determinations doubtful, but it should be pointed out that in all the earlier determinations the animals were in an abnormal condition. *Myxine* is extremely sensitive to changes in salinity and temperature. After being caught in the ordinary way it gives off incredible quantities of mucus and is unable to live for more than a day or two. Palmgren (1927) worked out methods for catching hag-fish without bringing them even for a moment in contact with water of higher temperature and lower salinity than in their natural habitat. These will keep perfectly normal for indefinite periods in aquaria and never give off any mucus, and Borei alone was able to make his determinations on such animals.

Of the three European species of Petromyzontidae one, *Petromyzon marinus*, lives most of the time in the sea but migrates into rivers to breed, while two others, *P. fluviatilis* and *P. planeri*, are fresh-water forms which can and do penetrate into brackish and perhaps even into sea water. These forms must therefore possess very effective regulatory mechanisms, but very little is known about them. According to Burian (1910) the serum of *P. marinus*, apparently taken in the Mediterranean ($\Delta = 2\cdot3°$), had a freezing-point depression of 0·586°. If this is confirmed the animal must have powerful machinery for resisting or compensating loss of water, and it would be extremely interesting to find out whether this is of the type to be described later for marine Teleostei. Dekhuyzen (1904) found for *P. fluviatilis* a Δ of 0·473–0·50°, and Galloway (1933) found for the same species 0·46°. Transferred to a mixture of 1 part sea water and 2 parts tap water with a Δ of 0·57° the osmotic pressure (determined by vapour tension) would rise in 22 hr. to $\Delta = 0·52°$ and the behaviour of the animals would become abnormal. Returned to tap water they would recover completely. Higher concentrations would produce a further rise, and pure sea water was lethal in less than 24 hr. It seems possible, however, that animals acclimatized slowly might have survived.

ELASMOBRANCHII

As Elasmobranchii or Plagiostomata are classed the sharks and rays and also the Holocephali comprising the single family of Chimaeridae. From the osmoregulatory point of view all these animals are mainly characterized by the high concentration of urea present in the blood and permeating all the tissues. The permeability of the skin is in most elasmobranchs of a low order, because the blood supply is small and mainly confined to the interior of the denticles which make up the larger part of the surface and can be taken as wholly impermeable. A current of water passes regularly through the mouth and branchial cavities, and an exchange of substances will take place through the mucous membranes of these cavities and through the gills proper which have a large thin-walled surface along which the whole of the circulating blood passes directly from the heart. The numerous kidney elements (30,000–50,000 per kg. fish, Smith and Smith, 1931) have large arterial glomeruli producing urine by filtration. Between the glomeruli and the proximal convoluted segments and again distal to these there are special segments, peculiar to the elasmobranchs, which are supposed to have as their chief function the reabsorption of urea from the glomerular filtrate. While the Chimaeridae are exclusively marine both the sharks and the rays have a certain number of representatives in fresh water. The evidence to be derived from the osmotic conditions and osmoregulatory mechanisms, which will be discussed below, points, in my opinion, to a marine origin of the group.

MARINE ELASMOBRANCHS

It was first shown by Staedeler and Frerichs (1858) that the blood of elasmobranchs contains large amounts of urea, and the fact has since been confirmed repeatedly and for so many forms that the universal occurrence cannot be doubted. The quantity varies within rather wide limits. Some of the older determinations giving very high values are perhaps not reliable. The more recent seem to show that in animals in more dilute sea water the urea content becomes lower as in the table reproduced on p. 124 from Homer Smith (1931). Recalculating as usual into mM. I divide the urea figures by 2 to make them directly comparable with the electrolyte concentrations.

In addition to urea the blood and tissues of elasmobranchs contain considerable amounts (100–120 mM.) of trimethylamine oxide (F. Hoppe-Seyler, 1930; Homer Smith, 1936), which being a weak base may be taken as osmotically active, like urea, in simple proportion to its concentration. Hoppe-Seyler has shown that the concentration of this substance in elasmobranch urine is only about 10 % of that in the blood, and we must assume therefore that it is actively retained to raise the osmotic concentration.

The total osmotic concentration of the blood in marine elasmobranchs is always close to that of the sea water, and Duval was the first to establish the fact, since amply confirmed, that it is normally slightly higher. This means a regular, but not very large, osmotic inflow of water through the exposed surfaces in so far as these are permeable, the main inflow no doubt taking place through the gills. Homer Smith (1931) has shown by an examination of the gut content of sharks and rays, kept for 24 hr. in sea water with added phenol red, that these fish do not habitually drink water, although they may occasionally swallow a little.

Smith gives analyses of the ionic composition of gastro-intestinal fluids in *Squalus acanthias* and *Raja stabuliforis*. These fish had been starved for 4–14 days before analysis, and the results are not therefore representative of quite normal conditions. They show that urea diffuses from the blood into the intestinal canal, and a comparison of the ionic concentrations in the stomach and intestine respectively makes it probable that the Mg^{++} and $SO_4^=$ ions are absorbed only to a slight extent, compared with K^+, Ca^{++} or Cl^-. In an earlier paper Smith (1929 *a*) compares the urea content of tissues with that of the blood and finds small differences only when calculations are made on the basis of water content. The perivisceral fluid contains an excess of Mg^{++} and $SO_4^=$ and the pericardial fluid an excess of K. These fluids are therefore characterized as secretions, and the power of cells to concentrate certain ions is again illustrated.

The rate of flow of urine has been measured repeatedly in several elasmobranchs, and the results are summarized by Smith. The figures are rather divergent, but all of them fairly small, the highest being 22 ml./kg./day, observed by Scott (1913) in *Mustelus canis*. The most reliable figure seems to be in the neighbourhood of 5 ml./kg./day, which should therefore represent approximately the volume of water absorbed osmotically. When food is absorbed its content of water will also be in the main excreted as urine, and the higher figures are possibly to be ascribed to this cause.

The urine is normally hypotonic to the blood and the difference is sometimes considerable, as shown in Table XXV compiled from the data of Smith. This table gives a great deal of interesting information, although it is clear that some of the determinations cannot be even approximately accurate, since in several cases the sum of Cl and urea in serum or urine exceeds the total concentration as found by freezing-point determinations, and both serum and urine contain in addition to the chloride both sulphate and phosphate. When the figures for Cl and urea in the urine are compared with those for the serum it is evident that both these substances are normally reabsorbed from the glomerular filtrate, and further that such reabsorption can take place in a very variable degree, that in other words it can be regulated according to the needs of the organism.

Table XXV

	Water	Serum			Urine				
	total conc. mM.	Total conc. mM.	Cl. mM.	Urea mM./2	Total conc. mM.	Cl. mM.	Urea mM./2	Phosphate mM.	$\dfrac{P}{N \times 0.028}$
Raja stabuliforis	546	583	—	248	495	64	179	79	16
,,	542	567	—	335	561	406	26	50	68
R. diaphanes	542	566	272	357	—	—	—	—	—
Squalus acanthias	542	572	—	—	548	157	123	79	23
Raja sp.	435	472	214	304	263	81	131	45	12
,,	320	360	183	253	231	25	60	66	40
,,	320	400	162	208	157	20	150	4	1*
,,	320	390	173	189	139	—	—	—	—

* Smith gives the figure 10, but this must be a misprint or an error in calculation.

Smith calculates what he calls the N/P ratio, but which I should prefer to designate as the P/N ratio, since it is defined by him as the number of millimoles of phosphate excreted with 1 g. N as urea + NH_3. In meat-fed or fasting animals (or man) this ratio is somewhat below 4 and is an expression of the ratio of P to N resulting from the combustion of protein. There is every reason to believe that the phosphate, which in the animal body must be mainly derived from protein, is quantitatively excreted through the urine and, since the P/N ratio in the table above is generally much higher than 4, Smith is probably right in concluding that a considerable proportion of the N is excreted extrarenally, although the extreme variability of the ratio does not inspire confidence.* It is, however, very probable, *a priori*, that the gills and other exposed membranes are not absolutely impermeable to urea and that a certain amount is constantly getting lost by diffusion. Margaria (1931) and Hukuda (1932) found in experiments in which specimens of dog-fish (*Scyllium*) were transferred to various dilutions of sea water that the limiting membranes were semipermeable, but the duration of their experiments was too short to establish the point.

By a similar reasoning from the ratio of Mg to Cl in the urine Smith endeavours to show that there must be an extrarenal excretion of Cl. This may be so, but I cannot accept the evidence as convincing.

FRESH-WATER ELASMOBRANCHS

Homer Smith and Carlotta Smith acquired merit in studying some species of fresh-water elasmobranchs in the Far East (1931). They give the table on p. 126 showing the concentrations in the blood of the species studied.

The main part of the experimental work was done on the saw-fish, *Pristis microdon*, which was obtained in numbers in perfectly fresh water about 40 miles from the mouth of the Perak river in Malaya. There is a tidal range of up to 4 m., but Smith is careful to point out that at Teluk Anson where the experiments

---

* There is the further objection that the urine according to Smith's own analyses contains a considerable proportion of N which is neither urea nor NH_3, but must nevertheless be derived in the last instance from the protein catabolized. When this is taken into account the ratio as given would be somewhat reduced and in the second specimen of *R. stabuliforis* even halved.

were made there was never at any depth any "detectable" chloride
which is stated to mean less than 1·0 mM./l. *P. microdon* is,
however, a marine fish, but "a frequent invader of rivers in the
tropics".

Table XXVI

	Serum		
	Cl mM.	Urea mM./2	Total mM.
Pristis microdon	170	130	299
"	169	93	272
Dasyatis uarnak	212	104	299
Carcharhinus melanopterus	158	103	264
Hypolophus sephen	146	81	—

The analyses of the blood and urine in *Pristis* can be summarized
as follows. In some cases the fishes were starved for 2 or 3 days
before the analyses were made. This did not seem to make any
difference. The total concentration of the blood corresponds to a
freezing point of 1·00 to 1·02° or 295 mM./l., the chloride being
about 170 mM. and the urea about 110 mM. The total concentration of the urine was only 29 mM. with 5·5 mM. Cl and 14 mM.
urea as an average of nine determinations. In one case the urine
is reported as Cl free. Phosphate is excreted on an average in much
higher quantities than corresponding to the N of the urine, and it
is concluded that urea is given off by diffusion through the gills and
mucous membranes. The urine flow measured by collecting urine
through a catheter in the urinary papilla (in the males) or in the
cloaca (in the females) is extremely copious, varying between 150
and 460 ml./kg./day and averaging 250 ml., which is fifty to a
hundred times more than in the sea-water elasmobranchs. If these
flows are really normal they indicate a much higher permeability
for water than in the marine species, because the driving force, the
difference in osmotic concentration, is about 290 mM. in the case
of *Pristis* and on an average 43 mM. in the marine forms listed in
Table XXV.

The urine flow was generally measured in experiments in which
a fish was kept over a period of 3–4 hr. in a known volume of water

in a long and narrow tank, and by analysis of the water the extra-renal excretion of urea, ammonia and chloride was studied.

In several of these experiments intravenous injections of urea, NaCl, Na_2SO_4, $NaHCO_3$, water or glucose were given, but with very small effects. The most remarkable fact is, perhaps, that the injection of urea could be tolerated only in a dose of 0·75 g.*/kg., corresponding to 35 mM., which would raise the urea content of the organism from the normal 110 to 145 mM., which is still less than half the concentration in marine elasmobranchs, while higher doses invariably caused convulsions and death.

The main result of the experiments was that urea and NH_3 were regularly excreted extrarenally and in quantities which varied only slightly. This is taken to prove an outward diffusion of these substances through the gills and mucous membranes, a conclusion which I am ready to accept, although I do not think that the total quantities observed are at all normal. The average excretion of (urea + NH_3) N is given as 450 mg./kg./day, "a figure that is not excessive for recently fed carnivorous fish kept at 80° F. (26·5° C.)". When the additional N of the urine is taken into account, as it should be, the excretion is well above 0·5 g./kg./day corresponding to over 12 Cal. from the combustion of protein, which is a very high figure, as seen by the following comparison.

From the phosphorus figures given for marine elasmobranchs an average urine concentration of 54 mM./l. can be calculated. With a P/N ratio of 3 (as defined by Smith) and a urine flow of 5 ml./kg./day, this would correspond to 0·005 . 54/3 = 0·09 g. N/kg./day or 2·3 Cal. from protein. There is no reason to think that *Pristis*, even if recently fed, should have a protein metabolism five times as high, and in my opinion it is a great deal more reasonable to assume that the *Pristis* specimens experimented upon by Smith were not really normal, but had their gill membranes damaged so as to absorb osmotically an excessive amount of water and producing the corresponding quantity of urine. The polyuria would make the reabsorption mechanisms less effective, and the damage to the gills might cause a direct loss by diffusion of substances like Cl and urea which are more concentrated in the serum than in the surrounding water.

* In the paper the dose is given as 0·75 mg./kg., an obvious misprint.

Smith observed a very variable extrarenal loss of chloride which he is inclined, because of its variability, to take as a regulated excretion. In one case, in a fish which had been starved for 6 days, he found no extrarenal loss, while in two others the urine was completely or almost Cl free. In view of the fact that we have observed in practically all fresh-water vertebrates and invertebrates studied a special mechanism for absorption of Cl it is much more natural to assume the presence of such a mechanism in the gills of *Pristis* and to explain the variations observed by Smith as variations in the activity of this mechanism. To *prove* its existence it would be necessary to keep the animals for some time in really Cl-free water. This would cause a loss of Cl both through the urine and by diffusion, and if the mechanism is present it should enable the fish after such treatment to absorb Cl from a dilute solution like ordinary fresh water.

Smith finds that the total Cl excretion averages in eight experiments about 20 mM./g. (urea+NH_3)N. "This value is about 3 times as large as in a dog fed upon canned salmon and 10 times as large as in a fasting dog", but in spite of that Smith does not think that it indicates an abnormal loss of Cl during the experiments. I am unable to agree.

I arrive at the following picture of the osmotic regulation in elasmobranchs generally. The salt content in the organism is reduced by the presence in blood and tissues of urea in a concentration which would be fatal to most other organisms. This urea is retained by reducing the permeability of the gills to urea to an unusually low figure and by a special reabsorption mechanism for urea in the kidney tubules. The total osmotic concentration of the blood is always higher than that of the surrounding water, and water flows in osmotically as a result of this difference which is fairly small in sea water, but considerable in fresh water. The water is excreted in the kidneys which produce a hypotonic urine by reabsorption from the glomerular filtrate. Both urea and chloride are regularly reabsorbed, and the resulting urine is usually only moderately hypotonic in sea-water elasmobranchs, but very dilute in fresh water in conformity with the general rule for fresh-water animals. In the fresh-water *Pristis* there is some indication of the presence of an extrarenal Cl-absorbing mechanism.

Smith seems to take it for granted that the elasmobranchs have a fresh-water origin. In my opinion physiological evidence, as derived from a study of the osmoregulation, points rather in the opposite direction. There would be no point for a fresh-water organism in reducing the salt content by substituting urea since the salt content tends always to become reduced by losses to the surrounding water, and special mechanisms are necessary to keep it up at about the same height as in a large number of other fresh-water forms. It would appear, although we are unable to see why, that a total salt concentration slightly below 1 % is essential for the high development reached within the vertebrate phylum, irrespective of their habitat in the sea, in fresh water or on land. The marine elasmobranchs approach this concentration, while retaining hypertonicity above the sea water by means of urea. The fresh-water elasmobranchs have reduced their urea content considerably, but still bear witness of their ancestry by a urea concentration roughly thirty times higher than that of teleosts.

TELEOSTOMI

The subclass of Teleostomi is here taken to comprise the Dipnoi, the Ganoidea and the Teleostei, but very little information is available about the lung-fishes and the different orders of ganoids. It is generally assumed that the fishes are derived from fresh-water ancestors and have secondarily penetrated into the sea and, while inconclusive as evidence, the mechanisms by which osmotic regulation is accomplished are on the whole in good agreement with this view.

The general circulation is modelled on the same lines as in the cyclostomes and elasmobranchs, the heart being on the venous side of the gills through which the blood passes before entering the dorsal aorta.

The kidneys (Marshall, 1934) are built up of a very large number (100,000 or more) of elements which in most fishes consist of an arterial glomerulus (Malpighian body) enclosed in a capsule. Through a ciliated neck segment the capsule is connected with a proximal convoluted tubule opening usually directly into a branch of the collecting tubes. In some cases there is a short intermedial segment and a distal convoluted tubule proximal to the collecting tube system. This arrangement appears to be the same in principle as the one met with in many invertebrates and specially well developed in the higher Crustacea. It provides for filtration under pressure of a fluid which must have very nearly the same ionic composition as the blood, with subsequent modification by reabsorption and in many cases probably by secretion.

Several marine species of fish like the goosefish (*Lophius*) and the toadfish (*Opsanus tau*) have aglomerular kidneys, and from the point of view of evolutionary history it seems very significant that in these a small number of arterial "pseudoglomeruli" unconnected with the tubules and non-functional (Grafflin, 1929) can be discovered microscopically. In one kidney of a goosefish seventy-eight such structures were found, while the number of tubules was estimated as 150,000. In this case the vascular supply of the tubular apparatus

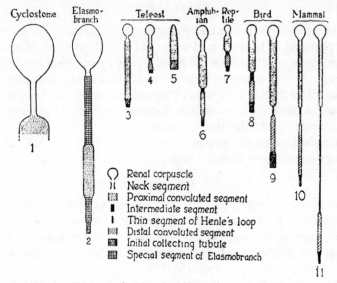

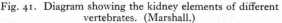

Fig. 41. Diagram showing the kidney elements of different vertebrates. (Marshall.)

Table XXVII

No. in fig.	Class	Genus	Renal corpuscle		Neck segment	
			Length mm.	Diameter mm.	Length mm.	Diameter mm.
I	Cyclostome	*Bdellostoma*	0·63	0·50	0·40	0·05
2	Elasmobranch	*Raia**	0·56	0·35	0·05	0·04
3	Teleost	*Myoxocephalus*	0·125	0·10	0·035	0·015
4	,,	*Ameiurus*	0·088	0·080	0·108	0·025
5	,,	*Opsanus*	—	—		

No. in fig.	Class	Genus	Proximal convoluted segment		Distal convoluted segment	
			Length mm.	Diameter mm.	Length mm.	Diameter mm.
I	Cyclostome	*Bdellostoma*	0·75	0·35	—	—
2	Elasmobranch	*Raia**	56·0	0·12	—	—
3	Teleost	*Myoxocephalus*	6	0·055	—	—
4	,,	*Ameiurus*	1·23	0·05	1·13	0·035
5	,,	*Opsanus*	4·27	0·07		

* The proximal convoluted segment is intercalated between two other segments which are not represented in other vertebrates. The first of these measured 7·6 × 0·050 and the second 28·0 × 0·050.

is almost exclusively venous. Functionally the aglomerular kidneys are probably to be compared with the Malpighian tubes in insects as organs in which urine is produced mainly by secretion and having conservation of water as a major task. Just as we have seen in aquatic insects that a copious elimination of water can be brought about on this basis we shall find that even aglomerular kidneys can be adapted to a fresh-water existence.

Marshall gives the measurements shown in Table XXVII on kidney elements in different fishes represented in Fig. 41.

FRESH-WATER FISHES

The osmotic conditions and mechanisms of fishes living permanently in fresh water are very similar to those of fresh-water invertebrates. The osmotic concentration of the blood and tissue fluids is in all cases much higher than that of the surrounding water and ranges from 130 to 170 mM.

Bottazzi (1908) gives the figures shown in Table XXVIII (recalculated into mM. from freezing-point determinations):

Table XXVIII

Barbus fluviatilis	140–147	(Fredericq)
Leuciscus dobula	132	,,
Leuciscus erythrophthalmus	145	(Dekhuyzen)
Cyprinus carpio	154–158	,,
Tinca vulgaris	135–151	,,
Abramis blicca	146	,,
Esox lucius	152–156	,,
Perca fluviatilis	149	,,
Amia calva (Ganoidea)	152	,,

Garrey found values about 147 mM. ($-0.50°$) for several fresh-water fishes of the Mississippi, and Duval obtained values very close to this for the carp. He finds in this fish that 74·5 % of the total concentration in the serum is made up by chlorides. It is to be concluded generally that in each species the concentration of the blood is maintained at a fairly constant level, and the differences between different fresh-water fishes seem to be small also.

The skin, mucous membranes and gills of fishes are generally permeable to water, but there seems to be rather large variations in the permeability. The permeability of the skin of scaly fishes is lower than that of naked forms (Sumner, 1905), but definite measurements are lacking and are quite difficult to make. On trout (*Salmo irideus*) Krogh (1937) observed a slow diffusion of heavy water through the skin. The main osmotic uptake of water no doubt takes place through the gills (and mucous membranes of mouth and gill cavity). The total osmotic uptake of water is represented in a fish not taking food by the urine excreted, since fresh-water fishes do not drink water (Homer Smith, 1930). Only a few measurements of the urine flow are available. Marshall states that the cat-fish (*Ameiurus*) may produce urine at the rate of 300 ml./kg./day. Smith gives the corresponding figures for *Cyprinus*, *Carassius* and *Anguilla* (in fresh water) as 60 to 150 ml., and I have observed in *Salmo irideus* a range of 60–106 ml. The flow is scarcely proportional to the weight, but more probably to the surface area.

The skin and gills are slightly permeable also to organic substances and ions. Homer Smith (1929) found in experiments on *Carassius auratus* and *Cyprinus carpio* made in a divided chamber and with a retention catheter for the urine that a very large proportion of the nitrogenous waste products are excreted extrarenally. The excretion takes place mainly as NH_3 through the gills, but small quantities are also lost through the skin. Urea, which makes up some 20 % of the total nitrogen, or less, is also mainly excreted through the gills, and the urine sometimes contains only nitrogenous substances which are neither NH_3 nor urea. I have confirmed on *Carassius auratus* the copious NH_3 excretion through the gills (Krogh, 1938). Smith showed that in the case of urea a simple diffusion takes place from the more highly concentrated blood, while in experiments of 24 hr. duration in a divided chamber the NH_3 concentration in the water surrounding the head of a carp might rise above that of the blood. In view of the complicated relations between combined and free NH_3 he comes to the conclusion that "the difference in total ammonia in blood and water is too small to justify the belief that secretory activity on the part of the gill membranes is involved in the escape of ammonia by this route". The point will come up for discussion below.

In experiments with a large carp of 1·5 kg., provided with a retention catheter and kept in a chamber, divided into compart-

ments enclosing the anterior and posterior parts of the body
respectively, the water after 24 hr. contained small, but measurable,
amounts of ions, and Smith gives the following example which I
have recalculated from concentrations to total quantities:

Table XXIX

	Front chamber (850 ml.) μM.	Back chamber (1470 ml.) μM.
Total base	1140	1940
K	280	280
Ca	150	320
Mg	85	40
Cl	370	910
SO$_4$	140	230

These quantities are certainly very small and do not indicate, as
Smith points out, any preferential permeability of the gills; but
they show that in a starving fish a loss of salt must take place con-
tinuously not only through the urine, but also by diffusion through
the surface, including the gills.

On *Salmo irideus* the loss of chloride taking place through
definite parts of the surface was measured and found to vary between 0·1 and 0·2 μM./cm.^{2}/hr. The total surface of a 200 g. fish
being 345 cm.^{2} (including 90 cm.^{2} fins), a loss per day of 1000 μM.
through the skin is to be expected (Krogh, 1937).

In experiments in which only total losses of chloride were
measured it was found (Krogh, 1937) that when fishes were transferred to distilled water, renewed each day, they would generally
lose a rather large quantity during the first day or two, but later at
a much slower rate. A small *Ameiurus* (19·5 g.) lost 300 μM. the
first day and later about 100 μM./day. Twenty-two sticklebacks
(*Gasterosteus aculeatus*) weighing 17 g. lost in 3 days 320 μM.

It seems to be generally known that the urine of fresh-water
fishes is very dilute, but I have been able to find only very few
actual determinations. Smith (1932) gives his own freezing-point
determinations on *Protopterus*, *Amia*, *Lepidosteus* and fresh-water
eels as from −0·07 to 0·09° C. = 22 mM. I found in the urine of
fresh-water trout a Cl concentration of 1·9–11·8 mM. On a goldfish

of 50 g. I have seen urine productions of 40–100 ml./kg./day with Cl concentrations from 2·5 to 4·1 mM. In this case the head only was in water, and the minimum urine production must correspond to the osmotic uptake of water through the gills. The gill surface was 55 cm.[2] The concentration difference was approximately 120 mM., corresponding to 5·4 atm. From these data a day number of 158 is calculated, indicating a low permeability for water.

In fish which are feeding normally the unavoidable losses of ions are probably made good mainly through the food and a constant composition of the body fluids maintained by regulation of the salt output through the urine, but it is well known that many fishes can stand fasting for very long periods, and it is therefore probable, *a priori*, that they possess like so many of the fresh-water invertebrates special mechanisms for the absorption of ions from the water. This has been confirmed (Krogh, 1937), but rather large differences between different species were brought to light. The fishes were washed out in a slow current of distilled water in the apparatus shown in Fig. 54, p. 216, for varying periods, according to the size and species, and then tested in known volumes usually of about millimolar solution. In most cases Cl only was determined at intervals in the solution.

The results obtained on single species are as follows.

Ameiurus had to lose a considerable proportion of Cl before it was induced to absorb, but when a fish of 19·5 g. had lost in 12 days a total of 740 μM. it absorbed Cl and Br from millimolar solutions of sodium salt without, however, reducing the concentration to anything approaching 0.

Gasterosteus, after washing out, absorbed from Ringer/100 (1·1 mM.) which was brought down to 0·32 mM., but the fishes failed to absorb from 0·2 mM.

Acerina cernua and *Perca fluviatilis*. Small specimens of ruffe and perch of 5–10 g. would continue to lose Cl whether in distilled water, in ordinary tap water or even in Ringer/10 (11·5 mM.), and would live only for 10–14 days without food. In one case a slight absorption was noted in tap water where a ruffe of 4 g. weight reduced the concentration in 60 ml. from 1·67 to 1·59 in 24 hr.

Salmo irideus. The ability to absorb Cl from about millimolar solutions was demonstrated on young trout of only 8 g. weight, and rates up to 57 μM./day were observed. On adult trout of 200 g. I did not succeed, but I have no doubt that this was due only to the experimental difficulties.

Leuciscus rutilus. Roach proved able to absorb Cl from extremely dilute solutions. One fish, probably of about 100 g. weight, was kept in 4 l. "distilled" water with a concentration of 0·042 mM. Cl and changed each day. During the first 5 days it continued to lose Cl, but after an aggregate loss of 400 μM. it began to absorb and in one day reduced the concentration to 0·02, absorbing 88 μM., and this absorption continued until the initial loss was made good.

A roach of 25 g., the skin of which was damaged, could only stand distilled water for 2 days when it became very weak. Transferred to 100 ml. tap water it absorbed Cl at an average rate of 4 μM./hr. and recovered. Continued experimentation made it clear that the loss of salt through damaged skin was an important factor in the lethal effect of distilled water. A special series of qualitative experiments on roach of 4–10 g. showed that these would die in distilled water in 2 days, but survive in Ringer/2000 (about 0·5 mM.). Damaged fish of 10–20 g. would die in distilled water or salt solutions up to 0·1 mM., but survive in stronger solutions and, if taken in time, could be restored in 5 mM. Ringer. In the damaged fish there is both an increased osmotic inflow of water and also a direct loss of salt through the damaged part of the skin which must be made good by the active uptake of ions.*

Carassius auratus. Preliminary experiments on goldfish showed that they could be readily washed out so as to absorb Cl at a fairly rapid rate and reduce the concentration from 1 to 0·2 mM., and for these fish a divided chamber was constructed in which the exchange in the head and in the body behind the pectoral fins could be studied separately. It turned out that the fish had to become accustomed by a series of trials of 1–3 hr. duration to the confined position in this chamber before a regular absorption could be expected. The experiments then showed that the active absorption takes place

* Fishes are often exposed to damage in nature. Otterstrøm (1935) mentions several cases of fishes lacking pelvic fins and thinks it probable that they have been attacked by eels. The chances of wounded fish to recover will be determined largely by the salt content of the water in which they are placed.

only in the head chamber. As the skin must behave in the same way in both chambers we can take it that the active absorption takes place through the gills.

By means of the divided chamber the absorption of single ions was studied (Krogh, 1938). Cl^- can be absorbed from NaCl, KCl, NH_4Cl and $CaCl_2$ and from mixtures of these salts with nitrates and iodides. The absorption from NH_4Cl especially is taken as proving the existence of a special anion-absorbing mechanism, active with regard to Cl^-. This mechanism also actively takes up Br^-, but neither I^-, NO_3^- nor CNS^-. I^- penetrates very slowly by diffusion, but no penetration of NO_3^- or CNS^- could be detected. The uptake of Cl^- (or Br^-) need not be accompanied by any absorption of cations, and Cl is absorbed alone from NH_4Cl or KCl and usually from $CaCl_2$. In such a case Cl^- must be exchanged against HCO_3^-, but when a cation is absorbed simultaneously with Cl^- the rate is more rapid and the total quantity absorbed definitely larger.

An independent mechanism for cation absorption exists and will take up Na^+ from NaCl, NaBr, $NaHCO_3$ and $NaNO_3$ or from mixtures of these, as well as from mixtures of $NaHCO_3$ with $KHCO_3$.

When this absorption is not accompanied by an approximately equivalent absorption of Cl^- it is sometimes compensated by a definite increase in the ammonia excretion through the gills, but in one case at least the Na^+ taken up was in excess of the NH_4^+ given off, and Na was apparently taken up with bicarbonate ions.

It is a very significant fact that K^+ is not absorbed at all, and from mixtures of K and Na salts the Na can be almost completely removed by the fish, while the K is left behind.

In most experiments Ca^{++} was not absorbed at all, but I have once seen Ca^{++} taken up with Cl^- and even at a slightly more rapid rate.

The two mechanisms for Cl^- and Na^+ seem to be similar in principle to those described above for *Eriocheir*, but they are definitely more selective.

Duval (1925) succeeded in acclimatizing carp to fairly salt water during the months October to March in the basement of the "Institut Oceanographique" (the temperature is not recorded). He raised the concentration gradually by adding small quantities of sea salt once or twice a day for a certain number of days, varying between 5 and 50. When the desired concentration had been reached the fish was left for 2 days more. The results of a series of experiments are given in the curve (Fig. 42). From a concentration corresponding to a freezing point of $0·7°$ (205 mM.) the concentration of the blood of the fish became identical with the surrounding water. This species at least, while able to tolerate an increase to about double of its normal concentration, does not seem to possess any mechanism to counteract the change.

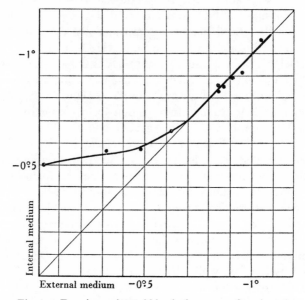

Fig. 42. Freezing points of blood of carp as a function of external medium. (Duval.)

MARINE FISHES

These show an osmotic concentration much lower than that of the surrounding water and maintain a constant composition of their internal medium by regulatory mechanisms of a very peculiar character.

The first determinations of the osmotic concentration of marine teleosts were made by Bottazzi in 1897 who measured the freezing-point depression of the serum of *Charax puntazzo* and *Serranus gigas* and obtained values of 1·035–1·04° or 305 mM.

A considerable number of careful determinations on many different genera and species and comparisons with the older results available were given by S. and S. Schmidt-Nielsen (1923). These range from Δ 0·66–0·78°, confirming the fact that marine fishes, while essentially independent of the surrounding sea water, have concentrations definitely higher than the fresh-water forms.

Smith (1932) gives the following (Table XXX) useful series of comparative values for water, blood and urine:

Table XXX

	Water	Blood	Urine	Observer
Anguilla rostrata	1·85°	0·82°	0·79°	Original
Orthagoriscus mola	2·15	0·80	0·69	Rodier, 1899
Anarrhichas lupus	1·73	0·68	0·63	Dekhuyzen, 1905
Gadus virens	1·73	0·76	0·63	Dekhuyzen, 1905
Gadus morrhua	1·73	0·73	0·65	Dekhuyzen, 1905
Lophius piscatorius	2·15	0·86	0·80	Bottazzi, 1906
Conger vulgaris	2·15	1·03	0·82	Burian, 1910
Scorpaena scrofa	2·15	0·71	0·65	Burian, 1910
Myoxocephalus octodecim-spinosus	1·85	0·82	0·78	Smith, 1930 *a*

When a fish possesses a lower concentration than the surrounding solution it must, unless the gills and integument are impermeable, face a steady loss of water by osmosis. When, moreover, it produces a hypotonic urine it must in addition obtain water from the sur-rounding solution for the urine.* This osmotic problem was clearly formulated and solved by Homer Smith (1930).

Smith demonstrated by adding phenol red to the aquarium water that marine teleosts actually drink large quantities of the water in which they swim. The dye becomes concentrated in the intestine, and by measuring the concentration it becomes possible to de-termine the extent of water absorption taking place. In an experi-

---

* To my mind Smith (1930, 1932) stresses unduly the observed fact that the teleost urine is hypotonic. There is clear evidence that water can be reabsorbed in the convoluted tubules of the sculpin (Marshall) and in the aglomerular kidney hypertonicity should be expected unless, indeed, ions secreted in the upper part of a tubule are reabsorbed before the urine is passed into the bladder.

ment upon an eel the intestine was first emptied as far as possible through a catheter. Thereupon the anus and urinary papilla were ligated and the eel placed in tinctured sea water. 20 hr. later 2·3 ml. of fluid could be obtained from the intestine which were found by colorimetry to correspond to 12·3 ml. of sea water. Thus the fish must have swallowed 12·3 ml. and absorbed 10·0 ml. A small amount of dye was present in the bile and urine, making the above figures for swallowed and absorbed water rather too small. Special experiments showed that the dye could not be absorbed through the gills or skin and could only get into the intestine by swallowing.

In the above experiment 2·3 ml. of urine was obtained from the bladder at the end of the 20 hr. period, and the eel was found to have lost weight from 143·5 to 142·2 g. It follows therefore that $10 - 2·3 + 1·3 = 9$ ml. had left the body by an extrarenal route and Smith speaks of an extrarenal excretion of water. When it is considered that the osmotic concentration of the body fluids of the eel was only about 240 mM. and that of the surrounding sea water 530 mM. there can be no doubt that water must be extracted by osmotic force through the gills and skin, and it appears most likely that the whole of the water lost is thus extracted.

A number of experiments on eels (*Anguilla rostrata*) and sculpin (*Myoxocephalus*) show that per kg. of weight these fish swallow from 40 to 225 ml. sea water per day of which they absorb on an average respectively 78 and 63 % and lose extrarenally 59 and 31 %.

The above would present a clear and complete picture if water could be absorbed from the intestine without the salts. This is not the case. If it were, the total concentration of the residual water left in the intestine should rise, whereas it falls to become approximately isotonic with the blood, as shown by Smith in a number of determinations on *Lophius*, *Anguilla* and *Myoxocephalus*. Salts are therefore absorbed with the water and even in excess. This absorption is not indiscriminate, however, but selective, and Smith shows by numerous analyses that the monovalent ions of Na^+, K^+ and Cl^- are absorbed to a very large extent, while Ca^{++} and especially Mg^{++} and $SO_4^=$ become concentrated in the residual fluid.

I select as examples analyses from a fasted eel, acclimatized in the sea-water aquarium for 10 days. From the rectum of this fish fluid can be obtained, without admixture from the upper intestine, representing the composition of the residue just before it is expelled. Special experiments made by Smith show that Mg and SO_4 are not excreted by the intestine, but are without any doubt residues from the sea water swallowed. From another table in Smith's paper I add the composition of the urine simultaneously collected (Table XXXI):

Table XXXI

mM./litre

	Δ	K	Ca	Mg	Cl	SO_4
Sea water	1·81°	8·3	10·3	44	457	31
Rectal fluid	0·75°	0·6	11·3*	139*	76	122
Urine	0·66°	5·7	7·5*	75	76	52

* It is pointed out by Smith that the samples were centrifuged and that the intestinal fluid contains solid matter in suspension, consisting of $CaCO_3$ and $Mg(OH)_2$, while the urine *may* contain solid calcium phosphate.

The urine, which shows the normal hypotonicity, is remarkable for its high content of Mg and SO_4, and again Smith is careful to show that these ions are not absorbed through the integument or gills, but must be derived from the sea water swallowed. The retention of these ions in the intestinal residue, although very considerable when compared with Cl or the alkali metals, is not absolute, and the quantities absorbed are excreted through the urine where, in the example given, the Mg concentration equals that of Cl. This makes it abundantly clear that the alkali chlorides taken up from the intestine with the water in concentrations and quantities many times higher than those of Mg must be excreted elsewhere.

Assuming that no Mg is excreted extrarenally and that all the Mg left in the intestine or excreted in the urine comes from the sea water ingested it becomes possible to calculate the amounts of water and Cl excreted extrarenally. Corresponding to 1 l. of urine + 1 l. of intestinal residue the total quantity of water swallowed must be represented by

$$\frac{\text{Mg concentration in urine} + \text{Mg concentration in residue}}{\text{Mg concentration in sea water}},$$

or, in the example given above, $\dfrac{139+75}{44}=4\cdot85$ l. containing 2220 mM. Cl⁻. Of this quantity 1 l. is excreted as urine containing 76 mM. Cl and 1 l. is intestinal residue also with 76 mM., and we have left 2·85 l. with 2086 mM. Cl.

Special experiments made on fresh-water eels by injection of salts point to the gills as by far the most probable route of the extrarenal excretion of alkali chloride, and show especially that the mucus covering the skin contains only negligible amounts.

A direct proof of the active elimination of chloride through the gills of the eel was given by Keys (1931 c), who worked out a special technique for perfusion of a heart-gill preparation (Keys, 1931) in which the heart and gills were perfused by one balanced solution, the volume of which could be fairly accurately measured, while the mouth and branchial cavities were bathed by an aerated circulating solution, the volume of which could be read off at any time. Utilizing the precision syringe pipettes described by Krogh and Keys (1931), Keys worked out further an extremely accurate micro-method for the determination of chloride (1931 b), and by means of these new tools he was able to demonstrate the active excretion of Cl through the gills from an internal medium with a Cl concentration of 196 mM. towards an external medium in which the Cl concentration was 534 mM. It should be remembered that the demonstration of an active Cl transport which is comparatively easy in fresh water, where the Cl concentration is about millimolar, requires a different order of analytical precision in solutions which are from 200 to 600 mM.

I give as an example an experiment in which the Cl concentration of the perfusion fluid was $6959\cdot8 \pm 0\cdot2$ mg./l. which was reduced by perfusion at the rate of 147 ml./hr. to $6912\cdot4 \pm 0\cdot2$ mg./l. In the same period the external fluid increased in volume from 130·60 to 130·74 ml. in 1 hr., and its Cl concentration rose in the whole period of 2 hr. 21 min. from $18{,}897\cdot0 \pm 0\cdot7$ mg./l. to $18{,}971\cdot4 \pm 0\cdot5$.

The general result is that the rate of chloride secretion is governed by the concentration of the internal medium. When the total concentration of this is not higher than the value normal for eels in fresh water generally no secretion takes place, and there is even sometimes a measurable diffusion of Cl from the outside medium. At higher concentrations, corresponding to the serum of eels in sea water, the Cl secretion may reach quite high figures as seen in

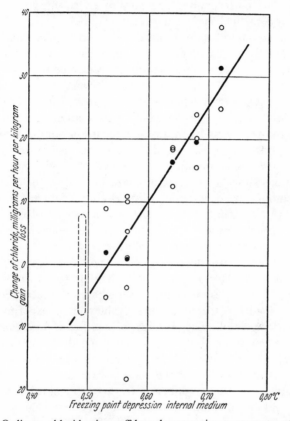

Fig. 43. Ordinate, chloride given off by eel preparation to sea water at varying concentrations of internal medium (abscissa). ○ Experimental results. ● Averages. Dotted area, limits of error in preliminary experiments. Errors in final experiments 1/10 of this only. (Keys.)

Fig. 43. This emphasizes the character of the process as a regulation to prevent an undue rise in concentration of the blood. The maximum rate of excretion shown in Fig. 43 is very nearly 1 mM./ kg./hr. When the example given above from Smith's paper is recalculated on the same basis I find an excretion of 1·75 mM./kg./hr., which is a very satisfactory agreement, especially when it is remembered that in the living eel employed by Smith the internal concentration corresponded probably to a freezing point of 0·82° instead of 0·72° in Keys's experiment.

A small amount of water is always transferred (osmotically) with the Cl, and Keys (like Smith) looks upon the process as an active transport of a chloride solution more concentrated than the outside sea water.

In a later paper by Bateman and Keys (1932) Keys's results were confirmed by experiments in which a circulation was maintained through the gills alone by means of a perfusion pump, and in most of the experiments it was found that the decrease in total concentration of the circulating fluid as measured by vapour-pressure determinations showed a satisfactory agreement with the decrease in Cl⁻, assuming alkali chlorides to be excreted. Again, it was explicitly assumed that the work done, which was calculated thermodynamically to represent 0·1–0·3 cal./g. of gill tissue/hr., consisted in the transport of a solution of chlorides.

This conception was opposed by Schlieper (1933 b, c), who modified the perfusion technique so as to be able to measure volume changes on both sides of the gills with greater accuracy. Schlieper also simplified the technique and evaluation of experiments by using eel-Ringer solutions on both sides either identical or in different concentrations, but always containing the same ions in the same relative proportions. Schlieper was able to show that the Cl secretion is independent of the water movement, just as we have since found on a large number of fresh-water animals. When the outside and inside fluids are identical (and sufficiently concentrated) a considerable Cl transport takes place without any water movement. In sea water the water permeability of the gills is on the whole very low, but becomes larger when the concentration of the internal medium is reduced, say, from 200 to 150 mM.

Schlieper studied also the mechanism by which an increased osmotic concentration of the internal medium stimulates secretion. He found that he could stimulate secretion by the addition of NaCl, Na_2SO_4, glucose or saccharose up to a suitable total concentration, but not by sodium nitrate or urea, and he explains this by assuming that the active substances extract water osmotically from the secreting cells and thereby raise the Cl concentration within them, while the inactive substances penetrate into the cells and have no power to increase their Cl concentration. He therefore takes the Cl concentration in the secreting cells as the only adequate stimulus. A careful perusal of Schlieper's paper fails now, as it did five years ago, to convince me that this view is substantiated or even definitely supported by the experimental evidence.

Keys and Willmer (1932) studied the gills of the eel histologically. At the base of the leaflets they found a number of very characteristic cells with large spherical nuclei. "The cytoplasm of these cells is finely granular and has a greater affinity for eosin than the rest of the epithelium." "The cells are ovoid in shape and may occupy the whole of the epithelial thickness, but they never, or only very rarely, appear to be more than one layer thick."

In two papers G. Bevelander (1935, 1936) maintains that these cells are mucus cells, and that similar cells are found not only on the gill filaments but everywhere in the mucous membrane of the mouth and gill cavity. Bevelander even goes so far as to doubt the special function of the gills as chloride secreting, maintaining that this power may be resident in the whole of the mouth and branchial cavity. While this must be admitted as a possibility the alternative that the whole of the respiratory epithelium might be also secretory appears to me more likely, because one would expect a considerable blood supply to the secreting surface and the vascularization of the mucous membranes is distinctly poor. A cytological study from the point of view of ion transport is highly desirable.

Although the histological evidence is doubtful and the direct demonstration of a branchial secretion of ions has been obtained only for the eel which is not a purely marine teleost I believe that it is safe, on the basis of Homer Smith's work, to assume that marine fishes generally solve the problem of maintaining a lower concentration of the internal medium by swallowing sea water and excreting the chlorides extrarenally.

It should be pointed out that we have, strictly speaking, no proof that the Cl⁻ ion is the one transported actively. It may, in analogy with the results obtained on fresh-water animals, generally, just as well be the Na^+ ion or even more probably both, but the task of solving this problem is very formidable because of the analytical difficulties. It may become possible to utilize radioactive isotopes, and something may perhaps be done by means of lithium and bromine.

When the swallowing of sea water is regulated so as to provide for the loss of water by osmosis through the gills and the skin the water for urine formation may become reduced to the point of waning. This appears to be the case both in the sculpin (*Myoxocephalus octodecimspinosus*) possessing glomerular kidneys and in the aglomerular toadfish (*Opsanus tau*) according to the very careful study made by Grafflin (1931). This author measured flows below 2·5 ml./kg./ day in the toadfish and below 4 ml. in the sculpin in the summer time when both species are at the height of their activity. In these cases the Cl concentration of the plasma was practically constant (at 151 mM. in the sculpin), while the urine was Cl free and the urinary total nitrogen above 100 mg. %. Grafflin will accept flows up to 10 ml./kg./day as possibly within normal limits in the sculpin when the urine is still Cl free, but all higher rates of flow are definitely abnormal and are usually caused by mechanical damage to the skin of the fish. The mode of action of such damage is rather peculiar. The immediate effect must be an increased loss of water to the higher concentrated outside medium, while salts will diffuse in. This might be supposed to stop the urine flow completely, were it not that the normal urine production is practically not concerned with osmotic regulation, but only with the regulation of divalent ions and the elimination of waste products. The only possibility seems to be, as emphasized by Grafflin, that the injury and consequent loss of water brings about an increased swallowing of sea water. This increases the plasma chloride, and figures up to 225 mM. are recorded. In such circumstances the chloride-excreting mechanism of the gills must be taxed to the utmost, and Grafflin's figures seem to show that in the sculpin under this stress the kidneys take over a significant part of the osmotic regulation. I reproduce Tables 2 and 3 (Table XXXII) from Grafflin's paper showing the gradual increase in urine flow under

the conditions of the experiments and the consequent changes in
composition in two sculpins. It is seen that in all the later periods
the Cl excretion through the urine is very large, and it is remarkable
that the Cl concentration is definitely higher than that of the blood,
utilizing probably to the utmost the power of concentration by reabsorption of water.

Table XXXII

Date	Flow	Analyses of urine		
		Cl	Total N	SO$_4$
July 16—original urine	—	—	107	—
	10·4	—	82	—
July 20	51·9	231	28	32
July 22	71·0	259	11	29
July 23	52·6	301	—	—

Plasma Cl after last period 212. Weight 162 g.

July 16	11·9	26	—	—
July 20	71·2	224	8	31
July 22	112·0	239	7	21
	—	310	—	—

Plasma Cl after last period 225. Weight 155 g.

EURYHALINE AND ANADROMOUS FISHES

A small number of teleosts are able to stand a fairly rapid transference from fresh water to sea water and vice versa, and some of
these undertake regular migrations between the two media, but the
peculiarities which are responsible for this power are not at all clear
in spite of the considerable amount of work spent upon the problem.

The fish most extensively studied in this respect is the eel, represented by the species *Anguilla vulgaris* in Europe and *A. rostrata*
in North America. As is now well known the eels breed within a
definite region of the Atlantic north and north-east of the West
Indian Islands. The larvae, Leptocephali, drift with the current for
1–3 years during which period they are stenohaline. They are
finally metamorphosed into elvers which in large numbers ascend
the rivers, while many develop in brackish or salt water. They are
very rapacious fishes showing normally a rapid rate of growth. On
reaching maturity they leave their habitat and, taking no more food,
swim out into the depths of the Atlantic to find their breeding place!

From the stage of elvers up to maturity they will stand abrupt changes in salinity, and Duval (1925) illustrates in the adjoined curve the corresponding slight change in the freezing point of the eel serum. A corresponding curve and table are given by Mme Boucher-Firly (1935) for the tissues of elvers. The figures were obtained after a sojourn of 8 hr. at each concentration, and since up

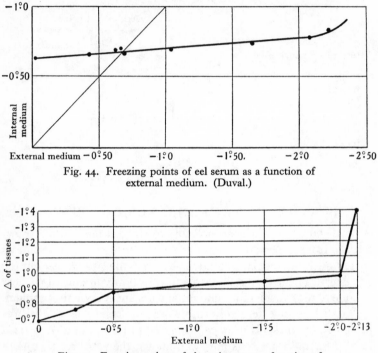

Fig. 44. Freezing points of eel serum as a function of external medium. (Duval.)

Fig. 45. Freezing points of elver tissues as a function of external medium. (Boucher-Firly.)

to a concentration of $\Delta = 0.9°$ the elvers show a definite increase in osmotic concentration and remain more concentrated than the surrounding water, they are apparently capable of active absorption of salt from a more dilute medium.

This point was studied in a large number of experiments both on eels of 70–200 g. and on elvers of 100–200 mg. weight (Krogh,

1937), but no evidence of absorption from fresh water or solutions of similar concentration could be found.

The eel exhibits a remarkable power of retaining Cl. An eel of 98 g. in a glass tube with a slow current of distilled water (0·6 l./hr.) lost Cl at the rate of less than 1 μM./hr. or a total loss of 280 μM. in 13 days, and repeated tests with Ringer/100 showed the same rate of loss, while one test with R/10 showed a seven times *larger* loss over 7 hr. In repeated experiments of this type absorption was never observed and the eels were killed—apparently by washing out—in about a month.

The loss of Cl was increased in one series of experiments by damaging the skin, and after a total loss of 1100 μM. had been obtained tests were made with tap water, R/10 and R/5, at a time when the loss in distilled water, which at first was at the rate of 50 μM./hr., had become reduced to about 10 μM. The losses in the salt solutions were now definitely smaller and in two periods of 6 hr. each even 0, but no definite uptake was observed.

On elvers the results obtained by Cl determinations on extracts of the animals were similar, but it was observed that R/100 would reduce the loss which was in distilled water over 8 days 9·3 mM./kg. tissue water, in R/100 only 2·3 mM.

In a final experiment three groups of six elvers were slightly damaged by burning along the tail and placed respectively in 1 l. distilled water, 1 l. R/100 and 1 l. R/10. In 24 hr. the animals in distilled water and R/100 were dead, but in R/10 three animals survived, and these showed 10 days later a normal Cl content. In the light of the result obtained by Mme Boucher-Firly I am now inclined to think that at least the elvers do have some power of actively absorbing Cl, but that it is insufficient to cover the losses in ordinary fresh water and only effective in stronger solutions, being of the same order as the power observed for instance in *Carcinus maenas.*

The eel survives then in fresh water mainly by absorption of salts from the food and is able to resist inanition for a considerable period by a highly developed power of retaining salt. This power resides partly in the kidneys, which must be able to reabsorb Cl from the glomerular filtrate practically down to 0.

It is believed, especially by Duval and Mme Boucher-Firly, that the mucus which normally covers the skin of an eel is very effective as a barrier to diffusion of ions. Numerous unpublished experiments made in this laboratory failed to support their contention, diffusion of ions and sugars through mucus taking place almost as rapidly as through water, but it may mean something that the mucus forms a relatively thick layer without any convection through which exchange is possible only by diffusion. The experiments of Duval in which the mucus was removed by wiping and the permeability found to become excessive are not really conclusive, because the skin must have become damaged as in Grafflin's experiments with the sculpin.

Experiments by Keys (1933) on the change in weight taking place in eels transferred from fresh to salt water and vice versa show a remarkably low permeability of the gills and integument to water, and this is perhaps the chief factor responsible for the power of the eel to starve in fresh water and to stand abrupt changes in salinity.

Keys worked with eels of 200–300 g. weight, and in comparative experiments he blocked the oesophagus of one eel by means of a rubber balloon to prevent the swallowing of water. Unfortunately he did not pay any attention to the urine production. When an eel is transferred from fresh water to sea water there is an initial rapid loss in weight, reaching 4 % in 10 hr., and brought about partly by the osmotic loss of water, partly, no doubt, by the urine formation which will continue for some time at the high fresh-water rate. When swallowing is prevented this loss continues, although at a slower rate, but a normal eel will begin to swallow sea water, the loss will be brought to a standstill, a gain in weight will set in and a steady state is reached in about 48 hr., when the original weight is reduced about 3–4 %, corresponding to the increase in osmotic concentration.

When an eel is transferred from sea water to fresh water it apparently goes on swallowing water for a few hours and gains weight rapidly (2 % in less than 6 hr.). Shortly afterwards the regulation sets in which means, as I think, that urine elimination becomes copious and water swallowing ceases. If the intake of water is prevented by the balloon the gain in weight is remarkably slow—about

2·5 % in 48 hr.—and if we may assume that the urine production is maintained at the sea-water level during this period, which shows a straight-line curve for the increase, it is evident that the water permeability of the eel taken as a whole must be very low. Assuming a weight of 200 g., a total surface, including the gills, of 700 cm.² and a concentration difference of 8 atm., I calculate a minute number corresponding to not less than 5 years.

The eel is essentially a marine fish, and there are several relatives like *Conger* and *Muraena* which never leave the sea. The salmons, on the other hand, breed in fresh water, and many representatives remain all their lives in lakes and streams, while others migrate and grow up to a large size in the sea before returning to fresh water for breeding purposes.

Greene (1904) made very careful determinations of freezing-point depressions on the blood, serum and other fluids of the Chinook salmon, *Oncorhynchus tschawytscha*, a fish reaching often a weight of 20 kg. He found an average Δ for the blood of specimens feeding in sea water of 0·762° with variations from 0·7° to 0·8°. When taken at the spawning grounds the mean for males was 0·668° and for females 0·610°, while the ovarian fluid surrounding the ripe eggs was definitely less concentrated (0·559°).

There is every reason to believe that the marine salmon swallows sea water and regulates its concentration by active excretion through the gills, but definite evidence is lacking. In fresh water the salmon spends a long time and travels, often very long distances, without taking any food. It is therefore scarcely conceivable that it can do without an ion-absorbing mechanism like that possessed by the fresh-water species, *Salmo irideus*. It would be interesting to find mechanisms in the gills capable of an ion transport in both directions.

The demonstration of such double mechanisms should also be possible in sticklebacks and in *Fundulus*, but experiments are lacking.*

Grafflin (1937) emphasizes the fact that several species of

---

* In a very recent paper Grafflin has shown that fluorescein is not absorbed by *Fundulus* in fresh water, but is taken up in sea water with the water swallowed.

syngnathids have migrated independently into fresh water in various widely separated localities in the tropics. In one of these, *Microphis boaja*, he has made a special study of the kidneys which follow the general rule within the family of being aglomerular. I would point out that the skin in these fishes is well protected and probably presents a very low permeability for water, and further, that the habits of the species known to me are very sluggish so that the gills may possibly have a very low permeability even for water. The fresh-water forms may or may not have developed the power to absorb salt from fresh water, and even aglomerular kidneys may, like the Malpighian tubes in insects, be able to produce a dilute urine in sufficient quantity. A study of the osmoregulation in this species would no doubt be interesting.

Considering the available evidence concerning osmoregulation in fishes as a whole I am inclined to agree with Homer Smith that it points towards a fresh-water origin of this subclass, but to my mind it appears much less conclusive than it does to him. It is true that a glomerular kidney capable of eliminating large amounts of fluid and reducing the concentration to a very low figure is an essential fresh-water adaptation, but it is doubtful whether it must have had its first development in fresh water.

The very peculiar form which the adaptation of fishes to sea water has taken in all the species so far studied may be an expression of their fresh-water origin, but if it is we have to assume that the habit of swallowing sea water and the power of active extrarenal excretion of salt has come into existence independently in all the species which originally migrated into the sea. As will be seen in the chapter on Amphibia such an assumption is not so unlikely as at first sight it would appear.

It would no doubt be possible to gather from the literature some information concerning the distribution of ions in blood and tissues of fishes, but precise results representing equilibria or steady states are not available, and it seems sufficient to give the following representative analyses (Table XXXIII) by Homer Smith (1930) on blood and muscle of *Protopterus*.

The figures show that the sodium and chloride of the blood is largely and perhaps completely replaced by potassium and phosphoric acid in the muscle. These ions must to a very large extent exist as free ions in the water of the muscle cells to provide the necessary osmotic concentration.

Table XXXIII. *Protopterus*

	K	Ca	Mg	Total base	Cl	SO$_4$	PO$_4$	CO$_2$
Plasma mM./l.	8·2	2·1	Trace	99	44·1	Trace	1·0	35
Muscle mM./kg.	60·5	—	—	—	—	0·5	45	—

AMPHIBIA

The Amphibia form the transition from an aquatic to a terrestrial existence, but almost all live in water at least during the breeding season and possess the adaptations characteristic of a life in fresh water. A few forms (several species of *Bufo*) may use brackish water for breeding places. The larvae are, with very few exceptions, regular fresh-water organisms.

The adult Amphibia generally breathe air by means of lungs, but in almost all cases the skin is an important accessory organ of respiration, and many forms among the Urodela and anuran larvae have fairly well-developed gills and are independent of the air as far as respiration is concerned. Also in these forms respiration takes place largely through the general surface which is well provided with blood and easily permeable to oxygen.

The circulatory system is rather complicated, and generally the organs of respiration (including a large part of the integument) receive venous blood and show a close network of capillaries which may be important also from the point of view of active salt absorption. The lymph system is specially well developed, and lymph hearts pumping lymph into the veins help to provide a rapid circulation of lymph filtering out from the capillary circulation.

The kidneys have in some of the Urodela (*Necturus*) a small number of exceptionally large glomeruli. In the frogs the glomeruli are rather small (about 0·1 mm. in diameter) and correspondingly numerous. The neck segment of the tubules is provided with cilia. Proximal and distal convoluted segments of the tubules are regularly present and 3–4 mm. long, and there is a very short intermediate segment, corresponding to the loop of Henle in mammals. The glomeruli are supplied with arterial blood, and when urine production is not excessive they close and open up in alternation. The tubuli are surrounded by a network of capillaries supplied with blood also from the veins of the legs (and tail).

Several species of frog (*Rana*) have been used in numerous experiments on the permeability of the skin for water and dissolved substances (Wertheimer, 1923-5; Pohle, 1920; Adolph and others and summarized by Adolph, 1933), but much of the work has given conflicting results and the interpretation is exceedingly difficult, because the power of the skin to absorb ions was unknown and often brought about experimental conditions which could not be reproduced.

The skin of frogs is permeable for water. This was clearly shown in the experiments by Overton, summarized in his thirty-nine theses (1904), which contain a great deal of very valuable information. It is a pity that this preliminary communication was not followed up by the elaborate publication for which the material was evidently at hand. I extract the following which has a direct bearing upon our problems.

Water evaporates freely from the surface, and at ordinary room temperature and moisture a frog of 60 g. will lose one-quarter of its weight in 8-11 hr. at a rate which remains constant so long as conditions as to temperature and moisture do not change. This loss produces an increase in osmotic pressure of the blood to about double the original value, from which it is concluded that part of the water in the tissues is not osmotically active and is held more firmly.

When such a frog is brought back into water it will keep quiet and absorb water through the skin by osmosis until the original weight is restored, and during this period it does not eliminate urine.

A normal frog also takes up water through the skin, but passes a corresponding quantity as urine. The rate of uptake depends upon the temperature and is 4-5 times as rapid at 30° C. as at 0°. The osmotic pressure of the urine is much lower than that of the blood and lower at low temperatures than at high. At 0° the osmotic concentration is stated to be less than one-tenth that of the blood, which is normally a little over 100 mM. (frog's Ringer is 110).

The rate of absorption of water through the skin is proportional to the difference in osmotic pressure between the blood and the surrounding fluid. In an isotonic solution (111 mM. NaCl) water is not at first absorbed, but later there is an increase in weight, ascribed by Overton to the production of osmotically active substances by metabolism.

In solutions of higher concentration, up to 200 mM., water is lost through the skin, and again the loss is approximately proportional to the difference in osmotic pressure, provided the animals are prevented from drinking. At concentrations above 200 mM. the skin loses its impermeability to salts.

While frogs in water or dilute solutions do not drink water Overton observed that in 140 mM. NaCl or more concentrated solutions they would drink the solution and produce large volumes of relatively concentrated urine. This observation, which has apparently been overlooked by later authors, is very striking. It was confirmed in experiments with KCl which would not in corresponding concentrations produce any poisoning in experiments lasting a week at 18–20° C. so long as the frogs were prevented from drinking. Frogs allowed to drink became paralysed in 115 mM. KCl in 24–36 hr., but recovered, when brought back into water, by excretion of K in the urine. When after recovery such frogs are again put into 106 mM. KCl, they may survive without paralysis for 10 days—and must refrain from drinking during most of that time.

The drinking of concentrated solutions is a most interesting phenomenon comparable to the drinking of sea water by marine fishes. It should be studied further from a quantitative point of view to see whether, as in the fishes, more salt than water is absorbed from the intestine and whether a mechanism exists, renal or extrarenal, for eliminating salt in excess of water.

Hevesy, Hofer and Krogh (1935), utilizing heavy water, found in experiments on whole frogs, on legs of frogs dipping in solutions and on isolated pieces of skin, that the permeability is the same in both directions, and they measured permeabilities for the diffusion of heavy water expressed by day numbers of 460–390 at 0·5–2° and at 20–22° C. varying from 175 to 100. The osmotic uptake of ordinary water was found to be a more rapid process showing day numbers at 2° of 160, at 10° of 60 and at 22° of 30, confirming Overton also on the point of the high temperature coefficient of the permeability.

Experiments by Rubinstein and Miskinowa (1936) on the osmotic water transport through isolated pieces of frog skin confirm that the rate is the same in both directions when the skin is normal and not exposed on the inside to lower concentrations than 3/4 or 1/2 Ringer, and unpublished experiments made by the writer have given the same result, so that I think it safe to affirm that an "irreciprocal" permeability for water does not exist in normal frogs.*

Adolph (1934), in partial confirmation of earlier experiments (Stirling, 1877; Pohle, 1920; Jungman and Bernhardt, 1923), found that damage to the midbrain or cutting of the medulla oblongata in frogs would for a time greatly increase the water intake through the skin which would rise from the normal 1·5 to 6 % of the weight during the first hour at 20° C. The effect would "wear off with time", but it is not clear whether this meant a real recovery from the condition, because in most cases the frogs died. Adolph himself says: "The increase is characterized by the fact that the intake of water is now proportional to the square root of the time elapsed and not directly to the time as in the normal frog. This criterion is of significance because it seems to indicate that a new process has begun, apparently one of passive and unretarded osmosis. It is as though there were two kinds of water influx, a normal one in the steady state and an abnormal one from which no recovery is possible." And later: "One is led by exclusion to the view that the skin's permeability to water may be directly controlled by a steady stream of impulses from the brain."

Since the isolated skin shows normal permeability it seems to me that the effect observed by Adolph must be in the nature of a nervous shock, increasing while it lasts the permeability of certain elements in the skin for water. The reaction should be studied further, but a few experiments in this direction made in my laboratory failed to reveal it. Rubenstein (1935) thought he could demonstrate a decrease in the osmotic uptake of water through the skin brought about by nerve stimulation, but it is rather more likely that what he observed was a contraction of skin glands by which fluid was expelled to the outside.

* Huf (1936) found in experiments in which osmosis took place from 1/10 Ringer to 1/1 Ringer through isolated pieces of skin that the rate was much more rapid with 1/10 Ringer on the inside than with 1/1 Ringer on the inside. Although the effect was completely reversible there can be little doubt that 1/10 Ringer bathing the inside of frog's skin is unphysiological and an increase in permeability is to be expected.

The kidney function has been carefully studied in frogs and *Necturus*, especially by Richards (1935) and his associates (Westfall, Findley and Richards, 1934), and the results may be summarized as follows. An ultrafiltrate from the blood is eliminated from the arterial glomeruli into the Bowman capsules. The concentration of sugar in this fluid is equal to that of the blood, and chloride is also present in substantially the same concentration as in plasma, the slight difference being explicable by the Donnan effect of the plasma proteins which are retained. During the passage down the tubuli certain substances become reabsorbed, and it is especially significant that sugar is normally completely reabsorbed in the proximal tubules while chloride can be reabsorbed more or less completely in the distal. Reabsorption of water takes place also, as shown by the concentration in the tubules of certain dyes introduced artificially, but normally the urine never becomes hypertonic to the blood and is almost always highly hypotonic.

Toda and Taguchi (1913) analysed urine from a very large number of *Rana esculenta* obtained in summer and presumably used very soon after being caught, so that the composition is probably determined largely by the food. They found an average freezing-point depression of 0·106° (corresponding to 31 mM. NaCl) with variations only from 0·08 to 0·13°. The solids made up 2·46 g./l., of which 0·53 g. were inorganic (ash). The single ions were determined on the ash from two samples of frog's urine of 2 l. each and gave the following results, recalculated into mM./l.:

Table XXXIV

mM.				mE.	mM.		
Na	K	Ca	Mg	Total base	Cl	SO$_4$	PO$_4$
2·44	0·95	0·78	0·40	4·57	1·89	0·49	2·35

Richards found in the glomerular urine of frogs 5·2 g. NaCl/l. corresponding to 88 mM. It is evident, therefore, that Na and Cl become reabsorbed to a very large extent and, as shown below, the Cl concentration can be even further reduced.

The osmotic uptake of water, at a rate which will replace all the water in a frog in about 2 days, and the elimination of this water as urine of roughly 5 mM. mineral concentration, involves a loss of salt which must be made good, and it is reasonable therefore to expect that a mechanism for salt uptake similar to that described for fresh-water fishes and a number of invertebrates is also present in the frog. It was first demonstrated by Huf (1935, 1936), who found that in the isolated frog's skin, bathed with neutral Ringer solution on both sides, a transport of Cl would take place from the outside in. This transport could be inhibited by cyanide (1 mM.) and increased by lactate (5 mM.) or pyruvate (5 mM.), while glucose and glucose-diphosphate were ineffective. Energy is therefore used in the process and probably derived from the breaking down of lactic or pyruvic acid.*

That this mechanism could actually be used by the frog to obtain salt from fresh water and similar dilute solutions was shown by Krogh (1937). Frogs were washed out in distilled water, and in a series of experiments single frogs (*R. esculenta*) of 60 g. weight were kept at 18° C. in 400 ml. distilled water changed each day, while the urine was collected in a rubber bag fixed by means of a cannula in the cloaca. Urine was produced at the rate of about 15 ml./day.

Water and urine were analysed for Cl and Ca and averaged for 3-day periods, and it was found that there is a loss of both ions through the skin as well as through the urine. The Cl concentration in the urine varied irregularly between 0·5 and 1 mM., while the loss through the skin to the water was fairly high at first and later became negligibly small, corresponding in the 400 ml. to a concentration of 0·003 mM. or less. The loss of Ca through the skin varied but little (5–6 μM./day), but in the urine the concentration was gradually reduced from 0·4 to 0·1 mM.

In frogs kept without food in distilled water the concentration of Cl in blood and tissues would gradually become reduced, while in tap water it was maintained at the normal level, and direct experimentation demonstrated the absorption through the skin of frogs, previously treated with distilled water, from very dilute solutions even down to concentrations of 0·01 mM. or less.

---

* Huf appears to believe in an active transport also of water, but his experiments do not bear this out, as the transference of salt must cause an osmotic flow of water in the same direction.

By dipping different parts of the skin no significant difference in the power of absorbing Cl could be detected, except in so far as the lower legs were, perhaps, less effective. The rate of absorption depends to some extent upon the concentration of the outside fluid. From a 10 mM. solution a maximum rate of 0·6 μM./hr./cm.^{2} was observed. The normal rate from millimolar solutions (Copenhagen tap water or R/100) is of the order 0·05 μM./hr./cm.^{2} There is no significant difference in rate as observed from water, where there is a simultaneous osmotic uptake of water, or from a sugar solution or Na_2SO_4 solution isotonic with the blood, from which no water is absorbed.

A study of the active absorption of single ions (Krogh, 1937, 1938) gave the following results.

Cl^- is absorbed with Na^+ from NaCl solutions, but from KCl, NH_4Cl, and $CaCl_2$ without being accompanied by cations, and in these cases the absorption, which may be rapid at first, comes to a standstill before the Cl supply is exhausted. The Cl^- is in such cases replaced in the outside solution by HCO_3^-.

Br^- can be taken up in all cases like Cl^-. The rate is somewhat slower in spite of the fact that Cl is taken up against a gradient of about 100 mM. inside, while varying from 1 to 0 outside, whereas Br^- is transported from an outside concentration diminishing from about 1 downwards practically to 0 against an inside concentration increasing from 0 to about 2. A frog taken directly from ordinary fresh water fails to absorb both Cl^- and Br^-.

I^- is taken up slowly by diffusion. The initial absorption is fairly rapid even from very dilute solutions, pointing to a certain amount of I being fixed in the skin. The inside concentration never reaches the outside, because I is excreted and concentrated to some extent in the urine. NO_3^- and CNS^- are both taken up by diffusion. It will be remembered that the gills of *Carassius auratus* were impermeable to both these ions.

Na^+ is absorbed with Cl from NaCl, but the rates may differ greatly, and in one case a frog was observed to absorb Na at the rate of 8·2 μM./hr., while losing Cl at the rate of 4·8 μM./hr. Na^+ is also absorbed from $NaHCO_3$, and the absorption can be accounted for by exchange with NH_3 only to a very slight extent, while the bicarbonate concentration in the outside solution is definitely reduced. Na^+ can also be absorbed from mixtures of $NaHCO_3$ and $KHCO_3$ leaving K^+ behind and from Na_2SO_4. In this latter case a definite exchange with NH_4^+ was found to take place.

K^+, NH_4^+ and Ca^{++} are not absorbed and no penetration by diffusion has been observed.

The two independent mechanisms present and normally responsible for the absorption of Cl^- and Na^+ are the same as those found in the goldfish, but the ion permeability is higher in the skin of *Rana esculenta*.

The biological significance of the active uptake of salt is clear and is probably of vital importance to the frogs in winter, when about 7 months are spent under water without any food.

On tadpoles of *Rana temporaria* at the stage with covered gills and before the legs make their appearance we did not succeed in demonstrating any salt uptake. During the process of washing there was a rapid reduction in weight due to the high rate of metabolism, and this was not changed when the animals were placed in R/100 to which rather large amounts of Cl were given off. In one experiment the animals showed after 4 days' washing an average weight of 120 mg. and a Cl content of $1\cdot49 \pm 0\cdot12$ mg. Cl/g. In an experiment of $11\cdot2$ hr. the average weight was reduced to 95 and the Cl content per g. was reduced to $1\cdot2$ mg./g. Experiments made on a number of tadpoles kept in the same basin are complicated by the fact that when given no food they will attack each other and the weaker individuals be devoured by the stronger ones. In spite of this we observed a constant fall in Cl concentration calculated per individual. It appears, therefore, that the tadpoles must normally obtain the necessary salts from their food, but the experiments made are not sufficient to exclude definitely the possibility that they may possess some power of active salt absorption, the more so as this power is present in the embryos just emerged from the eggs as shown below (p. 189).

Some experiments (unpublished) were made on the axolotl, the mature larva of *Amblystoma*. An animal of 27 g. weight was kept in 200 ml. tap water with an average Cl concentration of $1\cdot5$ mM. in which it continued to lose Cl at the rate of about 1 mg./day for

a fortnight. The loss was generally the same when it was transferred for periods of some hours to distilled water, to R/100 or
even to R/10, but occasionally no loss or even a very slight uptake
took place during a few hours. Finally, after 16 days, when the
total loss amounted to 15 mg., Cl was absorbed for 3 days at a rate
increasing from 0·14 to 0·66 mg./day. During the period the weight
had fallen to 22 g. Another specimen of 36 g. weight had to lose
21 mg. of Cl in 18 days before absorbing at a maximum rate of
1 mg./day from R/100.

These results indicate a rather poorly developed power of absorbing salt, and it seems natural to assume that this power is of
widespread or perhaps general occurrence in the Amphibia.

REPTILIA, AVES, MAMMALIA

The higher vertebrates are without exception air breathers by means of lungs and have taken the consequences from an osmotic point of view of this important step in having their integuments practically water impermeable.

The very low permeability for water was measured on man by Trolle (1937 b) by means of heavy water. It is probably impossible to calculate the osmotic passage of water into a man in fresh water from Trolle's figures, but it can be said to be of an order so low as not to affect the water balance in spite of the existence of numerous sweat glands. Evaporation from the skin of a dog (Trolle, 1937 a), in which the function of sweat glands is very slight, gave values of the same order, the evaporation into air with 60 % moisture at 20° C. being of the order of 1·2 g./hr. through about 3000 cm.^{2} surface. Indirect evidence is obtained from determinations of O_2 uptake through the skin which is in the warm-blooded animals studied (pigeon, man) about 0·5 ml./100 cm.^{2}/hr., and through the soft skin of a tortoise only 0·1 ml./100 cm.^{2}/hr. (Krogh, 1904).

Being practically impermeable to water, higher vertebrates living in fresh water, like crocodiles, beavers or others, are from the point of view of osmotic regulation in just the same position as terrestrial animals. They have to excrete the surplus of salts taken up with the food and the nitrogenous waste products, and the necessary water is derived partly directly from the food, partly from the H of organic substances metabolized and the rest from water drunk.

The case is somewhat different for marine forms which have no access to fresh water. In these it is a problem to be solved separately for each type whether enough water for evaporation and for the formation of urine can be obtained from the water of the food + the water formed by combustion of foodstuffs. This problem was raised by Portier in 1910, but could not at that time be solved. In the case of lactating mammals there is the further problem of providing water for the milk.

The groups of animals with which we have to deal are mainly the following: the sea snakes (*Hydrus*, *Platurus*) and turtles (*Chelonia*, *Thalassochelys*) among the Reptilia, and the seals, whales and Sirenia among the mammals. Although not marine in the sense that they live in water the oceanic birds should also be considered, because they present essentially the same problem, only intensified by the probable need of providing larger quantities of water for evaporation.

The osmotic concentration of the blood in the marine Reptilia and mammals seems to be somewhat higher than in the land or fresh-water forms. Bottazzi found a Δ of 0·60° in *Chelonia caouana* and gives for a whale (*Delphinus phocaena*) the figure 0·74°, and Portier (1910) found in *Phoca foetida* values from 0·66 to 0·72 and in *Tursiops tursio* even 0·83°. Also in marine birds like *Uria troile* and *Fulmarus glacialis* he observed values about 0·7°.

The organs of excretion are in the higher vertebrates developed to serve the function of conservation of water. In the reptiles and birds the main product of protein breakdown is uric acid which is eliminated to a large extent in the solid form. The urine coming from the kidneys is fluid, but in the cloaca so much water is absorbed that it is finally eliminated as a semifluid paste. It is doubtful, however, whether this holds for the turtles, since a large percentage of urea was found by Lewis (1918) to be present in the bladder of *Chelonia*. The urates of Na, K and NH_4 having a low solubility any surplus base can be excreted without producing a significant osmotic concentration, and it would seem as if the inorganic acid radicles, especially Cl^-, should be mainly responsible for the osmotic concentration of reptile and bird urine. Actual determinations would be more useful, however, than any speculations.

In mammals protein is broken down mainly to the highly soluble urea, but in the kidney tubules water can become reabsorbed to such an extent that the urine finally eliminated is hypertonic to an astonishing degree. Dreser (1892) observed on a cat, fed on meat and not allowed to drink water, urine concentrations corresponding to Δ values between 4 and 4·94°, and values of 4·1–4·2° were repeatedly observed by Bottazzi on dogs. In a seal, *Phoca vitulina*, H. Smith (1936) obtained values up to 4°, and Portier reports one case in *Phoca foetida* in which the depression approached 4·5° C. I have found only one determination of the Δ of whale urine, 2·46°, reported by Schmidt-Nielsen and Holmsen (1921). These authors made careful chemical determinations on several specimens of *Balaenoptera borealis*, living on Crustacea exclusively, and *Balaenoptera physalus*, eating fish (herring) mainly. There was no significant difference between the urines of the two species. The concentrations of bases in two representative specimens are given in Table XXXV:

Table XXXV

g./l. Total ash	Na	K	Ca	Mg	mE./l. Total base	mM. Cl
		mM./l.				
25·95	266	74	2·7	4·2	354	362

Similar determinations by Furuhashi (1927) on the same species and also on the cachalot (*Physeter*) gave somewhat higher values for total base and Cl, namely, on an average 423 and 375 mM. respectively.

Laurie (1933), who analysed the urine from a number of blue and fin whales on the fishing grounds in the South Seas where these whales feed on Crustacea, found very variable values for the Cl content, ranging from 120 to 455 mM. and with many values near the upper limit.

Lövenbach made for me a large number of Cl determinations mainly on *Megoptera boops* in Australian waters, where the whales spend the winter season and generally take no food at all. These investigations are being continued and will be published later. The urine values range from 75 to a maximum of 820 mM., but both the highest and the lowest values which were confirmed by repeated determinations on the same urine sample are no doubt exceptional. The usual range is between 280 and 520 mM.

A direct and exhaustive study of the water balance of a marine mammal has been made only by Irving, Fisher and McIntosh (1935) on the seal, *Phoca vitulina*. They state expressly that their seals were never observed to drink sea water, although four seals which were shipped to Toronto in a warm express car "drank fresh water greedily as soon as a clean supply was available". This very interesting observation is scarcely significant for seals leading a normal free life, because fresh water will never become available and because they can obtain the cooling necessary to maintain a constant temperature by convection to the surrounding water without having recourse to evaporation. The seals were fed on fresh herring and the water balance could be made out as follows.

According to analyses of the food 1250 g. would yield by oxidation 1000 Cal. and contain about 1000 g. water (80 %). Out of each 1000 Cal. 430 would be derived from fat and 570 from protein. The metabolic breakdown of the fat would yield 50 g. water and the protein 71 g. A total of $50 + 71 + 1000 = 1121$ g. water would therefore become available. This water would have to satisfy the following physiologic requirements, viz. evaporation from the lungs, water content of the faeces, and water for urine formation, while no water enters or leaves the body through the skin.

The evaporation is calculated as follows : 236 l. O_2 are required to metabolize the fat and protein making up 1000 Cal. Assuming a 6 % deficit in the expired air this means a total volume breathed of $\frac{236}{0\cdot06} = 3933$ l., and to raise the saturation of this volume from 15 to $35°$ C. 106 g. water are required.

The consistency of the faeces was such as to require not over 200 g. water per 1000 food Cal. and we have at least 800 g. water left for the urine. The metabolism would yield 48 g. urea from 139 g. protein, and this would produce a concentration of 6 % or just 1000 mM. The salts from the food would not amount to more than about 0·9 % or a concentration in the urine of 1·4 %. If this is taken as NaCl we can calculate a total concentration corresponding to a Δ of 2·7°. Both the urea and the total concentrations are well within the range possible for mammalian kidneys and show a satisfactory agreement with the actual values observed simultaneously by Homer Smith, and both studies make it probable that seals can swallow their food even under water without contamination with any significant amount of sea water.

The result arrived at by Irving and his collaborators, viz. that the water obtained from the food is sufficient for the normal requirements of the animal, can no doubt be safely extended to include all the seals and whales feeding exclusively or mainly on vertebrates, but for the walrus feeding on clams, the cachalot feeding on cephalopods, and most of the whalebone whales feeding on small Crustacea, the case is somewhat different. In all these food animals the "blood" is, practically speaking, sea water, and the blood volume, especially in clams, is quite high. The osmotic concentration of tissue cells is also equal to that of sea water, but this concentration is made up to a considerable extent both in molluscs and in Crustacea of organic substances. The substances known to be present in molluscs are taurin and glycocoll, both of which contain N. The organic substances making up the osmotic deficit in crustacean tissues are unknown (at least to me), but it is reasonable to suppose that they too contain N. This means that they will require practically the same amount of water for their excretion as the salts, and for our purposes we can take the water obtained with the food as sea water. We assume that only insignificant quantities of actual sea water are swallowed with the food, and as a matter of fact the whalebone filtering apparatus, with the enormous tongue acting as a press to squeeze out water, would appear well adapted to insure this. In addition we have the nitrogenous waste products from the breakdown of protein.

It may be of some interest so to modify the calculation of Irving, Fisher and McIntosh as to make it applicable to whales feeding on invertebrates. We assume as above that the whale obtains 1000 g. water directly and 120 g. by combustion of 1250 g. food. It is taken for granted that no evaporation of water is required for heat-regulation purposes, and the water lost by saturation of the expired air is probably much less than in the seal, because the whale increases the pressure in the lungs by diving and therefore probably uses up a much higher percentage of oxygen than the 6 % assumed for the seal.

We will assume that the water necessary for evaporation can be reduced to 50 g. and that in the faeces to 170 g. Irving and his collaborators assumed 200 g. and did not take the salts of this water into account. The faeces of course contain salts. Lövenbach found the Cl concentration in the rectum to vary greatly (from 17 to 200 mM.). There are good reasons for the assumption that divalent ions (including phosphate) are mainly excreted with the faeces and that the total concentration is not very far from that of the blood. This would eliminate 35 mM. salt (or more), and we would have 900 g. water left for the urine. This urine must contain the osmotically active substances taken with the food which is isotonic with sea water, that is 600 mM. less the 35 eliminated in the faeces. In addition we have the 48 g. urea produced from the combustion of food protein yielding a further 800 mM. (=400 when calculated as salt). The total concentration would correspond then to $565 + 400 = 965$ in 900 g. water or a concentration of 1070 mM. corresponding to a freezing-point depression of $3.7°$. This is no doubt well within the powers of the whale kidney to eliminate, as shown by the figures quoted above.

At certain periods the female whales and seals have to produce milk. This must be a very severe strain upon the water balance, and I would suggest that the fact that the milk of whales* contains from 70 down to 50 % water should not be considered principally in the light of providing food for the rapid growth of the young but from the point of view of the water economy of the mother.

If we can assume that whales are able to excrete a urine sufficiently concentrated to maintain them at an actual concentration of 220 mM. there should be no serious difficulties for the marine reptiles, and with regard to the birds everything depends upon the rate at which they evaporate water. If they can regulate their body temperature without using evaporation of water for cooling purposes it should be possible for birds feeding on vertebrates and even on marine invertebrates to manage on the water content of their food. The large birds of prey in zoological gardens obtain all the necessary water from their food and practically never drink.

Portier observed that the birds of polar regions make frequent visits to accessible sources of fresh water to drink, and he seems to believe that all birds have access to fresh water, but for the oceanic species this is certainly not the case, and their water economy must be precarious when they feed on invertebrates even if they do not require evaporation of water for cooling purposes. The tempera-

---

* The milk of seals is also highly concentrated (according to an oral communication by Prof. Schmidt-Nielsen).

ture at which the expired air is saturated when leaving the body must be a rather important consideration, and it seems possible that this temperature in birds during flight may become substantially lower than in mammals.

A study of the heat and water economy of marine birds would be sure to yield interesting results and is perhaps less difficult than the study of whales.*

* While reading the page proofs I was informed by Mr R. M. Lockley that a number of sea-birds including the shearwater (*Puffinus*), the storm-petrel (*Hydrobates*), the puffin (*Fratercula*) and the razorbill (*Alca*) habitually drink sea water, although usually not in large quantities. It is noted especially (Lockley, 1938, 1939) that the young shearwaters, when taking to the water for the first time, drink copiously. A study just completed by E. Zeuthen and not yet published shows conclusively that during flight large amounts of water must be evaporated from the air-sacs to prevent an undue rise of body temperature, and the oceanic birds will therefore have to drink corresponding quantities of sea water and excrete urine with a very high osmotic pressure.

OSMOTIC CONDITIONS IN EGGS
AND EMBRYOS

The relations of eggs and embryos of aquatic animals to their environment present many interesting features and it is difficult to separate osmotic conditions from the rest.

The eggs when produced in the ovaries grow like other cells of the organism and are subject to the general condition of osmotic equilibrium with the immediate surroundings, while the ionic composition of the egg plasma can be very different from that of the nutritive fluid or from surrounding cells. When they are shed into water the osmotic conditions are for many eggs profoundly altered, and our main object is the study of the reactions to such alterations. Eggs are distinguished by containing a certain amount, generally considerable, of inactive yolk material, part of which becomes built into the embryo while another part is metabolized during development. Eggs in which the amount of nutritive material is not excessive may have it distributed throughout the protoplasm, and generally present a holoblastic form of development in which the whole egg participates in cleavage, while yolk-rich eggs are more often meroblastic, only a localized part of the egg undergoing cleavage, and the rest remaining as a "yolk sac" until it is finally absorbed.

In holoblastic eggs active processes taking place at the surface are, at least theoretically, possible from the very first, but the membrane separating the yolk sac from the environment can only show variable degrees of passive permeability. In certain meroblastic eggs (insects) the yolk becomes completely enclosed in a superficial layer of cells, and these range, from our point of view, with the holoblastic, but unfortunately no information about their osmotic behaviour is available.

The ionic composition of mature eggs. A table giving the concentrations of cations and anions in a large number of different eggs calculated per 100 g. wet weight is given in J. Needham's standard work *Chemical Embryology* (vol. 1, p. 356, 1931). For my purposes it will be sufficient to discuss the representative results obtained by Bialaszewicz and published in two papers (1927, 1929).

In the first the concentrations of the elements K, Na, Ca, Mg, Cl and P are given in mg./g. of egg plasma for a certain number of fresh-water and marine animals. In most of these the eggs were taken from the ovary or at least before they were laid, and the analyses therefore represent the composition of eggs in equilibrium with the maternal organism. In the second paper this was followed up by an ingenious attempt to determine the distribution of the elements on the continuous and disperse phases of the eggs. A certain quantity of egg plasma was diluted so far that ultra-filtration became possible, and the elements were determined both in the suspension obtained and in the ultrafiltrate. By dilution the distribution of certain elements between the colloidal phase and the true solution is altered, but by making a series of solutions with increasing amounts of solvent and making determinations on each dilution it became possible to find the original distribution by extrapolation. I have studied the figures carefully and, although the method is theoretically sound, I cannot repress my doubts regarding a number of the numerical results.

Any analytical errors cannot avoid being seriously magnified by the calculations involved. The relative volumes of the disperse and continuous phase which it is possible to calculate show some rather wide discrepancies, and in cases where the disperse phase is found to be substantially lower than the dry substance in the eggs it cannot possibly be correct. There are, finally, certain grave discrepancies between the analytical results given in the first and second paper (e.g. the Cl content of the eggs of *Torpedo* and *Maia*). For these reasons I refrain from reproducing tables of figures and shall give only general conclusions which are of great importance and, I think, completely warranted. The osmotic concentrations of the egg contents, as determined by the freezing-point depression, in the eggs of the crab *Maia verrucosa*, the elasmobranch *Torpedo ocellata* and the fish *Salmo fontinalis*, are practically identical with the animal's serum, but the mineral concentrations are much lower. This is brought out clearly in experiments in which the egg contents of *Arbacia*, *Sepia*, *Maia* and *Torpedo* were diluted, the freezing points of the dilutions determined, the single cations analysed in the ultrafiltrates and the freezing points for the sum of cations calculated as for chlorides.

Table XXXVI

	Torpedo ocellata	Maia verrucosa	Sepia officinalis	Arbacia pustulosa
Dilutions to	1/2	1/3	1/3	1/3
Δ	0·726°	0·490°	0·471°	0·716°
Δ calculated for mineral constituents	0·167°	0·113°	0·042°	0·435°

The observed depressions are lower in the cases of *Torpedo*, *Maia* and *Sepia* than one would expect, but, whether they are correct or not, it cannot be doubted that the minerals make up only a fraction of the total osmotic concentration. In the ultrafiltrate from the *Torpedo* eggs urea was found in a concentration of 8·43 g./l., and in all the ultrafiltrates N and S were found in relatively large concentrations, calculated by Bialaszewicz as taurin, but probably present as a mixture of organic substance of low molecular weight. The quantity of these organic substances was quite small in the echinoderm eggs, much larger in the eggs of the crab and the cuttlefish where they made up about one-quarter of the total osmotic pressure, while in the *Torpedo* eggs they made up, together with the urea, about one-half. Regarding the single mineral constituents Bialaszewicz found that K is, as in cells generally, the dominant cation in all the eggs examined, comprising beyond those mentioned above those of *Rana temporaria*, *Salmo fontinalis* and *Paracentrotus lividus*. Most of the K is present as free ions, but a small part is combined with the colloids. Na is present, but in quantities only of a few per cent of the K. Ca and Mg are largely present in colloid combinations which are dissociated by dilution. In the "intermicellar" fluid they make up only a minor fraction of the total cation content. Cl is mainly present as free ions. The small part which is combined does not become dissociated on dilution, and Bialaszewicz bases his calculations of the relative volume of the continuous phase mainly on the Cl analyses. The greater part of the phosphate is present in combination with the colloids. The concentration of phosphate ions (taken to be divalent) varies, according to the analyses, greatly from one species to another. In frogs' eggs the phosphate ions exceed the chloride as 2/1, while in *Torpedo* and *Sepia* no free phosphate could be found. The sum of Cl and phosphate is almost equal to or exceeds the sum of cations, and in *Sepia* the excess of Cl over the cations is so considerable that the presence of an unknown base must be assumed.

MARINE INVERTEBRATE EGGS

From what is stated above it is evident that the eggs of marine invertebrates will, when laid, be in osmotic equilibrium with the surrounding sea water, but possess at the same time an ionic composition which differs greatly from the surrounding medium both qualitatively and in the higher forms quantitatively, in so far as a considerable fraction of the total concentration is made up not of ions, but of organic molecules. It is an unavoidable consequence that the eggs must show a high degree of impermeability to small molecules and ions.

Echinoderm eggs have been the subject of many permeability studies, and from some of these information concerning the problems of osmotic and ionic regulation can be obtained. R. S. Lillie (1916) studied the rate of osmotic inflow of water in fertilized and unfertilized eggs of *Arbacia* when these were transferred to hypotonic sea water. He measured the rate of swelling which, owing to the small size, is quite rapid. He found the rate of swelling much more rapid in the fertilized (curve A) than in the unfertilized (C) eggs (Fig. 46). Assuming perfect semipermeability and osmotic equilibrium between the eggs and the natural sea water he calculates an initial permeability of 9 μ^3/μ^2/min. for 11 atm. pressure difference, corresponding to a minute number of $8\frac{1}{2}$ days for the unfertilized eggs. In the fertilized eggs this is reduced to 41 hr.

In a later paper (1918) Lillie showed that the change in water permeability on fertilization is not immediate, but takes many minutes to develop and that it is arrested or retarded by cyanide, suggesting strongly that the change is brought about by metabolic processes. This increase in permeability on fertilization is not a universal phenomenon and was missed by Lillie in starfish eggs which were before fertilization much more permeable than the eggs of *Arbacia* or *Echinarachnius*.

Experiments by McClendon (1910 *a, b*) and Gray (1913) show a definite increase in electrical conductivity of echinid eggs after fertilization and make it probable that this is due to an increased permeability of the plasma membrane to ions which remains too low, however, to affect osmotic experiments of a few hours' duration.

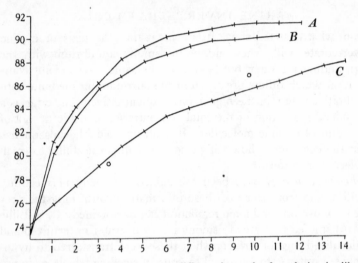

Fig. 46. Diameters of *Arbacia* eggs at different intervals after placing in dilute sea water. Ordinates are diameters in μ; abscissa, minutes after placing in the hypotonic medium. A, fertilized eggs; B, eggs with artificial membranes; C, unfertilized eggs. (Lillie.)

When the eggs are allowed to develop definite exchanges of ions take place. J. Runnström (1925), who studied the effects of varying the concentrations of single ions in the sea water in which the eggs of echinids (*Paracentrotus lividus* and others) were reared, observed profound changes in the protoplasm, especially when the eggs were exposed to K-free sea water, changes which are explicable only on the assumption that K will very slowly diffuse out from the eggs. It will be remembered that the concentration of K ions is very high.

J. Needham (1930), quoting Ephrussi and Rapkine (1928), stresses the fact that during development echinoderm eggs absorb large amounts of salt from the surrounding water and gives the following figures for the ash content of the eggs of *Strongylocentrotus lividus* at three points of time during development:

Table XXXVII

Hours after fertilization	8	12	40 (*Pluteus*)
Total ash % wet weight	0·34	2·06	3·56

. Needham and Needham (1930) found that relatively very large amounts of phosphate were absorbed from the water during the same period, although the phosphate concentration in sea water is always extremely low, amounting to $\frac{1}{2}$ μM. (16 γ) per litre or less. There can be no doubt, therefore, that the plasma membrane of echinoderm eggs is slightly permeable to ions, and that in spite of this permeability the egg content is not in ionic equilibrium with the surrounding water, but possesses the power to absorb and probably to reject ions according to requirements.

The most interesting problem from our point of view is whether the ions absorbed remain in a free state in the "intermicellar" fluid or are combined so as to exert no osmotic pressure. The ions used in the building up of the larval skeleton might possibly penetrate by diffusion, but K must, if at all, be absorbed against a concentration gradient, and in view of the extremely low phosphate concentration in sea water and the appreciable phosphate concentration within the egg cell there can be no reasonable doubt that phosphate also is absorbed against a concentration gradient.

Also water is taken up by the growing embryo. The metabolic processes give rise to the production of small osmotically active molecules, and it is reasonable to assume that these before diffusing out will be responsible for a certain osmotic uptake of water.

Sepia eggs. Ranzi (1930) studied the changes in weight, water and ash content of *Sepia* (*officinalis*) eggs during the whole course of embryonic development from the time of the first cleavage until hatching—a period of 90 days. The *Sepia* eggs are deposited by the female in small groups held together by a viscid mass. They are meroblastic, and the cleavage is confined to the germinal disc. When the larva hatches it contains in the mantle a small but distinctly visible shell. When just laid the eggs weigh on an average

77 mg. with 47·5 % dry substance and 1·04 % ash. The ash was determined by dry heating to a dull red heat and the values obtained are therefore probably too low.*

During development the weight increases to 132·8 mg. The water content increases from 52·5 to 75·8 % and the ash from 1·04 to 2·49 %. Analysing embryos and yolk separately Ranzi found that the yolk was absorbed during development without any large change in composition, while the growing embryo took up water and salt from the outside. Although it is unfortunate that the embryonic shells were not separately analysed there can be little doubt that ions are actively absorbed by the embryo during development, while water is attracted osmotically.

EGGS OF MARINE FISHES

The eggs of elasmobranchs are enclosed in a shell generally of a horny nature. Many elasmobranchs are viviparous or ovoviviparous and with those we are not concerned, but others lay their eggs before the embryo begins to develop.

The egg case is somewhat permeable both to salts and to urea, as shown by Peyrega (1914) for salts and by Needham and Needham (1930) for urea. The penetration is, however, quite slow. At a later stage the egg case opens up by four slits and the sea water gains free access. Nevertheless, only minimal amounts of urea are given off to the surrounding water, and according to Needham and Needham, it is probable that the walls of the yolk sac are impermeable to this substance. During development considerable amounts of urea are produced by the protein metabolism of the embryo, and these are in the main retained, so that the final concentration in the embryo comes very close to that of the adult.

When laid the eggs contain urea, as noted above for *Torpedo*, but in the case of *Scyllium canicula*, specially studied, the initial content is exceptionally low, 4·6 mg. in 5 g. wet weight of a single egg on an average, while some of the eggs gave even much lower values. It appears, therefore, that some urea may be lost just after laying. The

---

* Bialaszewicz found for the ovarial eggs as the sum of the elements $K + Na + Ca + Mg + Cl + P$ only 0·47 % of the fresh weight, and the "unknown base" which he failed to find is therefore, in all probability, inorganic. Wetzel (1907) found not less than 2·2 % total ash (1·6 % soluble ash) in the same eggs.

Scyllium eggs show in the main what Needham calls a cleidoic type of development, not depending on the supply of salts or water from the surrounding medium.

The eggs of teleosts, studied by Aug. Krogh, Agnes Krogh and C. Wernstedt (1938), exchange water and ions with the surrounding solution. Experiments were made on the eggs of *Pleuronectes flesus* and *Crenilabrus exoletus* which were pressed out into sea water from the ripe fishes. While in the oviduct they are in osmotic equilibrium with the surrounding opalescent fluid which contains proteins and, at least approximately, in equilibrium with the blood of the fish.

We observed them to sink in sea water of $10\text{--}15$ °/$_{oo}$, but to float in water of $25\text{--}34$ °/$_{oo}$. After a few minutes in the more concentrated water they became heavier and began to sink. The diameter decreases at first, but increases again and returns—at least approximately—to the original. This behaviour makes it probable that the eggs are permeable both to water and salt. To decide this point eggs were discharged into different concentrations of sea water and weighed, counted and analysed for Cl after a suitable interval. It turned out to be impossible to wash the eggs with any Cl-free solution without causing very great chloride losses. The eggs were therefore taken into a funnel of some 5 mm. diameter provided with an asbestos filter and rapidly sucked dry. The analyses were calculated both per 100 mg. fresh weight and per 100 eggs. When the osmotic equilibration takes place by loss of water to the more concentrated solutions it is to be expected that the Cl per 100 mg. will increase, while the Cl per 100 eggs should remain constant. When salts diffuse in both, the Cl per 100 mg. and the Cl per 100 eggs should increase. The results of a typical experiment on the eggs of the flounder (*Pleuronectes flesus*) are given in Table XXXVIII.

In spite of minor irregularities, due to individual variations and probably also to errors in the determinations, the table makes it clear that both water and Cl⁻ will penetrate into the eggs. The rate for salts is fairly slow, but after 6 hr. we are at least not far from an equilibrium, and the Cl content in the water of the eggs must become nearly the same as in the surrounding sea water.

Table XXXVIII

	100 eggs		100 mg.		Sea water Cl/100 mg.
	mg.	Cl⁻	No.	Cl⁻	
Fresh from fish	73·0	6·4	137	8·8	—
In 15 °/oo sea water	62·1	12·5	161	20·2	25·7
After 6 hr.	69·2	19·0	145	28·2	—
In 25 °/oo sea water	72·0	23·8	139	33·4	42·0
After 6 hr.	69·5	25·8	144	37·0	—
In 34 °/oo sea water	60·3	17·9	166	29·7	58·5
After 6 hr.	65·8	26·7	152	40·7	—

In these experiments we did not succeed in obtaining development and the results must be taken as representing unfertilized eggs.

A number of specific-gravity determinations on later stages of pelagic fish eggs can be found in the literature, but it is difficult to utilize them for the study of osmotic behaviour, because the determinations were made by plunging the eggs in different concentrations of sea water which do not leave the specific gravity unaltered. This effect was definitely noted by Jacobsen and Johansen (1908), and it follows from their observations that the eggs of plaice and cod are water permeable, but whether they are permeable also to salts cannot be decided. No material is available to explain the relatively low specific gravity of many pelagic fish eggs. It is not very likely that it is due to any osmoregulatory mechanism, but it may well be in relation to the fat content of the eggs.

Dakin (1911) made freezing-point determinations on the eggs of plaice (*Pleuronectes platessa*) from a hatchery and found a Δ of 0·78° for the eggs in sea water of $\Delta = 1·91°$.* Finding that treatment with distilled water for a few minutes would reduce the Δ to about 0·5° he concluded that the eggs are permeable to salts, and that in spite of this permeability a low salt concentration is kept up within them. As the eggs are meroblastic with a fairly large quantity of yolk this possibility seems rather remote, and the observations are to be explained in the light of experiments by Krogh,

---

* Dakin refers to the egg content as teleost larvae, and it would appear, therefore, that the embryos were in an advanced stage of development. This point is of some importance.

Krogh and Wernstedt (1938) on the eggs of pipefishes (Syngnathidae). In these fishes the female places the eggs on the abdomen of the male where they are fastened by a secretion and remain until hatching. We could obtain males of different species carrying eggs at different stages of development, and we had the further advantage that these eggs are large enough (weighing from 0·7 to 1·4 mg.) to allow simple dissections to be carried out.

The following determinations were made on the eggs of the small *Nerophis ophidium* taken from surface water with a Cl concentration of 412 mM. In the first batch of eggs the embryo could be clearly distinguished, but no eyes could be seen. These eggs weighed on an average 0·84 mg. and showed a Cl concentration calculated for the whole eggs of 274 mM.; 7 days later somewhat older eggs were obtained weighing 0·77 mg. and showing a Cl concentration of 235 Mm. In these eggs the embryos were very distinct and the eye pigment visible. Such eggs were opened and separate Cl determinations made on the "amniotic" fluid and the membranes + embryos. These showed for the fluid the same Cl concentration as the surrounding sea water (412 mM.), but the embryos + membranes had a concentration of only 180 mM.

The gradual reduction in the Cl content in the whole egg was confirmed on the larger eggs of *Nerophis aequoreus*, and in this case the embryos could be dissected out and gave on analysis a concentration of 97 mM., while that of the egg membrane was high.

The power to reduce the Cl content of the embryonal cells evidently appears very early and is probably present from the very first, but we do not know at what stage the power of the adult fish to reduce the total concentration of its blood and tissues comes into existence.

The osmotic conditions now described for certain eggs of marine fishes are probably not general. In certain syngnathids (*Hippocampus*) the eggs are enclosed in a brood pouch on the abdomen of the male, and Leiner (1934) found the fluid within this to have at first practically the same osmotic concentration as the blood of the adult fish, but to approach during development that of sea water.

The eggs of *Fundulus* maintain their original low concentration when laid, and after fertilization, as shown by the determinations of

Loeb and Wasteneys (1915), and the conclusion of these authors and others that the protoplasmatic membrane of the egg is impermeable to salts and almost impermeable to water seems to be unavoidable. It is a characteristic fact that the eggs of *Fundulus* (*heteroclitus*) can develop and hatch in distilled water. Manery, Warbritton and Irving (1933) found, however, that during development in sea water lasting 15 days *Fundulus* eggs would increase in weight from 3·4 to 3·75 mg., while the water content increased from 81 to 83 %, an increase in water content of 0·36 mg. for each egg. According to the curves given this increase seems to be rectilinear throughout the developmental period. Since the osmotic conditions would lead to loss of water we seem to face an unknown mechanism for active regulation.

EGGS OF FRESH-WATER ORGANISMS

With regard to the fresh-water organisms there is no reason to maintain a distinction between vertebrates and invertebrates. The problem is the same for all, viz. how to preserve the total concentration and single ions in the eggs from the moment they leave the maternal organism until the mechanisms of active control, present in the adult or in free-swimming larvae, come into play. A few forms only have been studied in such a way as to provide definite information.

Daphnia. In the Cladocera the eggs normally develop in the "brood pouch", and in some forms (*Moina, Polyphemus* and others) this acts as a kind of uterus into which nutritive material is secreted (Weissmann, 1876). In most forms, including the species of *Daphnia*, the brood pouch contains water only, and Ramult (1914) found that parthenogenetic eggs removed from the brood pouch and placed in tap water or even in distilled water would develop normally. They could not be removed, however, during the first hour of their stay without losing the power to develop. It is probable, therefore, that something essential to development enters the brood pouch with the egg, and that they are at first not so impermeable as they become later. This is borne out by the observation that a definite increase in volume takes place during the first hour in the brood pouch.

The osmotic pressure in developing *Daphnia* eggs, both parthenogenetic and fertilized, was studied by Przylecki in two papers (1921) in Polish of which I have been able to read only the French summaries. Przylecki measured the pressures by plasmolytic experiments with known sugar solutions. A few hours after the eggs had entered the brood pouch he found low concentrations corresponding to freezing-point depressions of 0·245° in the parthenogenetic eggs of *Simocephalus vetulus* and 0·186° in those of *Daphnia magna*, while the fertilized winter eggs gave for *D. pulex* 0·247° and for *D. magna* 0·240°. These figures correspond to concentrations of 57–72 mM.

From these starting-points there is a regular and large increase in the osmotic concentration of the eggs which reaches a value in 50 to 80 hr. of about 0·74° (216 mM.) During the first 20 hr. there is a considerable increase in volume of the eggs resisted by an elastic tension in the egg membrane which becomes evident when an egg is pricked. Later the volume remains constant over a considerable period, and finally the membrane is again stretched until it bursts and the larva emerges. Przylecki assumes a large initial drop in osmotic pressure occurring before he was able to start his determinations, but a comparison with Fritsches's results (p. 95), which have escaped the notice of Przylecki, makes it clear that the initial values are very close to the osmotic concentration of adult *D. magna*. The large, but comparatively slow, increase in concentration is to be explained probably by metabolic products, retained within the egg, and the increase in volume by an osmotic inflow of water. It is of course conceivable that an active absorption of salt takes place from the surrounding water, but this seems unlikely in view of the fact that normal development will take place in distilled water (Ramult).

In a later paper (1925) Ramult studied the influence of salt solutions upon the development of *Daphnia* eggs. He found the solutions acting only by their osmotic concentration irrespective of the nature of the salt. A concentration of 100 mM. or above would produce a "closed" development, the embryo undergoing the normal morphological changes, but without growing, and the final bursting of the membrane would be prevented. This again shows that the egg membrane is slightly permeable to water only and that the osmotic inflow of water is of vital importance for the normal development.

Salmo. Trout eggs have been studied repeatedly by Gray (1920, 1932), Runnström (1920), Svetlow (1929), Manery and Irving (1935), and Krogh and Ussing (1937). The results can be taken as representative for the Salmonidae and probably for a large number of fresh-water fishes. The ripe eggs, which are surrounded by a delicate, soft membrane, the "chorion", are in osmotic equilibrium with the blood of the maternal organism. Runnström found freezing-point depressions of 0·645° and 0·636° respectively. When they are shed into fresh water definite changes take place. The chorionic membrane hardens and becomes very tough, and a cytoplasmic membrane, referred to by Gray as the "vitelline" membrane, forms at the surface of the egg proper. During these processes, which take less than an hour, the egg swells by osmotic uptake of water. The chorion swells slightly more than the egg proper with the result that a perivitelline space is formed. The egg is suspended in the peri-vitelline fluid. In water it will occupy the position shown in Fig. 47 A, but in fluids of a sufficiently high specific gravity it will float at the top (B). These changes are brought about by the contact of the egg with fresh water, and fertilization is possible only at the very beginning. When eggs are shed into Ringer solution or sea-water dilutions (Runnström) the changes do not take place, and the eggs remain fertilizable for a period of at least a day. Manery and Irving definitely show that fertilization as such does not measurably influence the water inflow or the changes in the membranes. The swelling as measured by the increase in wet weight, from 65 to 77 mg. in experiments by Manery and Irving, is due only to water inflow, the salt content as measured by Cl determinations remaining constant.

The chorionic and vitelline membranes when fully formed show very different characteristic properties, specially studied by Gray (1932). The chorion is about 90μ thick and of a fibrous nature, able to stand pressures up to 7–8 atm. before rupturing. It is permeable both to water and salt, and perivitelline fluid at least very soon after the shedding of the eggs cannot be distinguished from the surrounding solution (Svetlow). The vitelline membrane is impermeable to water and salt. The impermeability was probable from the fact that the eggs maintain their osmotic concentration during development and do not swell, but this might be due to active processes. Gray demonstrated the water impermeability by placing eggs in salt solutions up to 8 times Ringer and noting that no shrinking would take place and the weight remain constant. The absolute impermeability was confirmed by Krogh and Ussing (1937) by means of heavy water. It was found that a slight permeability was present up to an age of 6 hr., while after that the eggs

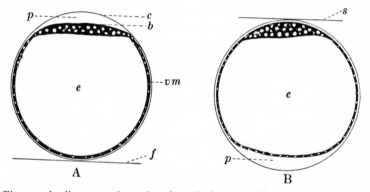

Fig. 47. A, diagrammatic section through the unfertilized egg of the trout in tap water; B, in a medium of slightly higher gravity. c, chorion; b, blastodisc; p, perivitelline space; vm, vitelline membrane; e, yolk; f, floor of container; s, surface, (Gray.)

remained impermeable for at least 13 days at a temperature of 10–12° C. Later, however, the eggs become again permeable, and when the eyes of the embryo have become visible D_2O will penetrate. In spite of this the weight of the eggs does not change, and we must assume, therefore, that the water flowing in osmotically is actively excreted. It is known that the urinary ducts become open to the outside about this age. During the period in which the vitelline membrane is impermeable to water O_2 is absorbed, and about the 11th day 4 mm.³ would penetrate per hour into one egg through a surface of very nearly 1 cm.² (Krogh and Ussing). It is evident, therefore, that in small eggs with a correspondingly large relative surface enough O_2 for development can be obtained by diffusion through a membrane which is completely impermeable to water, and the production of impermeable plasma membranes is probably a general mechanism for the protection of eggs in fresh water against osmotic swelling, a protection which can be dispensed with when mechanisms for the excretion of water become functional in the embryo, and which must be dropped when an exchange of ions is to take place. The observations of Ikeda on *Oryzias latipes* appear to furnish an example of this eventuality.

Oryzias latipes is a fish nearly related to *Fundulus* and living in fresh water and brackish water in Japan. The eggs will develop and hatch out both in tap water and in artificial salt solutions, and Ikeda (1937 *a*) noted the interesting fact that the number of days required from fertilization to hatching at a constant temperature of 28° C. could be lowered from 14 days in tap water to about 8 days in 200 mM. NaCl. 2 mM. of KCl would produce a similar increase in the rate of development, but 75 % of the eggs died. At higher concentrations of KCl the heart would be slowed down and stop and the embryos die in consequence. It is evident, therefore, that the egg membrane is (or becomes in later stages) permeable to cations.

In a second paper Ikeda studied the exchange of K ions between a certain number (about 50) of *Oryzia* eggs kept for 2 days in 50 ml. experimental solution. These solutions were made up by mixing o·1 molar NaCl with o·1 molar KCl so as to produce K concentrations varying from 100 mM. down to 2×10^{-8} mM. and to 0 (pure NaCl). It is necessary to examine the results in some detail, because Ikeda failed to see that his very high dilutions were fictive, since the NaCl or even distilled water would contain more K beforehand than he added. I shall recalculate his figures and add extra columns to his Table 3 to make this clear. Ikeda thought he found that at concentrations down to 2×10^{-6} mM. the eggs would absorb K, while at still lower concentrations K was eliminated from the eggs to the solution. All his results were obtained by determinations of K on the eggs and comparisons with a control batch kept for a few hours in tap water. The differences found between the control and experimental batches were supposed to be absorbed from or eliminated to the surrounding solutions. Fifty eggs have a volume according to Ikeda of 33 mm.³, and 1 mM. change in concentration in the eggs therefore corresponds to a K quantity of $33 \times 10^{-3} \mu M$.

Column 8 of Table XXXIX shows that the K absorbed from solutions I–VI is available in these and can be abstracted without seriously changing the concentration, but the alleged quantities taken from the following are much larger than the quantities originally put in, while the quantities said to be eliminated from the eggs into solutions IX, XII, XIII and XIV would raise these much beyond the point where absorption into the eggs is believed to take place. The results are probably due to variations in the K content of the eggs, but whatever the explanation the figures are unreliable. The important fact remains, however, that K is absorbed from solutions much more dilute with regard to K than the eggs themselves, certainly down to millimolar, and perhaps even beyond. Ikeda explains this by assuming that K within the egg is in organic combination with only a minimal concentration of free K ions, which Ikeda puts at 10^{-6} mM., while his experiments warrant at most 10^{-1}. We know of no other case in which K is thus combined, and it is much more likely that we have in Ikeda's results an example of the general rule that living cells are able to take up K from very dilute solutions. Ikeda is of opinion that such uptake (and elimination) can take place only by exchange with another ion, because he finds no change in the K content in eggs kept in distilled water. The argument does not hold, since the quantity which must be given off to the distilled water to raise the concentration to a steady state level is too small to be detected by his analytical technique.

Rana temporaria. The osmotic conditions in frogs' eggs were studied as early as 1912 by Backmann and Runnström. They made experiments on the development of the eggs in balanced salt solutions from the concentration of frog's Ringer downwards and were surprised to find that these in all higher concentrations down to R/5 were unfavourable and would not allow the embryos to hatch out. They concluded that the eggs themselves must have a very low osmotic concentration, and their determinations on egg contents at different stages showed indeed that the freezing-point depression, which in the eggs from the oviduct amounted to 0·48° (140 mM.),

Table XXXIX. Potassium contents of the eggs of *Oryzias latipes* (domesticated type) after being kept in the experimental solution for two days (25° C.)

1	2	3	4	5	6	7	8
						Outside quantity of K calculated from 2 and 6	
Outside solution	Original concentration mM. K^+	No. of eggs analysed	Inside K concentration mM.	Increase above "control" mM.	Amount absorbed or eliminated μM. $\times 10^{-3}$	Original μM.	Final μM.
I	100	500	88·7	26·1	860	5000	4999
II	50	—	—	—	—	—	—
III	25	565	75·5	12·9	425	1250	1249·5
IV	5	564	73·7	11·1	365	250	249·6
V	1	558	77·0	14·4	475	50	49·5
VI	2×10^{-1}	968	69·3	7·3	240	10	9·7
VII	2×10^{-2}	400	66·2	3·6	120	1	0·9
VIII	2×10^{-3}	400	67·0	4·4	145	10^{-1}	−0·045
IX	2×10^{-4}	400	58·6	−4·0	−130	10^{-2}	0·14
X	2×10^{-5}	400	68·0	5·4	180	10^{-3}	−0·179
XI	2×10^{-6}	400	64·7	2·1	70	10^{-4}	−0·07
XII	2×10^{-7}	300	59·6	−3·0	−100	10^{-5}	0·1
XIII	2×10^{-8}	300	56·0	−6·6	−220	10^{-6}	0·22
XIV	0 (100 mM. NaCl)	500	55·7	−6·9	−230	—	0·23
"Control"	—	500	62·6	—	—	—	—

dropped after fertilization to 0·045 and at the early blastopore stage even to 0·042 (12 mM.), which is about the same as that of the fresh water in which the eggs normally develop. A little later a sharp rise in osmotic pressure would take place and before the blastopore was closed would have reached a Δ of 0·215°. Thereupon a much slower rise would take place and reach in 20 days a value of 0·405 (118 mM.).

Backmann and Runnström, in trying to explain the large reduction in concentration observed, gave good reasons against the assumption that the salts diffused out of the eggs. They found that the eggs would develop in regularly renewed distilled water from which at least the salts lost at first could not later be recovered, and they point out also that the presence of the salts seems to be necessary at every stage (e.g. to prevent precipitation of globulins). They believe therefore that the salts must become provisionally adsorbed (to proteins ?), and quote figures in support of the theoretical possibility of such an adsorption.

In a separate paper by Backmann (1912) the existence of a very low osmotic pressure in the eggs after fertilization and during the first stage of development was confirmed by measurements of diameters on fertilized and unfertilized eggs of *Bufo vulgaris* and *Triton cristatus*. It was found that the unfertilized eggs would swell slowly in all NaCl solutions below the concentration of 120 mM., while the eggs in the morula stage would shrink in all concentrations and keep unaltered in tap water.

In spite of the evidently very careful work of Backmann and Runnström I have not found it possible to accept their results, mainly because of the difficulties inherent in the assumption of a provisional adsorption of nine-tenths of the osmotically active substances, but also because of the great difficulties inseparable from freezing-point determinations on such material as the contents of frogs' eggs or the yolk of hens' eggs, difficulties which have in more recent years caused a great deal of controversy regarding the osmotic relations between white and yolk in hens' eggs (cp. E. Howard, 1932). A series of determinations and experiments were therefore undertaken in this laboratory and are now published by A. Krogh, K. Schmidt-Nielsen and E. Zeuthen. We confirm the initial swelling of the eggs when laid in tap water or transferred to distilled water or millimolar salt solutions. In distilled water the swelling is more pronounced and continuous, but definitely more rapid in unfertilized than in fertilized eggs. In tap water and salt solutions the swelling of fertilized eggs reaches only some 15–20 % in volume during the first 2–4 hr. and practically ceases after the first cleavage to be resumed again after 24 hr. The inference that the eggs are at first permeable and then become for a time almost impermeable to water is confirmed by experiments with heavy water. This is in complete agreement with the measurements of Backmann and Runnström who observed swellings of 12·5–21 % before the first cleavage, 1·5 % between the 64-cell stage and well-developed multicellular blastula, and 1·3 % from this stage until the formation of the blastopore.

Osmotic pressures were measured by the vapour-tension method on the contents of single eggs, and in some cases we obtained for our determinations the clear and practically protein-free fluid from the blastocoele which will rise by itself in a micropipette. Cl determinations were made by means of the Wigglesworth technique on the mixed contents of a few eggs centrifuged in a sealed tube to obtain a clear liquid. The analyses of blastocoele fluid were made on single eggs. The results are summarized in Fig. 48, giving the concentrations found in millimoles. The time scale of this figure is logarithmic to allow a representation of later stages after hatching which takes place about the point marked i after 4 days. In spite of the rather large individual deviations (including of course the accidental errors) the curve shows the fall in total concentration to be expected as a result of the osmotic inflow of water, but nothing like the fall postulated by Backmann and Runnström. The fall in Cl concentration appears to be somewhat larger, but the large deviations in the initial determinations make it impossible to assign a definite value. There is a systematic difference in Cl concentration between the blastocoele fluid and the tissue, and it is remarkable that the blastocoele fluid is lower by about 12 mM.

During the later stages of development within the egg, from e to i on the curves, there is a definite increase in total osmotic concentration, while the chloride concentration remains practically constant. During this period there is, according to Schaper (1902), who made careful determinations of the growth of frog embryos, a slight increase in water content from 2·6 to 2·8 mg./egg, which should produce a corresponding decrease in concentration, and the increase found is almost certainly due to organic waste products which cannot escape owing to the very low permeability of the eggs. After the hatching the larvae grow rapidly (without food) by osmotic absorption of water which is increased in 2 days from 2·8 to

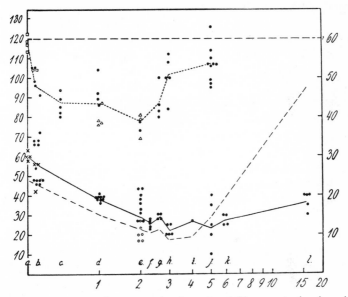

Fig. 48. Changes in total concentration (-----) and Cl concentration (——) in frogs eggs, during development. Time scale in days (logarithmic). *a–l*, developmental stages; *b*, first cleavage; *i*, hatching. Ordinate left, concentration in mM. Lowest curve (– –), total chloride in one egg; ordinate right, μM./100. (Krogh.)

7·9 mg. In spite of this absorption the Cl concentration rises, slightly at first and then definitely, and the only possible explanation is an active absorption of Cl from the water. This begins simultaneously with the appearance of the external gills, and it is to be supposed that the cells responsible are located in these. The quantities of Cl and alkali were determined on a large number of hatching larvae, and again 2 days later (without food), and the results were for the hatching larvae 0·20 μM. Cl and 0·19 μM. alkali, and 2 days later 0·31 and 0·40μM. respectively. This again shows the active absorption of both Cl and alkali.

We have also repeated on the morula stage of *Rana temporaria* eggs the experiments made by Backmann on *Bufo* and *Triton* eggs by placing them in different concentrations. We tried both glucose and NaCl and could not confirm Backmann's results. We found a regular shrinkage in concentrations higher than the osmotic pressure as determined by us, and a swelling at lower concentrations which became quite definite in tap water. The eggs were followed for 17 hr., during which time they passed into the blastula stage. The experiments were made very late in the season, and only a small number of eggs showed normal development, but the results obtained on these were uniform.

A few words should be said finally about the osmotic pressure in the perivitelline space, surrounding the egg from about the time of the first cleavage when it is first formed and growing larger, especially in the period from *f* to *g* in Fig. 48, when the embryo grows in length. We made determinations of osmotic concentration of the perivitelline fluid and found it slightly higher than that of the surrounding water. This corresponded to 7 mM., and the perivitelline fluid varied in three determinations from 10 to 18, average 14, of which 4 mM. was found to be due to chlorides. It seems possible, therefore, that the growth of this space is due to a small osmotic-pressure difference generated by substances diffusing out from the egg.

COMMENTS, CONCLUSIONS AND SUGGESTIONS

Permeability of cell surfaces and membranes. The problems of permeability in living organisms turn out to be extremely complicated. In what is usually called permeability we have to deal with the movements of molecules and ions in which the driving force is concentration gradients or, in the case of ions, electrical potentials, and when such movements take place across a protoplasmic surface that surface is *eo ipso* permeable. The rate of penetration can be measured and put in relation to the driving force, and if the concentration gradients or potentials are reversed the direction will also become reversed, while the same rate will obtain, provided the physicochemical properties of the membrane remain unaltered. In this sense protoplasmic surfaces are generally permeable to water, to dissolved gases, to a number of organic substances with which we are not here concerned, and sometimes also to ions.

In a number of cases, on the other hand, we have found special mechanisms by which ions, certain organic substances and sometimes even water are transported in one direction only and may be moved against gradients and potentials. It would be absurd to deny that in such cases the surfaces in question are permeable, but it would be just as absurd to put this "permeability" in the same category as the simple permeability defined above with which we shall deal exclusively in this section.

Complete impermeability for water is induced in the vitelline membrane of trout eggs by the contact with fresh water, and a corresponding mechanism is probably quite common in eggs of freshwater organisms. At early stages impermeability seems to be the only way to prevent osmotic swelling, since a fairly high osmotic concentration must be preserved, and no mechanism is available to remove water. The impermeability is biologically possible, because the egg can remain sufficiently permeable to O_2 and CO_2 to allow the necessary respiratory exchange. At later stages the membrane becomes again slightly permeable, and the inflow of water seems to be a biological necessity for the growing embryo. In other cases, like the eggs of frogs and Cladocera, there is at no stage a complete impermeability and, at least in the case of *Daphnia*, the *slow* osmotic inflow of water is biologically necessary.

There are very large differences in the permeability of animal integuments for water, but in all cases the permeability is of a low order, and minute numbers as determined range from 2 days to 5 years. Generally sea-water invertebrates are more permeable than fresh-water forms or than vertebrates. In some cases (integument of *Phascolosoma* and *Rana*) "irreciprocal" water permeability has been described. This does not mean that water will penetrate in one direction only, but that the rate was found to be more rapid in one direction. The evidence for such differential permeability is inconclusive, and the conception itself should be viewed with suspicion.

The permeability of integuments (including gills) for electroneutral substances and ions seems to have some relation to the permeability for water, in so far as minute numbers of a few days or even weeks are associated with a definite, but fairly low, permeability for dissolved substances, as found in most marine invertebrates. In several cases, among fishes and Crustacea, the gills are permeable to urea and NH_3 to such an extent that a major portion of nitrogenous waste products are excreted by this route.

Koizumi was able to show that regarding rate of penetration through the integument of *Caudina* ions could be arranged as follows:

$$K^+ > Na^+ > Ca^{++} > Mg^{++} \text{ and } Cl^- > SO_4^=,$$

and there is some additional evidence to show that generally monovalent ions will penetrate faster than divalent.

Impermeability of the integuments to ions and electroneutral substances, while being highly developed in the integuments of fresh-water organisms, is probably rarely absolute. When such animals are treated with distilled water they will lose ions slowly through the skin.

When marine forms penetrate into fresh water they may either develop a high degree of impermeability, like the eel, or remain relatively permeable like *Eriocheir*, but in the latter case they must develop very efficient mechanisms for the active absorption of ions by which the losses are made good.

Ionic independence of living cells. It appears to be a general property of living cells, both in plants and animals, that they are able to regulate their content of diffusible ions in the protoplasm and cell sap so as to be largely independent of the concentrations in the surrounding medium, subject in almost all cases to the condition of a nearly neutral reaction, and subject, in the case of cells not mechanically supported, to the condition of osmotic equilibrium with the medium. In the preceding sections many examples are given of such ionic independence of which the most notable are perhaps the presence (in large concentration) of NH_4Cl in the cell sap of *Noctiluca* and the absorption of K and phosphate by marine eggs. Even more striking instances can be found in plants, and I reproduce the following table from Osterhout (1933), in which analyses of the sap contained in very large cells of the marine algae *Valonia* and *Halicystis*, of the brackish-water *Chara* and of the fresh-water alga *Nitella* are put together. The cells of *Chara* and *Nitella* are mechanically supported and have a much higher total concentration than the surrounding water.

Table XL

mM.	Sea water	Valonia macro-physa	Hali-cystis	Brackish water	Chara	Pond water	Nitella
Cl	580	597	603	73	225	0·9	90·8
SO₄	36	Trace?	Trace	2·8	3·9	0·3	8·3
H₂PO₄	0	—	—	Trace	4·1	0·0002	3·6
NO₃	0	—	—	0·005	0·4	0·55	0
Na	498	90	557	60	142	0·2	10·0
K	12	500	6·4	1·4	88	0·05	54·3
Ca	12	1·7	8	1·8	5·3	0·78	10·2
Mg	57	Trace?	16·7	6·5	15·5	1·69	177·7

These figures show that almost any ion can become either concentrated or kept out. Cl is highly concentrated by *Nitella*, less so by *Chara*; SO₄ concentrated by *Nitella* and definitely kept out by the marine species. H₂PO₄ is concentrated almost 2000 times by *Nitella* and even more by *Chara*. NO₃ is concentrated by *Chara*, while kept out completely from *Nitella*. Na is concentrated by *Chara* and *Nitella*, K by all except *Halicystis*, Ca by *Chara* and *Nitella* and Mg also by *Chara* and *Nitella*, while kept out completely by *Valonia*.

Suggestive analyses on the same species of *Chara* from different habitats were published by Collander (1936) showing that the excess total concentration over the medium would remain practically the same in brackish as in fresh water, while the relative concentrations of single ions would vary enormously as shown in Table XLI:

Table XLI

	Cl mM.			Na mM.		
	Water	Sap	S./W.	Water	Sap	S./W.
Brackish water	80	232	2·9	68	148	2·2
Fresh water	0·13	176	1350	0·21	84	400
B./F.	615	1·3	—	320	1·8	—

	K mM.			Ca mE.		
	Water	Sap	S./W.	Water	Sap	S./W.
Brackish water	1·4	69	49	3·8	11	2·9
Fresh sater	0·04	77	1900	3·3	13	3·9
B./F.	35	0·9	—	1·1	0·8	—

I shall mention finally another paper by Collander (1937) in which a series of different plants were cultivated in the same solution, containing 2 mM. each of Na, K and Rb, and it was found that K and Rb cannot apparently be distinguished by the absorbing cells, since they were present in the ash in almost equivalent concentrations, showing minor but significant differences from one species to another. It was found further that the absorption of Na bore no relation whatever to the absorption of the two other ions, and the species could be arranged in a definite order (beginning with *Fagopyrum* and ending with *Salicornia* and *Atriplex*) showing an increasing affinity for Na (Fig. 49).

I do not think the time is at all ripe for a discussion of the mechanisms of ion absorption, but I shall refer briefly to experiments by Rosenfels (1935) on the uptake of bromide into *Elodea* cells from 2 mM. KBr, in which it was shown that such uptake is brought to a standstill by lack of O_2, but is not definitely affected whether CO_2 is eliminated (in the dark), stationary (in light, without a supply of CO_2 from outside) or absorbed (when an outside concentration of 0·2 % CO_2 is present in light). It would seem, therefore, that an exchange with HCO_3 can *not* be a part of the absorption machinery in this case.

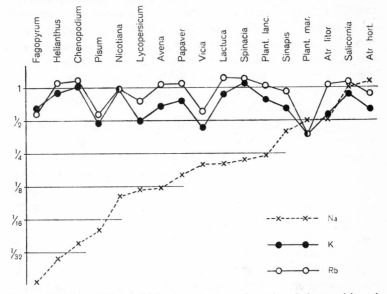

Fig. 49. Na, K and Rb in mM./g. dry substance of a series of plants cultivated in the same solution containing 2 mM./l. of these ions. (Collander.)

In a very suggestive paper by S. C. Brooks (1938) it is shown by means of radioactive K that in *Nitella* individual K atoms can be accumulated in the protoplasm for many hours before being transferred to the sap. This reveals as by a flash of lightning how complicated the machinery must be.

In plants the processes of active absorption would seem to be inseparable from the processes of growth. In animals such a restriction does not seem to exist, and while generally the examples that can be given of ion absorption from dilute media are less striking, because the internal medium directly bathing the cells of Metazoa is much less variable, we have the advantage that the medium can be changed reversibly and the consequent changes in composition of cellular fluids studied. A beginning in this direction was made on mussels and on *Eriocheir*, and although the technical difficulties have not so far been overcome it will no doubt be possible to demonstrate the active uptake of ions into tissue cells and to find out, at least, which steady states are approached in different conditions. Such experiments would involve that animals belonging to suitable species (*Eriocheir*, *Carcinus*, *Mytilus* or others) were brought to the lowest concentrations in their blood compatible with life and the composition of the continuous phase in cells of certain tissues ascertained. When thereupon the blood concentrations were raised in respect of one or several ions the consequent changes in the tissue cells could be followed.

Although we know from the fresh-water Protozoa and from specialized cells in many Metazoa that single cells may possess a power of active water regulation so as to maintain an osmotic concentration different from that of the medium, it appears that such a power is not normally present in metazoan tissues. This is probably mainly a question of specialization and economy, in so far as the active uptake or elimination of water to compensate the osmotic flow requires special machinery and the expenditure of energy necessary to run such machinery.

The isotonicity normally present between tissue cells and the surrounding medium need not mean, however, that the sum of free ions on both sides of the cellular membrane is the same. A very suggestive correlation seems to exist between the general height of organization, or possibly the perfection of the locomotor apparatus, and the total ionic concentration within cells, or more particularly within muscle fibres.

We find a very high concentration almost equal to that of sea water in the lower marine organisms like *Caudina* (p. 34). In the lower fresh-water organisms the concentration, maintained by active processes of regulation, seems, on the other hand, to be quite low.

In the higher marine invertebrates like the Mollusca (Gastropoda and Cephalopoda especially) and in the higher Crustacea a large proportion of the ions are replaced, at least in muscle cells, by organic substances (taurin and others) which make up the deficit in total concentration. This point of view holds also for the Elasmobranchii in which a considerable proportion both in the cells and in the blood is made up by urea and trimethylamine oxide, while the total concentration is slightly superior to that of sea water. These general relationships are well shown in the diagram (Fig. 50) published by Fredericq in 1901.

The ionic concentrations in cells of higher fresh-water invertebrates appear to be unknown.

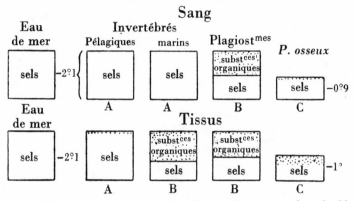

Fig. 50. Diagrammatic representation of osmotic concentrations in blood (upper row) and tissues (lower) of pelagic and marine invertebrates, plagiostomes and bony fishes compared with sea water. (Fredericq.)

In the teleosts and all higher vertebrates, whether on land, in fresh water or in the sea, the concentration of blood and tissue fluid varies only within the narrow limits of 250 to 150 mM., and the contribution of organic substances to this concentration is small only.

I can find no reason why an ionic concentration between 150 and 250 mM. should be more favourable for higher development or for muscle power than either higher or lower, and the above is only a suggestion which might be worth following up.*

* There is one apparent exception known to me. Wigglesworth found on the blood of mosquito larvae that chlorides made up only about 35–40 % of the total concentration which corresponded to 250 mM. In this case internal regulation is carried out largely by variation in the non-chloride fraction, and this may be of biological importance.

In any case determinations of ionic concentrations and of simple organic substances in the cells of higher invertebrates and elasmobranchs are highly desirable. If the organic substances are not there to make up osmotic concentration they must be supposed to fulfil some other function in the animal economy which would be worth investigating.

ACTIVE TRANSPORT MECHANISMS ACROSS MEMBRANES COMPOSED OF CELLS

I take it that the ability to transport ions, neutral substances or water across cellular membranes and accumulating them in an extracellular fluid or sap is something biologically different from the mere power of accumulation inherent in (probably) all living cells, although I have no doubt that it is derived by some further development from the latter, and that the accumulation in a large intracellular vacuole may possibly be very nearly related to extracellular accumulation. In animals this ability of extracellular accumulation is confined to certain specialized organs. In the higher plants, absorbing salts and water through a system of roots, it resides in the fine ramifications of the roots while these are growing, but is apparently lost at later stages. According to Lundegårdh (Lundegårdh and Burström, 1933, 1935; Lundegårdh, 1937) cations and anions are absorbed independently by roots (of wheat) and transferred at higher concentrations to the sap rising from the roots towards the leaves. In experiments with 1·25 mM. $HKCO_3$, K was absorbed without being accompanied by any anions. It is a very interesting fact that the absorption of anions depends upon a CO_2 production over and above the basal which stands in a constant relation to the anions absorbed. The absorption of 1 mM. of NO_3 requires 2 mM. of CO_2, while 1 mM. Cl requires 3 and 1 mM. of SO_4 requires 6 mM. CO_2. These quantities of CO_2 are the same both when, under normal conditions of oxygen supply, the respiratory quotient is about unity and when, at low O_2 pressures, the quotient rises to values of 2 or 3. The cations appear to be absorbed without any expenditure of energy, and quantitatively they stand in very variable relations to the anions taken up simultaneously. It would appear that when a cation like K^+ is absorbed from KNO_3 in excess of NO_3^- it must be exchanged against another cation.

There seems to be no power of discrimination in plant roots, all ions being absorbed mainly in accordance with their mobilities, but it should be remembered that in certain plants Collander observed a preferential absorption of Na as shown above (Fig. 49).

The organs doing active transport work in animals are very diverse. In the cases so far studied they are highly specialized, their activity is independent of growth processes, but is regulated in accordance with the requirements of the organisms, which can be briefly summarized as the maintenance of a constant internal environment.

Renal transport of organic substances and ions. It may be convenient to distinguish, at least provisionally, between renal and extrarenal organs of active transport. Renal organs seem to be distinguishable into two main types of which the one, represented by the Malpighian tubes in insects and by the aglomerular kidneys in certain marine fishes, works mainly by an active transport of waste products from the blood to the lumen of the glandular tubules. Very few details are known regarding the mechanisms here concerned, and from the point of view of osmotic regulation this type of kidney is of minor interest.

In the second type of kidney, of which the amphibian is the best known example, thanks to the brilliant researches of Richards and his collaborators, a blood filtrate is formed from which the final urine is elaborated by selective reabsorption. Westfall, Findley and Richards (1934) provided the final proof that the fluid issuing from the glomeruli is an ultrafiltrate, and Richards (1935) showed that sugar is completely reabsorbed from this filtrate by cells in the proximal tubules, while Cl can be similarly removed from the distal tubules.

Kidneys working mainly according to this principle seem to be widely distributed in the animal kingdom and to play an important part in osmotic regulation in fresh-water organisms. In many worms the nephridia begin as open tubes draining the coelomic cavity, but in the molluscs there is definite evidence of filtration into the pericardial sac, from which the ciliated nephridial tubes take their origin, and reabsorption of salts from the filtrate has also been shown to occur. In Crustacea and vertebrates the mechanism is the same in principle, but details regarding the power of selective absorption are almost completely lacking, except for the absorption of urea in specialized sections of the tubules in elasmobranchs. What we know is that osmotically active substances can be reabsorbed by the renal tubes of many fresh-water animals to such an extent that the urine becomes almost as dilute as the surrounding water, and that this regulating mechanism acts with even greater efficiency when animals are placed in distilled water.

Renal and intestinal reabsorption of water. The power of reabsorbing ions seems to be general in the filtration type of kidneys and to be closely related to a fundamental power of living cells to accumulate ions.

The ability to transport water actively against an osmotic gradient seems to be present only as a special development.

There is some evidence for water absorption in the hindgut of insects from the solution discharged by the Malpighian tubes, but it is scarcely conclusive and the absorption may be an osmotic inflow when the urine is more dilute than the body fluids.

In frogs it is known that certain substances present in the glomerular filtrate become somewhat concentrated in the final urine, but this may be and probably is a simple consequence of osmotic inflow of water, after the urine has become very dilute by the active absorption of salts.

In birds, and perhaps in reptiles, absorption of water takes place in the cloaca from the fluid urine discharged here by the kidneys, but it does not seem certain that the osmotic concentration of the resulting paste is definitely higher than that of the blood.

In mammals, finally, we have a very definite mechanism for active water absorption, probably located in the loop of Henle, which will raise the concentration of the urine to much higher figures than that of the blood.

The adaptation to a fresh-water life by extrarenal ion transport mechanisms. Animals living in fresh water and possessing integuments permeable to water have to face a constant loss of salts, due partly to the slight ion permeability of their integuments, but mainly taking place through the urine which, in the process of excreting all the water flowing in, cannot be made absolutely salt free. The loss of salt is no doubt in many cases, and perhaps generally, made good by the salts contained in the food, but a very large number of fresh-water animals are able to withstand starvation over long periods, and in these, at least, the mechanisms for ion absorption become essential, while they will also often preserve the life of individuals which have become damaged and lose an excessive amount of salt in consequence. Such mechanisms can be brought into action for experimental study, where they exist, when the salts of the organism are depleted by treatment with distilled water coupled with inanition. The active uptake of chloride ions by animals thus treated is generally easy to demonstrate and has been observed in so many forms within Annelida, Mollusca, Crustacea, Insecta, Teleostomi and Amphibia that it is no doubt of very common occurrence. It has been definitely shown on frogs and on *Eriocheir* that the active absorption of salt is independent of the osmotic inflow of water which normally takes place simultaneously, but will go on at about the same rate from solutions of sugar or sulphate isotonic with the blood. It is present also in some brackish-water species, of which *Carcinus maenas*, where it was first discovered, is the best known.

When animals penetrate from the ocean into brackish water this can take place in two essentially different ways. Some of them retain isotonicity and develop an increased tolerance towards low salt concentrations. This can carry them down to quite low salt concentrations, about 4 $^\circ/_{\circ\circ}$ as found in the Bay of Bothnia, but never into fresh water.

All brackish-water forms have concentrations lower than sea water, but some become definitely hypertonic to the surrounding water when this is diluted below a certain concentration. Such hypertonicity is active and is probably brought about generally by extrarenal absorption, but proofs are lacking except in the case of *Carcinus maenas*. A further development of the power to maintain hypertonicity enables a brackish-water animal to penetrate into fresh water. This adaptation is by no means rare, and even now animal forms (like *Hydrobia jenkinsii*) may suddenly gain (perhaps by mutation) the power of supporting life in fresh water.

The list given in Table XLII is a summary of the experimental results.

The power of absorbing chlorides varies greatly from one species to another. In the brackish-water forms Cl absorption is possible only from fairly high concentrations, but whether this is an inherent imperfection of the mechanism or is due to a simultaneous unavoidable loss future experimentation must decide. In the anadromous crab *Eriocheir* the power is very highly developed, but the loss is so large that below concentrations of about 0·3 mM. in the surrounding water it cannot be covered by the uptake. In some fresh-water forms the Cl concentration of a limited volume of water can become reduced practically to 0 which means analytically less than 0·005 mM. A highly developed power of Cl absorption is probably essential for animals living in waters containing a minimum of chlorides, the more so because also the food, animal or vegetable, must be either poor in Cl or depend for its Cl on active processes of absorption.

While in many parts of the earth chlorides are present in the soil and thence get into the fresh waters there are other parts where salts are mainly or almost exclusively derived from the rain. Chlorides are present in rain water, but the concentration depends largely upon the proximity to the sea, because the main source of salts is the spray from breaking waves. In Denmark the rain water collected during westerly gales may contain as much as 0·9 mM. Cl, while rain falling with southerly winds may contain as little as 0·07 mM. The students Mr K. Schmidt-Nielsen and Mr E. Krogh kindly made a survey for me in 1937 of the lake system of Grönningen at 64° N. latitude near the Norwegian-Swedish frontier. In one case they obtained rain water during a thunderstorm with as little as 0·027 mM. Cl. On another occasion the rain with westerly wind contained 0·037 mM. The lake water varied slightly from one place to another and at different depths between 0·056 and 0·080 mM. Cl, which is about 5 % of the Cl content in Copenhagen tap water and low enough to present difficulties to several fresh-water animals. A list of the fauna is

Table XLII

Group	Genus and species	Test solution mM.	Lowest concentration reached mM.	Power of absorption
Hirudinea	Haemopis sanguisuga	R/100, Cl 1·07; 2NaHCO₃, NH₄Cl	0·83 Cl; 1·26 Na; 0·84 Cl	Present both for Cl and Na, but not highly developed
Gastropoda	Limnaea stagnalis	R/100, Cl 1·17; CaCl₂, Cl 1·5	0·56 Cl; 0·9 Cl	Present for Cl
	Paludina vivipara	R/100, Cl 1·14	0·1 Cl	Well developed for Cl
	Dreissena polymorpha	R/100, Cl 1·15	0·15 Cl	Well developed for Cl
	Unio pictorum	NaCl, Cl 1·00	0·15 Cl	Well developed for Cl
		CaCl₂, Cl 1·5	0·7 Cl	Ca given off
	Anodonta cygnea	0·2 NaCl, Cl 0·2	0·1 Cl	Well developed for Cl
Crustacea	Carcinus maenas	R/100, Cl 1·1	1·9 Cl	Definite but not below 160 mM.
	Branchipus (grubii?)	NaCl, Cl 1	1·1 Cl	No absorption found
	Lepidurus productus	R/100, Cl 1·1	0·00 Cl	No absorption found
	Potamobius fluviatilis	CaCl₂, Cl 1·5	1·3 Cl	Very powerful absorption of Cl
	Eriocheir sinensis	NaCl, Cl 1·00; NaBr, Br 1·24	0·29 Cl; 0·35 Br	Powerful, but limited to concentrations above 0·2–0·3 mM.
Insecta	Chironomus sp.	NaCl, Cl 1·1; NaBr, Br 1·1	— ; —	Definite
	Culex pipiens	Tap water	—	Definite
	Aëdes aegypti	Tap water	—	Definite, better developed than in Culex
	Libellula sp.	R/100, Cl 1·1	0·9 Cl	Present for Cl and Na
Pisces	Acerina cernua	Tap water, Cl 1·7	1·58 Cl	Very poor
	Perca fluviatilis	Tap water, Cl 1·7	1·7 Cl	If present, very poor
	Ameiurus sp.	R/100, Cl 1·00	0·75 Cl	Definite
	Gasterosteus aculeatus	R/100, Cl 1·10	0·31 Cl	Definite, but seems to be limited to concentrations above 0·2
	Salmo irideus	Tap water, Cl 1·7, Cl 0·04; "Dist." water	Not determined	Definite
	Leuciscus rutilus		0·02 Cl	Very powerful
	Carassius auratus	R/100, Cl 1·16	0·11 Cl	Powerful
	Anguilla vulgaris	R/10, Cl 1·1	—	No absorption
	Anguilla vulgaris (elvers)	R/10, Cl 1·1	—	Slight absorption probable
Amphibia	Amblystoma (larva)	R/100, Cl 1·1	0·77 Cl	Definite
	Rana esculenta	NaCl, Cl 1·00	0·00 Cl	Powerful
	Rana temporaria. Newly hatched larvae	Tap water	—	Definite
	Rana temporaria. Older larvae	Tap water	—	If present, very poor

therefore of some interest. The following animals were observed or collected:

Ciliata, Infusoria, Rotatoria, Hirudinea, Oligochaeta: *Stylaria, Tubifex*; Gastropoda: *Planorbis albus, Limnaea ovata*; Lamellibranchiata: *Sphaerium, Pisidium*; Cladocera: *Daphnia* (several species), *Bosmina, Eurycercus lammelatus, Bythotrephes longimanus, Holopedium gibberum*; Copepoda: *Cyclops, Diaptomus*; Amphipoda: *Gammarus pulex*; Ephemeridae: *Ephemera, Cloëon*?, *Siphlonurus, Leptophlebia*; Dytiscidae, Culicidae, Chironomidae, Trichoptera, Odonata, Hydrachnida, Pisces: *Salmo trutta, Salmo alpinus, Lota lota*. Some of these may obtain the necessary salt from their food, but I have no doubt that the majority have very efficient mechanisms for ion absorption.

There can be no doubt that in the continents fresh waters with even lower salt content will be found, and their fauna will be of interest from the point of view of the ability to absorb salt from very dilute solutions.

Extrarenal ion transport mechanisms in marine animals. A few Crustacea have come to be known which are able to maintain a total osmotic concentration somewhat lower than the surrounding sea water. These are *Heloecius cordiformis, Pachygrapsus crassipes* and *marmoratus* and *Leptograptus*, to which must now be added the anadromous *Eriocheir sinensis*. The mechanisms here in operation have not been studied so far, but by analogy it is reasonable to assume that some ion transport mechanism is in operation, and the same holds also for *Artemia salina*, inhabiting highly concentrated saline waters.

The work of Homer Smith and Keys demonstrated the existence of a Cl transporting mechanism in the marine Teleostomi which eliminates chlorides from the body and operates therefore in the opposite direction to that found in fresh-water animals.

It is of considerable interest whether the same fish may possess both mechanisms and if they may possibly be located in the same cells which can reverse their action. From this point of view a study of euryhaline and anadromous fishes is of special importance. In the eel, where the branchial excretion of Cl was first established, we have found no evidence of active absorption in fresh water, but forms like *Fundulus*, *Gasterosteus* and *Salmo* are likely to possess both mechanisms.

An analysis of the ion absorption has been carried out on a few types (*Haemopis*, *Libellula*), *Eriocheir*, *Carassius*, *Rana*. In every case two independent mechanisms were found, viz. one for absorbing cations and one for absorbing anions, characterized respectively by the power to take up Na from $NaHCO_3$ and Na_2SO_4 without the anion, and by the power to absorb Cl from NH_4Cl and $CaCl_2$ without the cation. Each of these mechanisms can be more or less specialized.

In *Eriocheir* the cation mechanism will absorb Na^+ and K^+, but not NH_4^+ or Ca^{++}, the anion mechanism absorbs actively the chemically related ions Cl^-, Br^-, CNS^-, CNO^- and N_3^-, while NO_3^- will diffuse in rapidly, I^- slowly and $SO_4^=$ apparently not at all.

In the goldfish and in the frog the cation mechanism is specialized further to absorb only Na^+ and leave out K^+ from mixtures of the two ions, while the anion mechanism absorbs only Cl^- and Br^- actively. It is an interesting analogy that even in the mammalian kidney Br^- is not distinguished from Cl^- (Frey, 1937). The skin of the frog allows some diffusion of NO_3 and I^-, but the gills of the fish are almost impermeable to these ions.

Compared with the plant roots studied by Lundegårdh, which absorb all ions without distinction, these animals possess highly specialized mechanisms for ion absorption, and it seems specially significant that the nitrate ion which is taken up preferentially by plants is not absorbed at all by the animals. It is evident that more animals belonging also to other groups should be studied from this point of view and that the investigation should also be extended to a larger number of cations.

From the point of view of the animal economy mechanisms for absorption of K and, in the case of Crustacea and bivalves, also for Ca might be considered useful. As regards K the loss, even through long periods of starvation, seems to be slight and can be made good from the large stores of K in the tissue cells, the more so as K is made free by the oxidative breakdown of tissues. A special mechanism for Ca absorption is very likely, and a Ca uptake has been observed in a few cases, but the conditions necessary to demonstrate its existence have not so far been made out.

Ion absorption from the intestine. It is of considerable interest from a general and comparative point of view that ion transport mechanisms, similar in certain respects to those here under discussion, were recently discovered in the intestinal canal of higher animals and are probably of very general occurrence. Ingraham and Visscher describe in a series of papers (1936, 1937) the active absorption of chloride and sodium ions from isolated loops of the small intestine in dogs. They stress the fact that to demonstrate this absorption against the concentration gradient other ions must be present and especially a non-absorbable ion of the same sign, so as to make the total concentration equal to that of the blood. In this way they obtain a large reduction in concentration both of Na and Cl when present with $MgSO_4$. They find, however, a definite reduction in concentration also when the ions are present with a non-ionized crystalloid, like sucrose, which is absorbed only slowly. "In a few experiments sucrose was used and the concentration of NaCl fell to one-third of its plasma level, but practically all of such solutions are absorbed in 45 min. and therefore conditions are not optimal for the demonstration in question."

This seems to me to be an indication that the experimental difficulty lies in the extraordinary rapidity of osmotic water movement through the intestinal wall. From a dilute solution of NaCl both Na and Cl are absorbed rapidly, but the concentration may rise, because water flows into the intestinal wall with even greater rapidity. In order to obtain experimental proof of an absorption against a concentration gradient it is necessary to restrict the water movement by the presence in sufficient concentration of osmotically active substances, but in principle I take the mechanism present in the intestine to be of the same nature as the extrarenal absorption mechanisms under discussion in this book. A study of the selectivity of the mechanisms would be sure to yield valuable results. From the experiments mentioned I would expect them to be less selective than those mentioned above, but the evidence as given is not conclusive.

SUGGESTIONS FOR FUTURE WORK ON
ACTIVE ION TRANSPORT

The demonstration of active and selective ion-absorbing mechanisms in organs which are comparatively easy of access opens up interesting possibilities for further study, possibilities which must be followed up before we can hope to obtain any rational conception of what is going on.

The first desideratum is an accurate localization of the active cells, at least in certain forms, suitable for cytological or physiological investigation. We have reason to believe that in fishes and Crustacea the active cells are located in the gills, but the evidence for assuming special large cells, described by Keys and Wilmer, as being "chlorine" secreting, is inconclusive, and it seems quite possible that the general "squamous" epithelium of the gills does the work. *A priori*, one would expect the mechanism for cation and anion absorption respectively to be located in separate cells and these to show somewhat different reactions to stains and precipitants. Within the Arthropoda there is good reason to believe as first suggested by Koch (1934), but definitely proved only for certain mosquito and Harlequin fly larvae, that the special organs and cells which take up Ag from very dilute solutions and become stained by them (Figs. 33 and 34, p. 107) are responsible for the uptake of salts, and it appears most probable that the uptake of Ag represents a specific cation absorption.

When definitely located, suitable cells should be studied cytologically in the living state, during work and rest and under exposure to various stimulants and depressants. Very promising work in this direction was done by Wigglesworth (1933) even before the specific ion absorption was discovered.

Another very promising field of research is the study of the energetics of the absorption processes. This has been attempted repeatedly, but the quantitative results are far from convincing. When cyanide stops the ion transport we are justified in assuming that oxidative energy is involved, and that has been shown in several cases, but beyond that we *know* next to nothing. It is practically certain that the energy exchanges involved are not very large, and not of the order observed by Lundegård in plant roots. It will be necessary, therefore, to work on isolated organs and on such in which the active cells make up a fairly large fraction of the whole and may be responsible during rest for at least half the total metabolism. This condition is not fulfilled by frog's skin which might otherwise be suitable, but certain branchial organs will probably prove amenable to experimentation.

Possible mechanisms for the ion transport have been proposed in special cases (Osterhout, Lundegardh, Ingraham and Visscher, 1937) and models constructed, but I do not think that the time is at all ripe for this final step, and I submit that the most specialized mechanisms should be studied preferentially, because they are most likely to furnish clues.

NOTES ON METHODS

1. *The determination of total osmotic concentration* can be carried out by means of several different techniques of which each presents special difficulties and drawbacks.

The best known and most widely used method is the freezing-point determination according to Beckmann, in which a large thermometer, readable to 0·001° C., is used. This is extremely simple in principle, but it requires rather large quantities of fluid from about 1 ml. upwards. The objection sometimes raised that the osmotic concentration is determined at one temperature only and may change in biological fluids at higher temperatures is scarcely valid, but the actual determination of the freezing point is in some biological fluids by no means easy. This is borne out especially by the controversy concerning the freezing points of white and yolk in the hen's egg. Personally I accept the result arrived at by Atkins (1909) and confirmed in a very careful paper by Evelyn Howard (1932) by the critical application of Johlin's method (1931), in spite of the fact that Johlin himself (1933) obtained results confirming the alleged difference in concentration between white and yolk.

The essential points in the Johlin technique as applied by Howard are: The use of a cooling mixture which can be lifted by suction so as to surround the material to be determined for any desired length of time. Supercooling of this material to a limited degree not exceeding 0·4° C. Repeated seeding with small nichrome rings cooled in dry ice and just frosted from the moisture of the atmosphere before being dropped into the material. Observation of the temperature change at brief intervals (½ m.) until a *final* definite rise in temperature occurs, while the mixture is stirred by moving the thermometer up and down by hand. It appears to be essential that this mixing is somewhat irregular so that a false equilibrium between heat lost and gained is avoided.

The true freezing point is determined by a temperature plateau maintained over several minutes, just before this final rise, occurring when the ice is completely melted, and the important point brought out by the investigation of Howard is that both in natural egg yolk and in dialysates from the yolk there may be false plateaux at lower temperatures. It is absolutely essential, therefore, that the temperature is followed until the final rise shows that no more ice is present. The first seeding of the supercooled material must always cause a rise in temperature, but later on when ice is present it usually causes a drop of 0·01–0·02°. The accuracy to be obtained seems to be of the order of 0·002–0·005° when the average of readings at the final temperature plateau is taken.

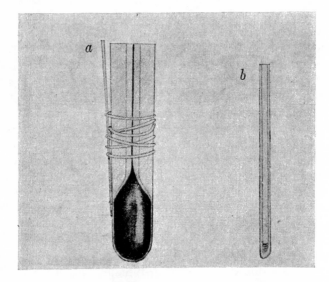

Fig. 51. Thermometer and glass capillary for micro freezing-point determination. (Fritsche.)

The micromethod for freezing-point determination of Drucker and Schreiner (1913), as used in the beautiful research by Fritsche on the osmotic concentration of *Daphnia* blood, consists essentially in observing the temperature at the moment when the frozen material, represented by a small drop in a glass capillary (Fig. 51), is just melting. The method can only be used on clear fluids in which the ice crystals can be observed by means of a lens. Fritsche describes the precautions necessary, and there can be no doubt that in his hands it has given results reliable within 0·01°, but the technique seems to be too difficult to come into general use. The main difficulty is to make sure that the temperature of the small drop in the tube is the same as that of the large thermometer bulb. The criterion must be that the same melting-point can be observed with different rates of temperature change. With a thermo-junction substituted for the Beckmann thermometer the micro freezing-point determination might still be worth trying out.

The thermoelectric vapour-pressure method as originally described by Hill and Kupalow (1930) has been greatly improved by Baldes (1934), who reduced the thermopile to have only two junctions shaped as eyes on a wire of 0·1 mm. and reduced the quantity of solution necessary for a determination to 1 mm.^{3} A very sensitive galvanometer and a room free from electric disturbances are required to obtain satisfactory determinations, and even so much caution and frequent control determinations are necessary to obtain reliable results.

It is a curious fact that the container built for the original Hill instrument was retained in the Baldes instrument, although its shape and volume are unsuitable for the single thermocouple. We have recently introduced a slightly modified instrument, shown in Fig. 52, which will reach a steady state more rapidly. There is, I believe, room for much further improvement, but the method will remain delicate and expensive.

Barger's method, in which the lengths of drops of different concentration in a capillary tube are measured and followed over a suitable period, is essentially a vapour-pressure method. The more concentrated drops which have a lower pressure will increase in length and the more dilute will decrease. In its original form and in several modifications this method has certain drawbacks and is difficult to use.

A modification, shown in Fig. 53, was described by Ursprung and Blum (1930) who studied the sources of error and the means to avoid them with exceptional care. If sufficient experimental fluid is available it is filled into the "salt cellar" shown, so as to leave a

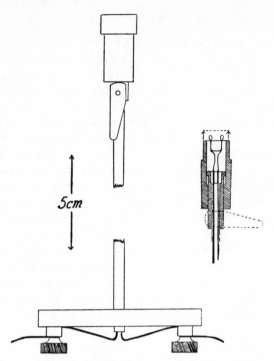

Fig. 52. A modified Baldes thermocouple for vapour-pressure
determination. (Krogh.)

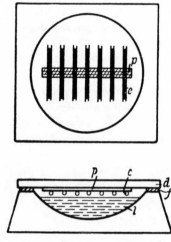

Fig. 53. Arrangement for vapour-pressure determination.
p, plastiline; c, glass capillaries. (Ursprung and Blum.)

minimum of air space, and a series of capillaries containing different known solutions are mounted on the cover-glass. The lengths of the drops are measured by a micrometer after the whole has been mounted in a bath, large enough to insure that temperature variations will be slow, and kept mixed so that no temperature difference can develop inside the salt cellars. The changes in length of the drops after a suitable time are recorded. A drop which does not change in length has the same concentration as the unknown solution. The authors have found it necessary to use tubing of hard glass (Pyrex, Jenaer Supremax or Jenaer Geräteglas 20) and between 0·5 and 0·3 mm. diameter. They recommend the insertion of a tube containing the experimental solution and to allow for the variations observed in this.

In work on small animals or eggs the quantity of fluid available will as a rule be so small as to allow only the filling of one or a few capillaries. These must be tested along with comparison tubes in cellars containing different known solutions, and if necessary transferred from one solution to another until the point of equilibrium is reached. When an accuracy of 0·01 mole is desired the solutions must be measured at intervals of several hours, and a final determination will often require 24 hr. or more. It is necessary, therefore, to guard against processes which may change the osmotic concentration. As for the thermocouple method it will often be necessary to suck up fluids for determination in capillary tubes, to seal these, dip them into boiling water, centrifuge and use the clear solution for determinations.

Blegen and Rehberg (1938) have recently worked out a method for a more direct determination of osmotic concentration. They prepare collodion tubes with permeabilities low enough to make them almost semipermeable. These tubes hold 0·2–0·4 ml. They are filled with the unknown solution which mounts into a horizontal capillary of 0·3–0·5 mm. diameter. When the collodion tube is placed in a fairly large volume of a known solution of slightly higher concentration the meniscus moves at a constant rate depending upon the concentration difference. It will usually be necessary to alternate between known and unknown solutions in the collodion tube. In the tests made on sea water, urine and blood the method has given the same results within 2 mM. as vapour-pressure determinations according to Baldes.

2. *Volume determinations* are used to determine the movements of water into and out of organisms. In larger organisms they are generally made indirectly by weighing, and the main difficulty is to obtain a reproducible removal of adhering water. On *Amoeba* Mast and Fowler obtained good results by sucking them into a narrow capillary and measuring their length, and Turbellaria and similar soft and small animals can be compressed slightly between glass plates a known distance apart and the area measured (Pantin, 1931).

Organisms of a very regular form like certain Infusoria and Rotatoria can be taken geometrically as produced by the revolution of a plane figure round the axis of symmetry. The volume is then determined by the area of this figure on one side of the axis multiplied by the circumference of the circle through which its centre of gravity revolves.

The volumes of spherical or approximately spherical bodies like a number of eggs are found by measuring diameters and applying the formula $v = \frac{1}{6}\pi d^3$. In eggs taking up a definite position in water it is often necessary to make sure that the vertical diameter is the same as the horizontal. When diameters agree within 1 % they can be averaged, otherwise a more complicated formula must be applied.

3. *Specific gravity determinations* are necessary only in special cases, generally on eggs. They cannot be made, as has often been attempted, by plunging the organisms in question in water of varied salinity, because the osmotic exchange of water is generally too rapid. It is necessary, therefore, to vary the specific gravity of the test solution without variation of the total osmotic concentration. This can be done by adding colloid or by substituting crystalloids with others having the same osmotic effect but a different specific gravity in solution. Lighter fluids can be obtained by substituting NH_4Cl for $NaCl$, but the solution must be sufficiently acid to reduce the concentration of free NH_3 to a minimum, because the unionized NH_3 will often penetrate organisms rapidly by diffusion. Heavier fluids can be obtained by substituting sugar in place of $NaCl$.

4. *The indiscriminate permeability to ions* can be studied by varying the concentration of certain ions, normally present in the surrounding water, but experiments with foreign ions are usually easier to perform and more conclusive. Berger and Bethe (1931) introduced the use of I^- for this purpose, and the ease and accuracy of its determination makes it eminently suitable in a number of cases. I have in a few cases used lithium salts, but only for qualitative spectroscopic tests.

5. *Drinking of water.* In all cases where hypotonicity against the surrounding medium is maintained it is important to know whether water is swallowed and absorbed from the intestine. Homer Smith (1930) introduced the use of phenol red for this purpose. The dye is added to the water in the aquarium and the content of the hind-gut examined for phenol red after a suitable time and, in certain cases, after ligaturing the anus. When phenol red is present it shows that water was swallowed, and when its concentration is increased above that of the medium an estimate of the absorption can be obtained. The choice of phenol red for this purpose seems to be rather accidental. The dye penetrates the intestinal wall, in the forms studied to a slight extent only, but a dye which was completely retained in the gut would be preferable. Vital red would probably serve, but has not been tested. Tests to show whether water is swallowed or not are often desirable also in experiments upon isotonic or hypertonic animals. I am aware that I ought to have carried out such tests in several cases.

6. *Active uptake of ions* is to be expected only in animals maintaining hypertonicity. The experimental study of such uptake must always be preceded by a period in which a definite reduction below the normal ion concentration of the internal medium is brought about. In fresh-water animals such reduction is carried out by washing with distilled water, and care must be exercised to make sure that the distilled water available is non-toxic. The *Daphnia magna* test introduced by Naumann (1933) is useful to settle this point. The washing can be carried out by automatic spraying in the case of Amphibia and by slow-flowing distilled water in the case of most fresh-water animals (Krogh, 1937, 1938) (Fig. 54). It will often be found useful to follow the depletion of chloride ions by

keeping the animals in a definite, fairly large volume of distilled water which is changed at suitable intervals and analysed for Cl according to the method described by Krogh (1937) for very dilute solutions. We have attempted in some cases to follow the depletion of ions generally by conductivity determinations, but the results were too irregular to be of much use.

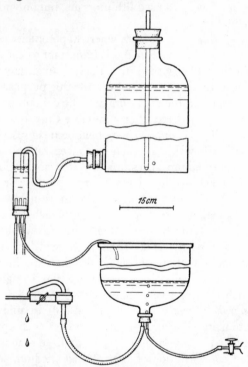

15 cm

Fig. 54. Apparatus for washing out fresh-water animals in slow flow of distilled water. (Krogh.)

Certain brackish-water animals will also stand washing with distilled water for a short time, but generally the depletion will have to be carried out by placing them in progressive sea-water dilutions.

The test for active uptake is carried out by placing the depleted animals in solutions containing the ion in question, but in definitely lower concentration than that of the internal medium. In general tests to establish the power of active absorption the Cl ion is utilized and either pure or balanced (natural) solutions are used. The test is carried out by Cl analysis of either the external or the internal medium after a suitable period for absorption. The question whether the external or the internal medium should be analysed depends upon a number of circumstances and is often difficult to decide. Methods for Cl determination in solutions ranging from sea water down to 0·01 mM. are described by Krogh (1937, 1938). An ultra-micro method for drops of 1 mm.^{3} or less of solutions or blood, containing not less than 10 mM., is described by Wigglesworth (1938).

Negative results of Cl absorption tests can only be accepted as conclusive when the period of washing and degree of depletion have been widely varied, when the conditions under which the test is made are as nearly natural as possible, or when the animal has been subjected to a suitable training (cp. Krogh, 1938), and when, finally, the Cl concentration and general composition of the test solution has been varied within wide limits. I am aware that I have made the mistake myself in several cases of not applying more concentrated solutions than 2 mM.

With regard to the study of the active absorption of other ions than Cl and the analytical methods for the determination of a number of ions I refer to the following papers: Krogh, 1938 *a, b, c.*

7. *The active secretion of ions*, so far demonstrated for chloride in the gills of fishes, is to be expected only in marine (saline) animals maintaining hypotonicity. The only technique at present available is the perfusion as worked out by Keys (1931) and Schlieper (1933), and a sufficient analytical accuracy has been obtained only for chloride (Keys, 1931). Owing to the high concentrations involved, and the comparatively small changes, of the order of $\frac{1}{2}$ mM., which can be expected, it seems unlikely that attempts involving the determination of other ions will be successful.

8. The methods for studying the exchange of ions between tissue cells and the internal medium have not reached such a state of perfection as to merit discussion. The following papers can be consulted: Lavietes, Bourdillon and Klinghoffer (1936), Hastings and Eichelberger (1937 *a–c*), Krogh (1938), and Brodie and Friedman (1937).

LIST OF REFERENCES

Adolph, E. F. (1925). Further experiments upon the regulation   52
    of body volume in earthworms. *Anat. Rec.* **31**, 340.
— (1926). The metabolism of water in amoeba as measured in   14, 16
    the contractile vacuole. *J. exp. Zool.* **44**, 355–81.
— (1927). The regulation of volume and concentration in the   52
    body fluids of earthworms. *J. exp. Zool.* **47**, 31–62.
— (1933). Exchanges of water in the frog. *Biol. Rev.* **8**, 224–40.   155
— (1934). Influences of the nervous system on the intake and   157
    excretion of water by the frog. *J. cell. comp. Physiol.* **5**,
    123–39.
— (1936). Differential permeability to water and osmotic ex-   46
    changes in the marine worm *Phascolosoma*. *J. cell. comp.*
    Physiol. **9**, 117–35.
Alexandrov, W. F. (1935). Permeability of chitin in some   102
    dipterous larvae and the method of its study. *Acta zool.*
    Stockh., **16**, 1–19.
Atkins, W. R. (1909). *Sci. Proc. R. Dublin Soc.* N.S. **12**, 123.   209

Backmann, E. L. (1911). Osmoregulation bei Wasserkäfern und   102
    Libellen. *Zbl. Physiol.* **25**, 779 and 835.
— (1911). Ueber die Entstehung der homoiosmotischen Eigen-   102
    schaften. *Zbl. Physiol.* **25**, 837–43.
— (1912). Die Einwirkung der Befruchtung auf den osmoti-   187, 190
    schen Druck der Eier von *Bufo vulgaris* und *Triton cristatus*.
    Pflüg. Arch. ges. Physiol. **148**, 141–66.
— (1913). Der osmotische Druck bei einigen Wasserkäfern.   102
    Pflüg. Arch. ges. Physiol. **149**, 93–114.
Backmann, E. L. & Runnström, J. (1912). Der osmotische Druck   185 ff.
    während der Embryonalentwicklung von *Rana temporaria*.
    Pflüg. Arch. ges. Physiol. **148**, 287–345.
Baldes, E. J. (1934). A micromethod of measuring osmotic   211
    pressure. *J. sci. Instrum.* **11**, 223–5.
Bateman, J. B. (1932). The osmotic properties of medusae.   28
    J. exp. Biol. **9**, 124–7.
— (1933). Osmotic and ionic regulation in the shore crab,   66, 73
    Carcinus maenas, with notes on the blood concentrations of
    Gammarus locusta and *Ligia oceanica*. *J. exp. Biol.* **10**,
    355–71.
Bateman, J. B. & Keys, A. (1932). Chloride and vapour-pressure   144
    relations in the secretory activity of the gills of the eel.
    J. Physiol. **75**, 226–40.
Baumberger, J. P. & Dill, D. B. (1928). A study of the glycogen   72
    and sugar content and the osmotic pressure of crabs during
    the molt cycle. *Physiol. Zoöl.* **1**, 545–9.
Baumberger, J. P. & Olmsted, J. M. D. (1928). Changes in the   66, 72
    osmotic pressure and water content of crabs during the
    molt cycle. *Physiol. Zoöl.* **1**, 531–44.

220 LIST OF REFERENCES

Beadle, L. C. (1931). The effect of salinity changes on the water content and respiration of marine invertebrates. *J. exp. Biol.* **8**, 211–27. — 39, 48

— (1934). Osmotic regulation in *Gunda ulvae*. *J. exp. Biol.* **11**, 382–96. — 41

— (1937). Adaptation to changes of salinity in the polychaetes. I. Control of body volume and of body fluid concentration in *Nereis diversicolor*. *J. exp. Biol.* **14**, 56–70. — 48

Berger, Eva (1931). Ueber die Anpassung eines Süsswasser- und eines Brackwasserkrebses an Medien von verschiedenem Salzgehalt. *Pflüg. Arch. ges. Physiol.* **228**, 790–807. — 80, 91

Berger, Eva & Bethe, A. (1931). Die Durchlässigkeit der Körperoberflächen wirbelloser Tiere für Jodionen. *Pflüg. Arch. ges. Physiol.* **228**, 769–89. — 33, 71, 215

Bethe, A. (1927). Der Einfluss der Ionen des Seewassers auf rhythmische Bewegungen der Meerestieren. *Pflüg. Arch. ges. Physiol.* **217**, 456. — 67

— (1929). Ionendurchlässigkeit der Körperoberfläche von wirbellosen Tieren des Meeres als Ursache der Giftigkeit von Seewasser abnormer Zusammensetzung. *Pflüg. Arch. ges. Physiol.* **221**, 344–62. — 54, 70

— (1930). The permeability of the surface of marine animals. *J. gen. Physiol.* **13**, 437–44. — 55

— (1934). Die Salz- und Wasserdurchlässigkeit der Körperoberflächen verschiedener Seetiere in ihrem gegenseitigen Verhältnis. *Pflüg. Arch. ges. Physiol.* **234**, 629–44. — 46, 55, 71

Bethe, A. & Berger, E. (1931). Variationen im Mineralbestand verschiedener Blutarten. *Pflüg. Arch. ges. Physiol.* **227**, 571–84. — 33, 46, 56, 68

Bethe, A., Holst, E. v. & Huf, E. (1935). Die Bedeutung des mechanischen Innendrucks für die Anpassung gepanzerter Seetiere an Aenderungen des osmotischen Aussendrucks. *Pflüg. Arch. ges. Physiol.* **235**, 330–44. — 71

Bevelander, G. (1935). A comparative study of the branchial epithelium in fishes, with special reference to extrarenal excretion. *J. Morph.* **57**, 335–48. — 145

— (1936). Branchial glands in fishes. *J. Morph.* **59**, 215–22. — 145

Bialaszewicz, K. (1927). Contributions à l'étude de la composition minérale des cellules-œufs. *Pubbl. Staz. zool. Napoli*, **8**, 355–69. — 171

— (1929). Recherches sur la répartition des électrolytes dans le protoplasme des cellules ovulaires. *Protoplasma*, **6**, 1–50. — 171 ff., 176

— (1932). Sur la régulation de la composition minérale de l'hémolymphe chez le crabe. *Arch. int. Physiol.* **35**, 98–124. — 70

Blegen, E. & Brandt Rehberg, P. (1938). A method for the determination of the osmotic pressure of biological fluids. *Skand. Arch. Physiol.* **80**, 40–5. — 213

Bogucki, M. (1932). Recherches sur la régulation osmotique chez l'isopode marin, *Mesidotea entomon*. *Arch. int. Physiol.* **35**, 197–213. — 79

Bogucki, M. (1934). Recherches sur la régulation de la com- 87, 93
position minérale du sang chez l'écrevisse (*Astacus fluviatilis*
L.). *Arch. int. Physiol.* **38**, 172–9.

Bond, R. M., Cary, M. K. & Hutchinson, G. E. (1932). A note 120
on the blood of hag-fish *Polistotrema stouti*. *J. exp. Biol.* **9**,
12–14.

Borei, H. (1935). Ueber die Zusammensetzung der Körper- 120
flüssigkeiten von *Myxine glutinosa* L. *Ark. Zool.* **28** B, no. 3.

Bottazzi, F. (1897). La pression osmotique du sang des animaux 139
marins. *Arch. ital. Biol.* **28**, 61.

— (1908). Osmotischer Druck und elektrische Leitfähigkeit 28, 54, 56,
der Flüssigkeiten der einzelligen, pflanzlichen und tieri- 132, 164
schen Organismen. *Ergebn. Physiol.* **7**, 161–402.

Boucher-Firly, S. (1935). Recherches biochimiques sur les 148
Téléostéens Apodes (Anguille, Congre, Murène). *Ann.
Inst. Océanogr.* **15**.

Brodie, B. B. & Friedman, M. M. (1937). The determination of 217
thiocyanate in tissues. *J. biol. Chem.* **120**, 511–16.

Brooks, S. C. (1938). The penetration of radioactive potassium 195
chloride into living cells. *J. cell. comp. Physiol.* **11**, 247–52.

Buchthal, F. & Péterfi, T. (1937). Messungen von Potential- 26
differenzen an Amoeben. *Protoplasma*, **27**, 473–83.

Burian, R. (1910). Funktion der Nierenglomeruli und Ultra- 120
filtration. *Pflüg. Arch. ges. Physiol.* **136**, 741.

Claus, A. (1937). Vergleichend-physiologische Untersuchungen 101, 118
zur Oekologie der Wasserwanzen, mit besonderer Berück-
sichtigung der Brackwasserwanze *Sigara lugubris* Fieb.
Zool. Jb., Abt. allg. Zool. Physiol. Tiere, **58**, 365–432.

Collander, R. (1936). Der Zellsaft der Characeen. *Protoplasma*, 35, 194
25, 201–10.

— (1937). Ueber die Kationenelektron der höheren Pflanzen. 194ff., 199
Ber. dtsch. bot. Ges. **55**, 74–81.

Conklin, Ruth & Krogh, A. (1938). A note on the osmotic be- 60, 80
haviour of *Eriocheir* in concentrated and *Mytilus* in dilute
sea water. *Z. vergl. Physiol.* **26**, 239–41.

Dayley, Mary E., Fremont-Smith, F. & Carroll, Margaret P. 99
(1931). The relative composition of sea water and the blood
of *Limulus polyphemus*. *J. biol. Chem.* **93**, 17–24.

Dakin, W. J. (1911). Notes on the biology of fish eggs and 178
larvae. *Int. Rev. Hydrobiol.* **3**, 487–95.

— (1912). Aquatic animals and their environment. The con-
stitution of the external medium and its effect upon the
blood. *Int. Rev. Hydrobiol.* **5**, 53–80.

Dakin, W. J. & Edmonds, E. (1931). *Aust. J. exp. Biol. med.* 77
Sci. **8**, 169–87.

Dekhuyzen, M. C. (1904). Ergebnisse von osmotischen Studien, 119ff.
namentlich bei Knochenfischen. *Bergens Mus. Aarb.* no. 8.

— (1921). Sur la semiperméabilité biologique des parois ex- 46
térieures des Sipunculides. *C.R. Acad. Sci., Paris*, **172**,
238.

Dreser, H. (1892). Ueber Diurese und ihre Beeinflussung durch 164
pharmakologische Mittel. *Arch. exp. Path. Pharmak.* **29**,
303–19.

Drilhon, A. (1933). La glucose et la mue des Crustacés. *C.R.* 72
Acad. Sci., Paris, **196**, 506–10.

Drucker, C. & Schreiner, E. (1913). Mikrokryoskopische Ver- 94, 210
suche. *Biol. Zbl.* **33**, 99–103.

Duval, M. (1925). Recherches physico-chimiques et physiolo- 56, 64, 66 ff.,
giques sur le milieu intérieur des Animaux Aquatiques. 73 ff., 86, 94,
Modifications sous l'influence du milieu extérieur. *Ann.* 123, 132, 137,
Inst. océanogr. **2**, 232–407. 148

Duval, M., Portier, P. & Courtois, A. (1928). Sur la présence 103
de grandes quantités d'acides amines dans le sang des
Insectes. *C.R. Acad. Sci., Paris,* **186**, 652–3.

Edmonds, Enid (1935). The relations between the internal fluid 66, 77
of marine invertebrates and the water of the environment,
with special reference to Australian Crustacea. *Proc. Linn.*
Soc. N.S.W. **60**, 233–47.

Ellis, T. E. (1926). *British Snails.* Oxford Univ. Press. 53

Ellis, W. G. (1933). Calcium and the resistance of *Nereis* to 48
brackish water. *Nature, Lond.,* **132**, 748.

— (1937). The water and electrolyte exchange of *Nereis diversi-* 49
color (Müller). *J. exp. Biol.* **14**, 340–50.

Enriques, P. (1902). Digestione, circolazione e assorbimento 32
nelle Oloturie. *Arch. zool. (ital.) Napoli,* **1**.

Ephrussi, B. & Rapkine, L. (1928). *Ann. Physiol. Physicochim.* 174
biol. **4**, 386.

Finley, H. E. (1930). *Ecology,* **11**, 337–47. 25

Florkin, M. (1935). Influence des variations de l'abaissement 61
cryoscopique du milieu extérieur sur celui du sang et de
l'urine de l'Anodonte. *Bull. Acad. Belg. Cl. Sci.* pp. 432–5.

— (1937). Contributions à l'étude du plasma sanguin des in- 102 ff.
sectes. *Mém. Sav. étr. Acad. R. Belg.* **16**, 1–69.

— (1938). L'abaissement cryoscopique du milieu intérieur de 62
l'Anodonte au cours d'une inanition prolongée. *Bull. Acad.*
Belg. Cl. Sci. pp. 24–8.

— (1938). Concentration du milieu extérieur et hydratation 61
chez un Lamellibranche d'eau douce. *Bull. Acad. Belg.*
Cl. Sci. pp. 143–6.

Fox, H. Munro & Baldes, E. J. (1935). The vapour pressures 102
of the blood of arthropods from swift and still fresh waters.
J. exp. Biol. **12**, 174–8.

Fredericq, L. (1901). Sur la concentration moléculaire du sang 28, 36, 47, 54,
et des tissus chez les animaux aquatiques. *Bull. Acad. Belg.* 56, 197
Cl. Sci. p. 428.

— (1904). Sur la concentration moléculaire du sang et des 73
tissus chez les animaux aquatiques. *Arch. Biol.* **20**, 701–39.

— (1905). Note sur la concentration moléculaire des tissus 51
solides de quelques animaux d'eau douce. *Arch. int.*
Physiol. **2**, 127.

Frey, E. (1937). Bromausscheidung und Bromverteilung.   205
   Arch. exp. Path. Pharmak. **187**, 275–81.
Frisch, J. A. (1935). Experimental adaptation of freshwater   25
   ciliates to sea water. *Science*, (1), 537.
Fritsche, H. (1916). Studien über die Schwankungen des osmo-   94 ff.,   181,
   tischen Druckes der Körperflüssigkeiten bei *Daphnia magna.*   211
   Int. Rev. Hydrobiol. **8**, 22–80, 125–203.
Furuhashi, Y. (1927). Ueber den Gesamtbasengehalt des Harns.   165
   Jap. J. med. Sci. Biochem. **1**, 135–6.

Galloway, T. McL. (1933). The osmotic pressure and saline   121
   content of the blood of *Petromyzon fluviatilis.* *J. exp. Biol.*
   10, 313.
Galtsoff, P. S. (1934). The biochemistry of the invertebrates   64
   of the sea. *Ecol. Monogr.* **4**, 481–90.
Garrey, W. E. (1905). The osmotic pressure of sea water and of   99, 132
   the blood of marine animals. *Biol. Bull. Wood's Hole*, **8**,
   257–70.
Gicklhorn, J. & Keller, R. (1925). *Z. Zellforsch.* **2**, 515.   106, 109
Goethard, W. C. & Heinsius, H. W. (1892). *Report on Noctiluca*   11
   (Dutch). *Nederlandsche Staatscourant.*
Grafflin, A. L. (1929). The pseudoglomeruli of the kidney of   130
   Lophius piscatorius. Amer. J. Anat. **44**, 441.
— (1931). Urine flow and diuresis in marine teleosts. *Amer. J.*   146
   Physiol. **97**, 602–10.
— (1937). The problem of adaptation to fresh and salt water   151
   in the teleosts, viewed from the standpoint of the structure
   of the renal tubules. *J. cell. comp. Physiol.* **9**, 469–76.
— (1938). The absorption of fluorescein from fresh water   151
   and salt water by *Fundulus heteroclitus*, as judged by a study
   of the kidney with the fluorescence microscope. *J. cell.*
   comp. Physiol. **12**, 167–70.
Gray, J. (1913). The electrical conductivity of fertilised and   174
   unfertilised eggs. *J. Mar. biol. Ass. U.K.* N.S. **10**, 50–9.
— (1920). The relation of the animal cell to electrolytes. I. A   182
   physiological study of the egg of the trout. *J. Physiol.* **53**,
   308–19.
— (1932). The osmotic properties of the eggs of the trout   182
   (*Salmo fario*). *J. exp. Biol.* **9**, 277–99.
Greene, C. W. (1904). Physiological studies of the Chinook   119, 151
   salmon. *Bull. U.S. Bur. Fish.* **24**, 431.
Grobben, C. (1880). Die Antennendrüse der Crustaceen. *Arb.*   94
   Zool. Inst. Univ. Wien, **3**, 93–110.
Gross, F. (1934). Zur Biologie und Entwicklungsgeschichte   13
   von *Noctiluca miliaris. Arch. Protistenk.* **83**, 178–96.
Gurney, R. (1923). Some notes on *Leander longirostris* and   78
   other British prawns. *Proc. zool. Soc. Lond.* **13**, 97 f.

Harnisch, O. (1934). Osmoregulation und osmoregulatorischer   102, 105 ff.
   Mechanismus der Larve von *Chironomus thummi. Z. vergl.*
   Physiol. **21**, 281–95.

Harvey, Ethel B. (1917). A physiological study of specific   13
gravity and of luminescence in *Noctiluca*, with special
reference to anesthesia. *Publ. Carneg. Instn*, **11**, 237–53.

Hastings, A. & Eichelberger, L. (1937). The exchange of salt   217
and water between muscle and blood. I. *J. biol. Chem.*
117, 73.

— — (1937). III. *J. biol. Chem.* **118**, 205.   217

Hazelhoff, E. H. (1926). *Regeling der Ademhaling bij Insecten*   101
en Spinnen. Utrecht.

Henri, V. & Lalou, S. (1904). Régulation osmotique des   32
liquides internes chez les Échinodermes. *J. Physiol. Path.*
gén. **6**, 9.

Henze, M. (1904–5). Beiträge zur Muskelchemie der Octo-   57
poden. *Hoppe-Seyl. Z.* **43**, 477–93.

Herfs, A. (1922). Die pulsierende Vakuole der Protozoen, ein   25, 43
Schutzorgan gegen Aussüssung. Studien über Anpassung
der Organismen an das Leben im Süsswasser. *Arch. Pro-*
tistenk. **44**, 227–60.

Herrmann, F. (1931). Ueber den Wasserhaushalt des Fluss-   86, 91
krebses. *Z. vergl. Physiol.* **14**, 479–524.

Hevesy, G. v., Hofer, E. & Krogh, A. (1935). The permeability   156
of the skin of frogs to water as determined by D_2O and
H_2O. *Skand. Arch. Physiol.* **72**, 199–214.

Hill, A. V. & Kupalow, P. S. (1930). The vapour pressure of   211
muscle. *Proc. roy. Soc.* B, **106**, 445–77.

Hoppe-Seyler, F. A. (1930). Ueber Vorkommen und Herkunft   123
des Trimethylamins im tierischen Stoffwechsel. *Verh.*
phys.-med. Ges. Würzburg, **53**, 24–36.

Hosoi, K. (1935). The exchange of calcium ion and water be-   30
tween sea-anemones and the surrounding medium. *Sci.*
Rep. Tôhoku Univ. IV, **10**, 377–86.

Howard, Evelyn (1932). Osmotic relationships in the hen's   187, 209ff.
egg, as determined by colligative properties of yolk and
white. *J. gen. Physiol.* **16**, 107–23.

Huf, E. (1933). Ueber die Aufrechterhaltung des Salzgehaltes   90ff.
bei Süsswasserkrebsen (*Potamobius*). *Pflüg. Arch. ges.*
Physiol. **232**, 559–73.

— (1934). Ueber den Einfluss der Narkose auf den Wasser-   61, 87, 91
und Mineralhaushalt bei Süsswassertieren. *Pflüg. Arch.*
ges. Physiol. **235**, 129–40.

— (1935). Versuche über den Zusammenhang zwischen Stoff-   159
wechsel, Potentialbildung und Funktion der Froschhaut.
Pflüg. Arch. ges. Physiol. **235**, 655–73.

— (1936). Ueber irreziproke (gerichtete) Osmose durch die   157
Froschhaut. *Protoplasma*, **26**, 614–19.

— (1936). Ueber aktiven Wasser- und Salztransport durch die   157, 159
Froschhaut. *Pflüg. Arch. ges. Physiol.* **237**, 143–66.

— (1936). Der Einfluss des mechanischen Innendrucks auf die   71, 73ff.
Flüssigkeitsausscheidung bei gepanzerten Süsswasser- und
Meereskrebsen. *Pflüg. Arch. ges. Physiol.* **237**, 240–50.

Hukuda, K. (1932). Change of weight of marine animals in   125
diluted media. *J. exp. Biol.* **9**, 61–8.

Ikeda, Y. (1937). Effect of sodium and potassium salts on the rate of development in *Oryzias latipes*. *J. Fac. Sci. Tokyo Imp. Univ.* **4**, 307–12.   184

— (1937). Potassium accumulation in the eggs of *Oryzias latipes*. *J. Fac. Sci. Tokyo Imp. Univ.* **4**, 313–28.   184ff.

Ingraham, R. C. & Visscher, M. B. (1936). The production of chloride-free solutions by the action of the intestinal epithelium. *Amer. J. Physiol.* **114**, 676–80.   206

— — (1937). Further studies on intestinal absorption with the performance of osmotic work. *Amer. J. Physiol.* **121**, 771–85.   206, 208

Irving, L., Fisher, K. C. & McIntosh, F. C. (1935). The water balance of a marine mammal, the seal. *J. cell. comp. Physiol.* **6**, 387–91.   165ff.

Jacobs, M. H. (1935). Diffusion processes. *Ergebn. Biol.* **12**, 1–160.   7

Jacobs, W. (1937). Beobachtungen über das Schweben der Siphonophoren. *Z. vergl. Physiol.* **24**, 583–601.   30

Jacobsen, J. P. & Johansen, A. C. (1908). Remarks on the changes in specific gravity of pelagic fish eggs and the transportation of same in Danish waters. *Medd. Komm. Havundersøg.*, Ser. Fiskeri, **3**, nr. 2, 1–24.   178

Johlin, J. M. (1931). The freezing point determination of physiological solutions. The usual errors and their elimination. *J. biol. Chem.* **91**, 551–7.   209

— (1933). Osmotic relationships in the hen's egg. *J. gen. Physiol.* **16**, 605–13.   209

Jungman, P. & Bernhardt, H. (1923). Experimentelle Untersuchungen über die Abhängigkeit der Osmoregulation vom Nervensystem. *Z. klin. Med.* **99**, 84.   157

Kamada, T. (1935). Contractile vacuole of *Paramaecium*. *J. Fac. Sci. Univ. Tokyo*, **4**, 49–62.   17

— (1936). Diameter of contractile vacuole in *Paramaecium*. *J. Fac. Sci. Univ. Tokyo*, **4**, 195–202.   17

Kawamoto, N. (1927). The anatomy of *Caudina chilensis* (J. Müller) with especial reference to the perivisceral cavity, the blood and the water vascular systems in their relation to the blood circulation. *Sci. Rep. Tôhoku Univ.* IV, **2**, 239–64.   32

Kelly, A. (1904). Beobachtungen über das Vorkommen von Ätherschwefelsäuren, von Taurin und Glycin bei niederen Tieren. *Hofmeister's Beitr.* **5**, 377–83.   57

Kepner & Yoe (1933). Reactions of *Stenostomum* K. and C. to distilled water. *J. exp. Zool.* **66**, 445–75.   42

Keys, A. B. (1931). The determination of chlorides with the highest accuracy. *J. chem. Soc.* pp. 2440–7.   142, 217

— (1931). The heart-gill preparation of the eel and its perfusion for the study of a natural membrane *in situ*. *Z. vergl. Physiol.* **15**, 352–63.   142, 217

— (1931). Chloride and water secretion and absorption by the gills of the eel. *Z. vergl. Physiol.* **15**, 364–88.   142ff.

Keys, A. B. (1933). The mechanism of adaptation to varying   150
salinity in the common eel and the general problem of
osmotic regulation in fishes. *Proc. roy. Soc.* B, **112**, 184–99.

Keys, A. B. & Willmer, E. N. (1932). "Chloride secreting   145
cells" in the gills of fishes, with special reference to the
common eel. *J. Physiol.* **76**, 368–78.

King, R. L. (1928). The contractile vacuole in *Paramaecium*   15
trichium. Biol. Bull. Wood's Hole, **55**, 59–69.

Kitching, J. A. (1934). The physiology of contractile vacuoles.   18 ff.
I. Osmotic relations. *J. exp. Biol.* **11**, 364–81.

— (1936). II. The control of body volume in marine Peri-   18 ff.
tricha. *J. exp. Biol.* **13**, 11–27.

— (1938). III. The water balance of fresh-water Peritricha.   18 ff.
J. exp. Biol. **15**, 143–51.

Koch, H. (1934). Essai d'interprétation de la soi-disant "ré-   106, 207
duction vitale" de sels d'argent par certains organes d'Ar-
thropodes. *Ann. Soc. Sci. méd. nat. Brux.* Ser. B, **54**,
346–61.

— (1938). The absorption of chloride ions by the anal papillae   106
of diptera larvae. *J. exp. Biol.* **15**, 152–60.

Koch, H. & Krogh, A. (1936). La fonction des papilles anales   106
des larves de Diptères. *Ann. Soc. Sci. méd. nat. Brux.*
Ser. B, **56**, 459–61.

Koizumi, T. (1932). Studies on the exchange and the equili-   33, 34, 192
brium of water and electrolytes in a holothurian, *Caudina
chilensis* (J. Müller). I. Permeability of the animal surface
to water and ions in the sea water, together with osmotic
and ionic equilibrium between the body fluid of the animal
and its surrounding sea water, involving some corrections
to our previous paper (1926). *Sci. Rep. Tôhoku Univ.* IV,
7, 259–311.

— (1935). III. (*a*) On the velocity of permeation of K˙, Na˙,   34
Ca¨ and Mg¨ through the isolated body wall of *Caudina*;
(*b*) an acidimetric micro method for the determination of
Na as triple acetate; (*c*) a volumetric micro method for the
determination of K as iodoplatinate. *Sci. Rep. Tôhoku
Univ.* IV, **10**, 269–75.

— (1935). IV. On the inorganic composition of the corpuscles   34
of the body fluid. *Sci. Rep. Tôhoku Univ.* IV, **10**, 277–
80.

— (1935). V. On the inorganic composition of the longitudinal   34
muscles and the body wall without longitudinal muscles.
Sci. Rep. Tôhoku Univ. IV, **10**, 281–6.

Konsuloff, S. (1922). Untersuchungen über *Opalina*. *Arch.*   25
Protistenk. **44**, 285–345.

Krogh, A. (1904). Some experiments on the cutaneous respira-   163
tion of vertebrate animals. *Skand. Arch. Physiol.* **16**,
348–57.

— (1935). Syringe Pipets. *Industr. Engng. Chem.* **7**, 130–1.

— (1937). Osmotic regulation in the frog (*R. esculenta*) by   159 ff., 215 ff.
active absorption of chloride ions. *Skand. Arch. Physiol.*
76, 60–73.

Krogh, A. (1937). Osmotic regulation in fresh water fishes by active absorption of chloride ions. *Z. vergl. Physiol.* **24**, 656–66.
31, 133 ff., 149, 215 ff.

— (1938). The active absorption of ions in some freshwater animals. *Z. vergl. Physiol.* **25**, 335–50.
82, 133, 138 ff., 160 ff., 217

— (1938). Extracellular and intracellular fluid. *Acta med. scand. Suppl.* **90**, 9–18.
59, 217

Krogh, A. & Keys, A. (1931). A syringe-pipette for precise analytical usage. *J. chem. Soc.* Sept. 1931, pp. 2436–40.
142

Krogh, A., with the collaboration of Agnes Krogh & C. Wernstedt (1938). The salt concentration in the tissues of some marine animals. *Skand. Arch. Physiol.* **80**, 214–22.
56, 177, 179 ff.

Krogh, A., Schmidt-Nielsen, K. & Zeuthen, E. (1938). The osmotic behaviour of frogs' eggs and young tadpoles. *Z. vergl. Physiol.* **26**, 230–8.
187 ff.

Krogh, A. & Ussing, H. H. (1937). A note on the permeability of trout eggs to D_2O and H_2O. *J. exp. Biol.* **14**, 35–7.
182 ff.

Laurie, A. H. (1933). Some aspects of respiration in blue and fin whales. *Discovery Reports*, **7**, 363–406.
165

Lavietes, P. H., Bourdillon, J. & Klinghoffer, K. A. (1936). The volume of the extracellular fluids of the body. *J. clin. Invest.* **15**, 261–8.
59, 217

Leiner, M. (1934). Der osmotische Druck in den Bruttaschen der Syngnathiden. *Zool. Anz.* **108**, 273–89.
179

Lenz, F. (1930). Ein afrikanischer Salzwasser-Chironomus aus dem Mageninhalt eines Flamingos. *Arch. Hydrobiol.* **21**, 447–53.
114

Lewis, H. B. (1918). Some analyses of the urine of reptiles. *Science* (2), **48**, 376.
164

Lienemann, Louise (1938). The green glands as a mechanism for osmotic and ionic regulation in the crayfish (*Cambarus clarkii* Girard). *J. cell. comp. Physiol.* **11**, 149–61.
86

Lillie, R. S. (1916). Increase of permeability to water following normal and artificial activation in sea-urchin eggs. *Amer. J. Physiol.* **40**, 249–66.
173

— (1918). The increase of permeability to water in fertilized sea-urchin eggs and the influence of cyanide and anaesthetics upon this change. *Amer. J. Physiol.* **45**, 406–30.
173

Lockley, R. M. (1938). The seabird as an individual. *Proc. Roy. Inst.* **30**, III.
169

— (1939). *Nature, Lond.*, **143**, 141–4.

Loeb, J. (1900). *Amer. J. Physiol.* **3**, 382.
29

Loeb, J. & Wasteneys, H. (1915). Note on the apparent change of the osmotic pressure of cell contents with the osmotic pressure of the surrounding solution. *J. biol. Chem.* **23**, 157–62.
180

Ludwig, W. (1928). Permeabilität und Wasserwechsel bei *Noctiluca miliaris* Suriray. *Zool. Anz.* **76**, 273–85.
13

— (1928). Der Betriebsstoffwechsel von *Paramaecium caudatum* Ehrbg. Zugleich ein Beitrag zur Frage nach der
15

Funktion der kontraktilen Vacuolen. *Arch. Protistenk.*
62, 12–40.

Lundegårdh, H. (1937). Untersuchungen über die Anionen-   83, 198, 208
atmung. *Biochem. Z.* **290**, 104–24.

Lundegårdh, H. & Burström, H. (1933). Untersuchungen über   198
die Salzaufnahme der Pflanzen. III. Quantitative Beziehungen zwischen Atmung und Anionenaufnahme. *Biochem.
Z.* **261**, 235–51.

—— —— (1935). Untersuchungen über die Atmungsvorgänge in   198
Pflanzenwurzeln. *Biochem. Z.* **277**, 223–49.

Macallum, A. B. (1903). On the inorganic composition of the   28
Medusae *Aurelia flavidula* and *Cyanea arctica. J. Physiol.*
29, 213–41.

— (1926). The paleochemistry of the body fluids and tissues.
Physiol. Rev. **6**, 316–55.

Maloeuf, N. S. R. (1937). The permeability of the integument   90
of the crayfish (*Cambarus bartoni*) to water and electrolytes.
Zbl. Biol. **57**, 282–7.

Manery, J. F. & Irving, L. (1935). Water changes in trout eggs   182
at the time of laying. *J. cell. comp. Physiol.* **5**, 457–64.

Manery, J. F., Warbritton, Virgene & Irving, L. (1933). The   180
development of an alkali reserve in *Fundulus* eggs. *J. cell.
comp. Physiol.* **3**, 277–90.

Margaria, R. (1931). The osmotic changes in some marine   74, 125
animals. *Proc. roy. Soc.* B, **107**, 606–24.

Marshall, E. K. (1934). The comparative physiology of the   130 ff.
kidney in relation to theories of renal secretion. *Physiol.
Rev.* **14**, 133–59.

The Kidney in Health and Disease. Philadelphia (1935).

Martini, E. (1923). Ueber Beeinflussung der Kiemenlänge von   112
Aëdeslarven durch das Wasser. *Verh. int. Ver. theoret.
angew. Limnologie,* **1**, 235–59.

Mast, S. O. (1938). The contractile vacuole in *Amoeba proteus*   15
(Leidy). *Biol. Bull. Wood's Hole,* **74**, 306–13.

Mast, S. O. & Fowler, C. (1935). Permeability of *Amoeba*   14, 16, 24,
proteus to water. *J. cell. comp. Physiol.* **6**, 151–67.   214

McCance, R. A. & Masters, M. (1937). The chemical composi-   57
tion and the acid base balance of *Archidoris Britannica.
J. Mar. biol. Ass. U.K.* **22**, 273–9.

McCance, R. A. & Shackleton, L. R. B. (1937). The metallic   57
constituents of marine gastropods. *J. Mar. biol. Ass. U.K.*
22, 269–72.

McClendon, J. F. (1910). Electrolytic experiments showing in-   174
crease in permeability of the egg to ions at the beginning
of development. *Science,* **32**, 122–4.

— (1910). Further proofs of the increase in permeability of   174
the sea-urchin egg to electrolytes at the beginning of development. *Science,* **32**, 317–18.

Medwedewa, N. B. (1927). Ueber den osmotischen Druck der   98
Hämolymphe von *Artemia salina. Z. vergl. Physiol.* **5**,
547–54.

Mendel, L. B. (1904). Ueber das Vorkommen von Taurin in   57
den Muskeln von Weichtieren. *Hofmeister's Beitr.* **5**, 582.
Müller, R. (1936). Die osmoregulatorische Bedeutung der   15 ff.
contractilen Vakuolen von *Amoeba proteus, Zoothamnium
hiketes* und *Frontonia marina. Arch. Protistenk.* **87**, 345–
82.

Nagel, H. (1934). Die Aufgaben der Exkretionsorgane und der   71, 73 ff., 91
Kiemen bei der Osmoregulation von *Carcinus maenas. Z.
vergl. Physiol.* **21**, 468–91.
Naumann, E. (1933). Das destillierte Wasser gegenüber der   96, 215
Daphnia magna-Probe. *Kungl. Fysiografiska Sällsk. Lund
Handl.* **3**, 1–6.
Needham, J. (1930). On the penetration of marine organisms   174
into fresh water. *Biol. Zbl.* **50**, 504–9.
— (1931). *Chemical embryology*, vols. 1–3. London.   170
Needham, J. & Needham, Dorothy (1930). Nitrogen-excretion   176
in selachian ontogeny. *Brit. J. exp. Biol.* **7**, 7–18.
— — (1930). On phosphorus metabolism in embryonic life.   175
I. Invertebrate eggs. *Brit. J. exp. Biol.* **7**, 317–48.

Oesting, R. B. & Allee, W. C. (1935). Further analysis of the   42
protective value of biologically conditioned fresh water
for the marine turbellarian, *Procerodes wheatlandi.* IV. The
effect of calcium. *Biol. Bull. Wood's Hole,* **68**, 314–26.
Okazaki, K. & Koizumi, T. (1926). Ueber die Leibeshöhlen-   33
flüssigkeit von Holothurien, *Caudina chilensis* (J. Müller).
Sci. Rep. Tôhoku Univ. IV, **2**, 139–42.
Osterhout, W. J. V. (1933). Permeability in large plant cells   35, 193, 208
and in models. *Ergebn. Physiol. exp. Pharm.* **35**, 967–1021.
Otterstrøm, C. V. (1935). Ueber das Fehlen der Bauchflossen   136
bei Plötzen, Brachsen und Karpfen. *Arch. Hydrobiol.* **29**,
178–9.
Otto, I. P. (1937). Ueber den Einfluss der Temperatur auf den   94
osmotischen Wert der Blutflüssigkeit bei der Wollhand-
krabbe (*Eriocheir sinensis* H. Milne-Edwards). *Zool. Anz.*
119, 98–105.
Overton, E. (1904). Neununddreissig Thesen über die Wasser-   155 ff.
ökonomie der Amphibien und die osmotischen Eigenschaften der Amphibienhaut. *Verh. phys.-med. Ges.
Würzburg,* **36**, 277–95.

Pagast, F. (1936). Ueber Bau und Funktion der Analpapillen   108, 114
bei *Aëdes aegypti* L. *Zool. Jb. Abt. Physiol.* **56**, 184–218.
Palmgren, A. (1927). Aquarium experiments with the hag-fish   120
(*Myxine glutinosa* L.). *Acta zool.* **8**, 135–50.
Palmhert, H. W. (1933). Beiträge zum Problem der Osmoregu-   31
lation einiger Hydroidpolypen. *Zool. Jb. Abt. allg. Zool.
Physiol.* **53**, 212–60.
Pantin, C. F. A. (1931). The adaptation of *Gunda ulvae* to   37 ff.
salinity. I. The environment. *J. exp. Biol.* **8**, 63–72.
— (1931). III. The electrolyte exchange. *J. exp. Biol.* **8**, 82–94.   37 ff., 214

Pantin, C. F. A. (1931). The origin of the composition of the body fluids in animals. *Biol. Rev.* **6**, 459–82. 214

Peters, H. (1935). Ueber den Einfluss des Salzgehaltes im Aussenmedium auf den Bau und die Funktion der Exkretionsorgane dekapoder Crustaceen (nach Untersuchungen an *Potamobius fluviatilis* und *Homarus vulgaris*). *Z. Morphol. Ökol. Tiere*, **30**, 355–81. 87 ff., 92

Peyrega, E. (1914–15). Sur la perméabilité osmotique de la coque des œufs de sélaciens. *Bull. Soc. zool. Fr.* **39**, 211–14. 176

Pfeffer, W. (1877). *Osmotische Untersuchungen.* Leipzig. 2

Philippson, M., Hannevart, G. & Thieren, J. (1910). Sur l'adaptation d'*Anodonta cygnea* à l'eau de mer. *Arch. int. Physiol.* **9**, 460–72. 64

Picken, L. E. R. (1936). A note on the mechanism of salt and water balance in the heterotrichous ciliate, *Spirostomum ambiguum*. *J. exp. Biol.* **13**, 387–92. 11, 17

— (1936). The mechanism of urine formation in invertebrates. I. The excretion mechanism in certain Arthropoda. *J. exp. Biol.* **13**, 309–28. 73 ff., 86 ff.

— (1937). II. The excretory mechanism in certain Mollusca. *J. exp. Biol.* **14**, 20–34. 61

Pieh, Sylvia (1936). Ueber die Beziehungen zwischen Atmung, Osmoregulation und Hydratation der Gewebe bei euryhalinen Meeresevertebraten. *Zool. Jb. Abt. Allg. Zool. Physiol. Tiere*, **56**, 129–60. 77

Pohle, E. (1920). Der Einfluss des Nervensystems auf die Osmoregulation der Amphibien. *Pflüg. Arch. ges. Physiol.* **182**, 215–31. 155, 157

Portier, P. (1910). Pression osmotique des liquides des oiseaux et mammifères marins. *J. Physiol. Path. gén.* **12**, 202–8. 163, 168

Portier, P. & Duval, M. (1927). Concentration moléculaire et teneur en chlore du sang de quelques Insectes. *C.R. Soc. Biol., Paris*, **97**, 1605. 103

Pratje, A. (1921). *Noctiluca miliaris* Suriray. Beiträge zur Morphologie, Physiologie und Cytologie. I. Morphologie und Physiologie (Beobachtungen an der lebenden Zelle). *Arch. Protistenk.* **42**, 1–98. 11

Przylecki, St. (1921). Recherches sur la pression osmotique chez les embryons de Cladocères, provenants des œufs parthénogénétiques. *Trav. Inst. Nencki*, **1**. 181

— (1921). Recherches sur la pression osmotique chez les embryons de Cladocères, provenants des œufs fécondés. *Trav. Inst. Nencki*, **1**. 181

Quinton, R. (1904). *L'eau de mer, milieu organique.* Paris. 54

Ramult, M. (1914). Untersuchungen über die Entwicklungsbedingungen der Sommereier von *Daphnia pulex* und anderen Cladoceren. *Bull. Inst. Acad. Sci. Cracovie*, pp. 481–514. 180

— (1925). Development and resisting power of *Cladocera* embryos in the solutions of certain inorganic salts. *Bull. Inst. Acad. Sci. Cracovie*, pp. 135–94. 181

Ranzi, S. (1930). L' accrescimento dell' embrione dei cefalopodi   175
(Ricerche sugli scambi tra ovo ed ambiente). *Arch. Entw-
Mech. Org.* **121**, 345–65.
Richards, A. N. (1934–5). *Urine Formation in the Amphibian*   158, 199
Kidney. Harvey Lect. pp. 93–118.
The Kidney in Health and Disease. Philadelphia (1935).
Robertson, J. D. (1937). Some features of the calcium meta-   72
bolism of the shore crab (*Carcinus maenas* Pennant). *Proc.
roy. Soc.* B, **124**, 162–82.
Rogenhofer, A. (1909). Zur Kenntnis des Baues der Kieferdrüse   94
bei Isopoden und des Grössenverhältnisses der Antennen-
und Kieferdrüse bei Meeres- und Süsswasserkrustazeen.
Arb. Zool. Inst. Univ. Wien, **17**, 139–56.
Rosenfels, R. S. (1935). The absorption and accumulation of   194
potassium bromide by *Elodea* as related to respiration.
Protoplasma, **23**, 503–19.
Rubenstein, B. B. (1935). The effect of salt and sugar solutions   157
on water exchange through the skin of frogs. *J. cell. comp.
Physiol.* **6**, 85–99.
Rubinstein, D. L. & Miskinowa, T. (1936). Untersuchungen   156
über einseitige Permeabilität. I. Ist die Froschhaut für
Wasser einseitig permeabel? *Protoplasma*, **25**, 56–68.
Runnström, J. (1920). Ueber osmotischen Druck und Eimem-   182
branfunktion bei den Lachsfischen. *Acta zool., Stockh.*, **1**,
321–36.
— (1925). Ueber den Einfluss des Kaliummangels auf das   174
Seeigelei. Experimentelle Beiträge zur Kenntniss des
Plasmabaues, der Teilung und der Determination des Eies.
Pubbl. Staz. zool. Napoli, **6** (1).

Schaper, A. (1902). Beiträge zur Analyse des thierischen   188
Wachsthums. *Arch. EntwMech. Org.* **14**, 307–400.
Schlieper, C. (1928). Die biologische Bedeutung der Salzkon-
zentration der Gewässer. *Naturwissenschaften*, **16**, 229–37.
— (1929). Ueber die Einwirkung niederer Salzkonzentra-   47ff.,55,73ff.,
tionen auf marine Organismen. *Z. vergl. Physiol.* **9**,   76, 94
478–514.
— (1929). Neue Versuche über die Osmoregulation wasser-   66
lebender Tiere. *S.B. Ges.ges.Naturw. Marburg*, **64**, 143–56.
— (1930). Die Osmoregulation wasserlebender Tiere. *Biol.
Rev.* **5**, 309–56.
— (1933). Ueber die osmoregulatorische Funktion der Aal-   144
kiemen. *Z. vergl. Physiol.* **18**, 682–95.
— (1933). Die Brackwassertiere und ihre Lebensbedingungen,
vom physiologischen Standpunkt aus betrachtet. *Verh.
Int. Ver. theoret. angew. Limnologie*, **6**, 113–46.
— (1933). Ueber die Permeabilität der Aalkiemen. I. Die   144, 217
Wasserdurchlässigkeit und der angebliche Wassertransport
der Aalkiemen bei hypertonischem Aussenmedium. *Z.
vergl. Physiol.* **19**, 68–83.
— (1935). Neuere Ergebnisse und Probleme aus dem Gebiet
der Osmoregulation wasserlebender Tiere. *Biol. Rev.* **10**,
334–60.

Schlieper, C. & Herrmann, F. (1930). Beziehungen zwischen   94
Bau und Funktion bei den Exkretionsorganen dekapoder
Crustaceen. *Zool. Jb. Abt. Anat. Ontog.* **52**, 624–30.

Schmidt-Nielsen, S. & Holmsen, J. (1921). Sur la composi-   165
tion de l'urine des baleines. *Arch. int. Physiol.* **18**, 128–32.

Schmidt-Nielsen, Signe & Sigval (1923). Beiträge zur Kenntnis   119, 139
des osmotischen Druckes der Fische. *K. norske Vidensk.
Selsk. Skr.* Nr. 1.

Scholles, W. (1933). Ueber die Mineralregulation wasser-   81, 84, 91
lebender Evertebraten. *Z. vergl. Physiol.* **19**, 522–54.

Schwabe, E. (1933). Ueber die Osmoregulation verschiedener   66, 76, 86, 92 ff.
Krebse (Malacostracen). *Z. vergl. Physiol.* **19**, 183–236.

Scott, G. G. (1913). A physiological study of the changes in   124
Mustelus canis produced by modifications in the molecular
concentration of the external medium. *Ann. N.Y. Acad.
Sci.* **23**, 1.

Smith, H. W. (1929). The composition of the body fluids of the   123
elasmobranchs. *J. biol. Chem.* **81**, 407.

— (1929). The excretion of ammonia and urea by the gills of   133
fish. *J. biol. Chem.* **81**, 727.

— (1930). The absorption and excretion of water and salts by   133, 139 ff.,
marine teleosts. *Amer. J. Physiol.* **93**, 480.   215

— (1930). Metabolism of the lung-fish, *Protopterus aethiopicus*.   152
J. biol. Chem. **88**, 97.

— (1931). The absorption and excretion of water and salts by   123 ff.
the elasmobranch fishes. II. Marine Elasmobranchs. *Amer.
J. Physiol.* **98**, 296–310.

— (1932). Water regulation and its evolution in fishes. *Quart.*   119, 134, 139,
Rev. Biol. **7**, 1–26.   152

— (1936). The composition of urine in the seal. *J. cell. comp.*   164, 166
Physiol. **7**, 465–74.

— (1936). The retention and physiological role of urea in the   123
Elasmobranchii. *Biol. Rev.* **11**, 49–82.

Smith, H. W. & Smith, Carlotta (1931). The absorption and   122, 125 ff.
excretion of water and salts by the elasmobranch fishes.
I. Fresh-water Elasmobranchs. *Amer. J. Physiol.* **98**, 279–95.

Spek, J. (1923). Ueber den physikalischen Zustand von   25
Plasma und Zelle der *Opalina ranarum*. *Arch. Protistenk.*
46, 166–202.

Staedeler & Frerichs (1858). Ueber das Vorkommen von   122
Harnstoff, Taurin und Scyllit in den Organen der Plagio-
stomen. *J. Prakt. Chem.* **73**, 48.

Stirling, W. (1877). On the extent to which absorption can take   157
place through the skin of the frog. *J. Anat., Paris,* **11**, 529.

Sumner, F. B. (1905). The physiological effects upon fishes of   133
changes in the density and salinity of water. *Bull. U.S.
Bur. Fish.* **25**, 55–108.

Svetlow, P. (1929). Entwicklungsphysiologische Beobachtungen   182
an Forelleneiern. *Arch. EntwMech. Org.* **114**, 771.

Tchakotine, S. (1935). L'effet d'arrêt de la fonction de la   17
vacuole pulsatile de la Paramécie par micropuncture ultra-
violette. *C.R. Soc. Biol., Paris,* **120**, 782–4.

Toda, S. & Taguchi, K. (1913). Untersuchungen über die   158
physikalischen Eigenschaften und die chemische Zusam-
mensetzung des Froschharns. I. Mitteilung. *Hoppe-Seyl.*
Z. **87**, 371–8.

Trolle, C. (1937). A study of the insensible perspiration from   163
the skin of a dog. *Skand. Arch. Physiol.* **76**, 220–4.

— (1937). A study of the insensible perspiration in man and   163
its nature. *Skand. Arch. Physiol.* **76**, 225–46.

Ursprung, A. & Blum, H. (1930). Zwei neue Saugkraft-Mess-   211
methoden. *Jb. Bot.* **72**, 254–334.

Ussing, H. H. (1935). The influence of heavy water on the
development of amphibian eggs. *Skand. Arch. Physiol.* **72**,
192–8.

Weatherby, J. H. (1927). The function of the contractile   15
vacuole in *Paramaecium caudatum*: with special reference
to the excretion of nitrogenous compounds. *Biol. Bull.*
Wood's Hole, **52**, 208–18.

Weil, E. & Pantin, C. F. A. (1931). The adaptation of *Gunda*   37 ff.
ulvae to salinity. II. The water exchange. *J. exp. Biol.* **8**,
73–81.

Weissmann, A. (1876–9). *Beiträge zur Naturgeschichte der*   180
Daphnoiden. Leipzig.

Wertheimer, E. (1923–5). A series of papers. *Pflüg. Arch. ges.*   155
Physiol. **199**, 201, 208.

Wesenberg-Lund, C. (1937). *Ferskvandsfaunaen biologisk*   78
belyst. Invertebrata, **1–2**, København.

Westblad, E. (1922). Zur Physiologie der Turbellarien. II. Die   37, 43
Exkretion. *Lunds Univ. Årsskr.* **18**, no. 6.

Westfall, B. B., Findley, T. & Richards, A. N. (1934). Quanti-   158, 199
tative studies of the composition of glomerular urine. XII.
The concentration of chloride in glomerular urine of frogs
and necturi. *J. biol. Chem.* **107**, 661–72.

Wetzel, G. (1907). Die chemische Zusammensetzung der Eier   176
des Seeigels, der Seespinne, des Tintenfisches und des
Hundshaies. *Arch. Anat. Physiol., Lpz.*, pp. 507–42.

Widmann, Erna (1935). Osmoregulation bei einheimischen   78, 94
Wasser- und Feuchtluft-Crustaceen. *Z. wiss. Zool.* **147**,
132–69.

Wigglesworth, V. B. (1933). The effect of salts on the anal gills   109, 116, 207
of the mosquito larva. *J. exp. Biol.* **10**, 1–15.

— (1933). The function of the anal gills of the mosquito larva.   103, 106
J. exp. Biol. **10**, 16–26.

— (1933). The adaptation of mosquito larvae to salt water.   109
J. exp. Biol. **10**, 27–37.

— (1938). A simple method of volumetric analysis for small   217
quantities of fluid: estimation of chloride in $0.3 \mu l$. of tissue
fluid. *Biochem. J.* **31**, 1719–22.

— (1938). The regulation of osmotic pressure and chloride   103, 109 ff.,
concentration in the haemolymph of mosquito larvae. *J. exp.*   197
Biol. **15**, 235–47.

LIST OF LATIN GENERIC NAMES

GENERAL INDEX

Accumulation of
    salts in eggs, 175
    sulphates, 35
    potassium—see Potassium
Active transport, 198 ff.
    water, 11, 21, 39 ff.
    increase in metabolism by, 39, 48,
        76 ff., 92, 207
    methods for studying, 215 ff.
    Na and Cl in *Haemopis*, 51
    Cl in *Limnaea, Paludina, Dreissena,
        Anodonta, Unio*, 62 ff.
    Cl in *Carcinus*, 74 ff.
    Na, K, Cl, Br, CNS, CNO, N₃ in
        Eriocheir, 82 ff.
    anions into plant roots, 83
    Cl in *Potamobius*, 91
    in *Daphnia*, 96
    Cl in mosquito larvae, 108 ff.
    Cl, Br and Na in *Libellula* and
        Aeschna, 117
    Cl in fresh-water fishes, 135 ff.
    Cl, Br and Na in *Carassius*, 136 ff.
    Cl in marine fishes, 142 ff., 204
    Cl in eels, doubtful, 149
    Cl, Br and Na in frogs, 159 ff.
    salts into marine eggs, 175 ff.
    Cl into frog's eggs, 189
Amino acids in insect blood, 103
Ammonia
    ammonium chloride in *Noctiluca*, 12
    elimination through gills in *Erio-
        cheir*, 82
    elimination through gills in fresh-
        water fishes, 133
Amphibia, 154 ff.
    eggs, 185 ff.
Anal papillae of mosquito larvae
    function, 103
    salt absorption, 106 ff.
    size, 112 ff.
"Anionenatmung", 83 ff.
Annelida, 45
Arachnomorpha, 99 ff.
Aves, 163
Axolotl, 161

Bound water, 1

Bromide
    active absorption of with chloride,
        108, 135, 137, 160, 205
Bryozoa, 44

Calcium
    active absorption of, 64, 137
    effect on membrane permeability,
        38 ff., 48 ff.
Cestoda, 43
Chloride
    content of fresh waters, 126, 202
    "secreting" cells, 145, 207
Coelenterata, 28 ff.
    inorganic constituents, 29
Crustacea, 65 ff.
    Stenohaline, 66 ff.
    Euryhaline, 73 ff.
    Fresh-water, 86 ff.
    eggs of, 180 ff.
Cyanide, effect on
    Noctiluca, 13
    Ciliates, 22 ff.
    Gunda, 40 ff.
    Nereis, 48
    Carcinus, 74
    frog's skin, 159
    Arbacia eggs, 173
Cyclostomata, 119 ff.

Deuterium—see Heavy water
Diffusion of solutes, 6
    ammonia and ions in *Eriocheir*, 82
    urea in elasmobranchs, 125 ff.
    urea and ammonia in *Pristis*, 127
    urea and ammonia in fresh-water
        fishes, 133
    ions in carp, 134
    Cl in fresh-water fishes, 134
    through mucus, 150
    ions in frog, 159
    ions in marine eggs, 174 ff.
Disperse phase of solutions, 1, 171
Distilled water
    poisonous action of, 17, 31, 96, 215
    washing out with, 51, 62 ff., 82, 91,
        96, 106 ff., 117, 135 ff., 149, 159 ff.
Donnan equilibrium, 6, 99

Drinking of sea water
  measurement of, 139, 215
  in Elasmobranchs, 123
  in marine fishes, 139 ff., 146
  in *Fundulus*, 151
  in frogs, 156
  in marine mammals, 165
  in birds, 169

Echinoderma, 32
  inorganic constituents, 35
  eggs, osmotic conditions, 173
Eggs
  osmotic conditions in, 170 ff.
  ionic composition of, 170 ff.
Elasmobranchii, 122 ff.
  marine, 122 ff.
  fresh-water, 125 ff.
  eggs, 176
Elvers, 147 ff.
Embryos
  osmotic conditions in, 170 ff.
Euphyllopoda, 97 ff.
Excretory organs, 199 ff.
  Protozoa, 15 ff., 27
  Turbellaria, 37
  Trematoda, 43
  Rotatoria, 43
  Annelida, 45
  Mollusca, 53
  Crustacea, 65, 68 ff., 87 ff., 94
  Insecta, 101
  Cyclostomata, 119
  Elasmobranchii, 122
  Teleostomi, 130
  Amphibia, 154
  higher vertebrates, 164
Extracellular fluid, 34
  determination of, in *Mytilus*, 59
Extrarenal excretion, 127, 133, 140 ff.

Fishes
  fresh-water, 132
  marine, 138
  euryhaline and anadromous, 147
  eggs, 177 ff., 182 ff.
Freezing-point depression, 3
  determination methods, 209 ff.
  micromethod of Drucker and
    Schreiner, 94
  see Osmotic concentration

Gastrotricha, 44

Glycin
  in muscles of *Pecten*, 57

Heavy water
  diffusion of, 7, 96, 98, 117, 133,
    156, 163, 183
Hirudinea, 50
Holothuria, 33 ff.
Homoiosmosis, definition, 8
Hydrostatic pressure, 3
  in Protozoa, 11
  of haemolymph in Crustacea, 71, 76
Hypertonicity of marine animals
  Nereis, 47 ff.
  euryhaline Crustacea, 73 ff.
Hypotonicity
  marine Crustacea, 66, 77, 80

Impermeability
  for water, 183, 188, 191
Inorganic constituents
  Coelenterata, 29
  Echinoderma, 35
  Mollusca, 56 ff.
  Marine animals, 69
  Chiridotea, 79
  in blood, urine and tissues of
    Eriocheir, 82, 85
  in blood of *Potamobius*, 93
  in blood and muscle of *Protopterus*,
    153
  in mature eggs, 171 ff.
  in Teleost embryos, 179
  independence of living cells, 193 ff.
  in plant cells, 193 ff.
Insecta, 101 ff.
Intestinal absorption
  of water in insects, 106
  of water and salts in marine fishes,
    140 ff.
  of water in birds, 200
  of ions in dogs, 206
Intracellular fluids in
  Mytilus muscle, 60
  Eriocheir muscle, 85
  mature eggs, 170 ff.
  developing eggs, 176 ff.
Ions
  independence of, in living cells, 193
  selective absorption of, 51, 82 ff.,
    117, 137, 160, 205
  see Active transport

CATALOGUE OF DOVER BOOKS

BOOKS EXPLAINING SCIENCE AND MATHEMATICS
General

WHAT IS SCIENCE?, Norman Campbell. This excellent introduction explains scientific method, role of mathematics, types of scientific laws. Contents: 2 aspects of science, science & nature, laws of science, discovery of laws, explanation of laws, measurement & numerical laws, applications of science. 192pp. 5⅜ x 8.
S43 Paperbound **$1.25**

THE COMMON SENSE OF THE EXACT SCIENCES, W. K. Clifford. Introduction by James Newman, edited by Karl Pearson. For 70 years this has been a guide to classical scientific and mathematical thought. Explains with unusual clarity basic concepts, such as extension of meaning of symbols, characteristics of surface boundaries, properties of plane figures, vectors, Cartesian method of determining position, etc. Long preface by Bertrand Russell. Bibliography of Clifford. Corrected, 130 diagrams redrawn. 249pp. 5⅜ x 8.
T61 Paperbound **$1.60**

SCIENCE THEORY AND MAN, Erwin Schrödinger. This is a complete and unabridged reissue of SCIENCE AND THE HUMAN TEMPERAMENT plus an additional essay: "What is an Elementary Particle?" Nobel laureate Schrödinger discusses such topics as nature of scientific method, the nature of science, chance and determinism, science and society, conceptual models for physical entities, elementary particles and wave mechanics. Presentation is popular and may be followed by most people with little or no scientific training. "Fine practical preparation for a time when laws of nature, human institutions . . . are undergoing a critical examination without parallel," Waldemar Kaempffert, N. Y. TIMES. 192pp. 5⅜ x 8.
T428 Paperbound **$1.35**

FADS AND FALLACIES IN THE NAME OF SCIENCE, Martin Gardner. Examines various cults, quack systems, frauds, delusions which at various times have masqueraded as science. Accounts of hollow-earth fanatics like Symmes; Velikovsky and wandering planets; Hoerbiger; Bellamy and the theory of multiple moons; Charles Fort; dowsing, pseudoscientific methods for finding water, ores, oil. Sections on naturopathy, iridiagnosis, zone therapy, food fads, etc. Analytical accounts of Wilhelm Reich and orgone sex energy; L. Ron Hubbard and Dianetics; A. Korzybski and General Semantics; many others. Brought up to date to include Bridey Murphy, others. Not just a collection of anecdotes, but a fair, reasoned appraisal of eccentric theory. Formerly titled IN THE NAME OF SCIENCE. Preface. Index. x + 384pp. 5⅜ x 8.
T394 Paperbound **$1.50**

A DOVER SCIENCE SAMPLER, edited by George Barkin. 64-page book, sturdily bound, containing excerpts from over 20 Dover books, explaining science. Edwin Hubble, George Sarton, Ernst Mach, A. d'Abro, Galileo, Newton, others, discussing island universes, scientific truth, biological phenomena, stability in bridges, etc. Copies limited; no more than 1 to a customer.
FREE

POPULAR SCIENTIFIC LECTURES, Hermann von Helmholtz. Helmholtz was a superb expositor as well as a scientist of genius in many areas. The seven essays in this volume are models of clarity, and even today they rank among the best general descriptions of their subjects ever written. "The Physiological Causes of Harmony in Music" was the first significant physiological explanation of musical consonance and dissonance. Two essays, "On the Interaction of Natural Forces" and "On the Conservation of Force," were of great importance in the history of science, for they firmly established the principle of the conservation of energy. Other lectures include "On the Relation of Optics to Painting," "On Recent Progress in the Theory of Vision," "On Goethe's Scientific Researches," and "On the Origin and Significance of Geometrical Axioms." Selected and edited with an introduction by Professor Morris Kline. xii + 286pp. 5⅜ x 8½.
T799 Paperbound **$1.45**

BOOKS EXPLAINING SCIENCE AND MATHEMATICS
Physics

CONCERNING THE NATURE OF THINGS, Sir William Bragg. Christmas lectures delivered at the Royal Society by Nobel laureate. Why a spinning ball travels in a curved track; how uranium is transmuted to lead, etc. Partial contents: atoms, gases, liquids, crystals, metals, etc. No scientific background needed; wonderful for intelligent child. 32pp. of photos, 57 figures. xii + 232pp. 5⅜ x 8.
T31 Paperbound **$1.50**

THE RESTLESS UNIVERSE, Max Born. New enlarged version of this remarkably readable account by a Nobel laureate. Moving from sub-atomic particles to universe, the author explains in very simple terms the latest theories of wave mechanics. Partial contents: air and its relatives, electrons & ions, waves & particles, electronic structure of the atom, nuclear physics. Nearly 1000 illustrations, including 7 animated sequences. 325pp. 6 x 9.
T412 Paperbound **$2.00**

CATALOGUE OF DOVER BOOKS

FROM EUCLID TO EDDINGTON: A STUDY OF THE CONCEPTIONS OF THE EXTERNAL WORLD, Sir Edmund Whittaker. A foremost British scientist traces the development of theories of natural philosophy from the western rediscovery of Euclid to Eddington, Einstein, Dirac, etc. The inadequacy of classical physics is contrasted with present day attempts to understand the physical world through relativity, non-Euclidean geometry, space curvature, wave mechanics, etc. 5 major divisions of examination: Space; Time and Movement; the Concepts of Classical Physics; the Concepts of Quantum Mechanics; the Eddington Universe. 212pp. 5⅜ x 8.   T491 Paperbound **$1.35**

PHYSICS, THE PIONEER SCIENCE, L. W. Taylor. First thorough text to place all important physical phenomena in cultural-historical framework; remains best work of its kind. Exposition of physical laws, theories developed chronologically, with great historical, illustrative experiments diagrammed, described, worked out mathematically. Excellent physics text for self-study as well as class work. Vol. 1: Heat, Sound: motion, acceleration, gravitation, conservation of energy, heat engines, rotation, heat, mechanical energy, etc. 211 illus. 407pp. 5⅜ x 8. Vol. 2: Light, Electricity: images, lenses, prisms, magnetism, Ohm's law, dynamos, telegraph, quantum theory, decline of mechanical view of nature, etc. Bibliography. 13 table appendix. Index. 551 illus. 2 color plates. 508pp. 5⅜ x 8.

Vol. 1 S565 Paperbound **$2.00**
Vol. 2 S566 Paperbound **$2.00**
The set **$4.00**

A SURVEY OF PHYSICAL THEORY, Max Planck. One of the greatest scientists of all time, creator of the quantum revolution in physics, writes in non-technical terms of his own discoveries and those of other outstanding creators of modern physics. Planck wrote this book when science had just crossed the threshold of the new physics, and he communicates the excitement felt then as he discusses electromagnetic theories, statistical methods, evolution of the concept of light, a step-by-step description of how he developed his own momentous theory, and many more of the basic ideas behind modern physics. Formerly "A Survey of Physics." Bibliography. Index. 128pp. 5⅜ x 8.   S650 Paperbound **$1.15**

THE ATOMIC NUCLEUS, M. Korsunsky. The only non-technical comprehensive account of the atomic nucleus in English. For college physics students, etc. Chapters cover: Radioactivity, the Nuclear Model of the Atom, the Mass of Atomic Nuclei, the Disintegration of Atomic Nuclei, the Discovery of the Positron, the Artificial Transformation of Atomic Nuclei, Artificial Radioactivity, Mesons, the Neutrino, the Structure of Atomic Nuclei and Forces Acting Between Nuclear Particles, Nuclear Fission, Chain Reaction, Peaceful Uses, Thermocular Reactions. Slightly abridged edition. Translated by G. Yankovsky. 65 figures. Appendix includes 45 photographic illustrations. 413 pp. 5⅜ x 8.   S1052 Paperbound **$2.00**

PRINCIPLES OF MECHANICS SIMPLY EXPLAINED, Morton Mott-Smith. Excellent, highly readable introduction to the theories and discoveries of classical physics. Ideal for the layman who desires a foundation which will enable him to understand and appreciate contemporary developments in the physical sciences. Discusses: Density, The Law of Gravitation, Mass and Weight, Action and Reaction, Kinetic and Potential Energy, The Law of Inertia, Effects of Acceleration, The Independence of Motions, Galileo and the New Science of Dynamics, Newton and the New Cosmos, The Conservation of Momentum, and other topics. Revised edition of "This Mechanical World." Illustrated by E. Kosa, Jr. Bibliography and Chronology. Index. xiv + 171pp. 5⅜ x 8½.   T1067 Paperbound **$1.00**

THE CONCEPT OF ENERGY SIMPLY EXPLAINED, Morton Mott-Smith. Elementary, non-technical exposition which traces the story of man's conquest of energy, with particular emphasis on the developments during the nineteenth century and the first three decades of our own century. Discusses man's earlier efforts to harness energy, more recent experiments and discoveries relating to the steam engine, the engine indicator, the motive power of heat, the principle of excluded perpetual motion, the bases of the conservation of energy, the concept of entropy, the internal combustion engine, mechanical refrigeration, and many other related topics. Also much biographical material. Index. Bibliography. 33 illustrations. ix + 215pp. 5⅜ x 8½.   T1071 Paperbound **$1.25**

HEAT AND ITS WORKINGS, Morton Mott-Smith. One of the best elementary introductions to the theory and attributes of heat, covering such matters as the laws governing the effect of heat on solids, liquids and gases, the methods by which heat is measured, the conversion of a substance from one form to another through heating and cooling, evaporation, the effects of pressure on boiling and freezing points, and the three ways in which heat is transmitted (conduction, convection, radiation). Also brief notes on major experiments and discoveries. Concise, but complete, it presents all the essential facts about the subject in readable style. Will give the layman and beginning student a first-rate background in this major topic in physics. Index. Bibliography. 50 illustrations. x + 165pp. 5⅜ x 8½. T978 Paperbound **$1.00**

THE STORY OF ATOMIC THEORY AND ATOMIC ENERGY, J. G. Feinberg. Wider range of facts on physical theory, cultural implications, than any other similar source. Completely non-technical. Begins with first atomic theory, 600 B.C., goes through A-bomb, developments to 1959. Avogadro, Rutherford, Bohr, Einstein, radioactive decay, binding energy, radiation danger, future benefits of nuclear power, dozens of other topics, told in lively, related, informal manner. Particular stress on European atomic research. "Deserves special mention . . . authoritative," Saturday Review. Formerly "The Atom Story." New chapter to 1959. Index. 34 illustrations. 251pp. 5⅜ x 8.   T625 Paperbound **$1.60**

CATALOGUE OF DOVER BOOKS

THE STRANGE STORY OF THE QUANTUM, AN ACCOUNT FOR THE GENERAL READER OF THE GROWTH OF IDEAS UNDERLYING OUR PRESENT ATOMIC KNOWLEDGE, B. Hoffmann. Presents lucidly and expertly, with barest amount of mathematics, the problems and theories which led to modern quantum physics. Dr. Hoffmann begins with the closing years of the 19th century, when certain trifling discrepancies were noticed, and with illuminating analogies and examples takes you through the brilliant concepts of Planck, Einstein, Pauli, de Broglie, Bohr, Schroedinger, Heisenberg, Dirac, Sommerfeld, Feynman, etc. This edition includes a new, long postscript carrying the story through 1958. "Of the books attempting an account of the history and contents of our modern atomic physics which have come to my attention, this is the best," H. Margenau, Yale University, in "American Journal of Physics." 32 tables and line illustrations. Index. 275pp. 5⅜ x 8. T518 Paperbound **$1.50**

THE EVOLUTION OF SCIENTIFIC THOUGHT FROM NEWTON TO EINSTEIN, A. d'Abro. Einstein's special and general theories of relativity, with their historical implications, are analyzed in non-technical terms. Excellent accounts of the contributions of Newton, Riemann, Weyl, Planck, Eddington, Maxwell, Lorentz and others are treated in terms of space and time, equations of electromagnetics, finiteness of the universe, methodology of science. 21 diagrams. 482pp. 5⅜ x 8. T2 Paperound **$2.25**

THE RISE OF THE NEW PHYSICS, A. d'Abro. A half-million word exposition, formerly titled THE DECLINE OF MECHANISM, for readers not versed in higher mathematics. The only thorough explanation, in everyday language, of the central core of modern mathematical physical theory, treating both classical and modern theoretical physics, and presenting in terms almost anyone can understand the equivalent of 5 years of study of mathematical physics. Scientifically impeccable coverage of mathematical-physical thought from the Newtonian system up through the electronic theories of Dirac and Heisenberg and Fermi's statistics. Combines both history and exposition; provides a broad yet unified and detailed view, with constant comparison of classical and modern views on phenomena and theories. "A must for anyone doing serious study in the physical sciences," JOURNAL OF THE FRANKLIN INSTITUTE. "Extraordinary faculty . . . to explain ideas and theories of theoretical physics in the language of daily life," ISIS. First part of set covers philosophy of science, drawing upon the practice of Newton, Maxwell, Poincaré, Einstein, others, discussing modes of thought, experiment, interpretations of causality, etc. In the second part, 100 pages explain grammar and vocabulary of mathematics, with discussions of functions, groups, series, Fourier series, etc. The remainder is devoted to concrete, detailed coverage of both classical and quantum physics, explaining such topics as analytic mechanics, Hamilton's principle, wave theory of light, electromagnetic waves, groups of transformations, thermodynamics, phase rule, Brownian movement, kinetics, special relativity, Planck's original quantum theory, Bohr's atom, Zeeman effect, Broglie's wave mechanics, Heisenberg's uncertainty, Eigen-values, matrices, scores of other important topics. Discoveries and theories are covered for such men as Alembert, Born, Cantor, Debye, Euler, Foucault, Galois, Gauss, Hadamard, Kelvin, Kepler, Laplace, Maxwell, Pauli, Rayleigh, Volterra, Weyl, Young, more than 180 others. Indexed. 97 illustrations. ix + 982pp. 5⅜ x 8.
T3 Volume 1, Paperbound **$2.00**
T4 Volume 2, Paperbound **$2.00**

SPINNING TOPS AND GYROSCOPIC MOTION, John Perry. Well-known classic of science still unsurpassed for lucid, accurate, delightful exposition. How quasi-rigidity is induced in flexible and fluid bodies by rapid motions; why gyrostat falls, top rises; nature and effect on climatic conditions of earth's precessional movement; effect of internal fluidity on rotating bodies, etc. Appendixes describe practical uses to which gyroscopes have been put in ships, compasses, monorail transportation. 62 figures. 128pp. 5⅜ x 8. T416 Paperbound **$1.00**

THE UNIVERSE OF LIGHT, Sir William Bragg. No scientific training needed to read Nobel Prize winner's expansion of his Royal Institute Christmas Lectures. Insight into nature of light, methods and philosophy of science. Explains lenses, reflection, color, resonance, polarization, x-rays, the spectrum, Newton's work with prisms, Huygens' with polarization, Crookes' with cathode ray, etc. Leads into clear statement of 2 major historical theories of light, corpuscle and wave. Dozens of experiments you can do. 199 illus., including 2 full-page color plates. 293pp. 5⅜ x 8. S538 Paperbound **$1.85**

THE STORY OF X-RAYS FROM RÖNTGEN TO ISOTOPES, A. R. Bleich. Non-technical history of x-rays, their scientific explanation, their applications in medicine, industry, research, and art, and their effect on the individual and his descendants. Includes amusing early reactions to Röntgen's discovery, cancer therapy, detections of art and stamp forgeries, potential risks to patient and operator, etc. Illustrations show x-rays of flower structure, the gall bladder, gears with hidden defects, etc. Original Dover publication. Glossary. Bibliography. Index. 55 photos and figures. xiv + 186pp. 5⅜ x 8. T662 Paperbound **$1.35**

ELECTRONS, ATOMS, METALS AND ALLOYS, Wm. Hume-Rothery. An introductory-level explanation of the application of the electronic theory to the structure and properties of metals and alloys, taking into account the new theoretical work done by mathematical physicists. Material presented in dialogue-form between an "Old Metallurgist" and a "Young Scientist." Their discussion falls into 4 main parts: the nature of an atom, the nature of a metal, the nature of an alloy, and the structure of the nucleus. They cover such topics as the hydrogen atom, electron waves, wave mechanics, Brillouin zones, co-valent bonds, radioactivity and natural disintegration, fundamental particles, structure and fission of the nucleus,etc. Revised, enlarged edition. 177 illustrations. Subject and name indexes. 407pp. 5⅜ x 8½. S1046 Paperbound **$2.25**

OUT OF THE SKY, H. H. Nininger. A non-technical but comprehensive introduction to "meteoritics", the young science concerned with all aspects of the arrival of matter from outer space. Written by one of the world's experts on meteorites, this work shows how, despite difficulties of observation and sparseness of data, a considerable body of knowledge has arisen. It defines meteors and meteorites; studies fireball clusters and processions, meteorite composition, size, distribution, showers, explosions, origins, craters, and much more. A true connecting link between astronomy and geology. More than 175 photos, 22 other illustrations. References. Bibliography of author's publications on meteorites. Index. viii + 336pp. 5⅜ x 8. T519 Paperbound **$1.85**

SATELLITES AND SCIENTIFIC RESEARCH, D. King-Hele. Non-technical account of the manmade satellites and the discoveries they have yielded up to the autumn of 1961. Brings together information hitherto published only in hard-to-get scientific journals. Includes the life history of a typical satellite, methods of tracking, new information on the shape of the earth, zones of radiation, etc. Over 60 diagrams and 6 photographs. Mathematical appendix. Bibliography of over 100 items. Index. xii + 180pp. 5⅜ x 8½. T703 Paperbound **$2.00**

BOOKS EXPLAINING SCIENCE AND MATHEMATICS

Mathematics

CHANCE, LUCK AND STATISTICS: THE SCIENCE OF CHANCE, Horace C. Levinson. Theory of probability and science of statistics in simple, non-technical language. Part I deals with theory of probability, covering odd superstitions in regard to "luck," the meaning of betting odds, the law of mathematical expectation, gambling, and applications in poker, roulette, lotteries, dice, bridge, and other games of chance. Part II discusses the misuse of statistics, the concept of statistical probabilities, normal and skew frequency distributions, and statistics applied to various fields—birth rates, stock speculation, insurance rates, advertising, etc. "Presented in an easy humorous style which I consider the best kind of expository writing," Prof. A. C. Cohen, Industry Quality Control. Enlarged revised edition. Formerly titled "The Science of Chance." Preface and two new appendices by the author. Index. xiv + 365pp. 5⅜ x 8. T1007 Paperbound **$1.85**

PROBABILITIES AND LIFE, Emile Borel. Translated by M. Baudin. Non-technical, highly readable introduction to the results of probability as applied to everyday situations. Partial contents: Fallacies About Probabilities Concerning Life After Death; Negligible Probabilities and the Probabilities of Everyday Life; Events of Small Probability; Application of Probabilities to Certain Problems of Heredity; Probabilities of Deaths, Diseases, and Accidents; On Poisson's Formula. Index. 3 Appendices of statistical studies and tables. vi + 87pp. 5⅜ x 8½. T121 Paperbound **$1.00**

GREAT IDEAS OF MODERN MATHEMATICS: THEIR NATURE AND USE, Jagjit Singh. Reader with only high school math will understand main mathematical ideas of modern physics, astronomy, genetics, psychology, evolution, etc., better than many who use them as tools, but comprehend little of their basic structure. Author uses his wide knowledge of non-mathematical fields in brilliant exposition of differential equations, matrices, group theory, logic, statistics, problems of mathematical foundations, imaginary numbers, vectors, etc. Original publication. 2 appendices. 2 indexes. 65 illustr. 322pp. 5⅜ x 8. S587 Paperbound **$1.75**

MATHEMATICS IN ACTION, O. G. Sutton. Everyone with a command of high school algebra will find this book one of the finest possible introductions to the application of mathematics to physical theory. Ballistics, numerical analysis, waves and wavelike phenomena, Fourier series, group concepts, fluid flow and aerodynamics, statistical measures, and meteorology are discussed with unusual clarity. Some calculus and differential equations theory is developed by the author for the reader's help in the more difficult sections. 88 figures. Index. viii + 236pp. 5⅜ x 8. T440 Clothbound **$3.50**

THE FOURTH DIMENSION SIMPLY EXPLAINED, edited by H. P. Manning. 22 essays, originally Scientific American contest entries, that use a minimum of mathematics to explain aspects of 4-dimensional geometry: analogues to 3-dimensional space, 4-dimensional absurdities and curiosities (such as removing the contents of an egg without puncturing its shell), possible measurements and forms, etc. Introduction by the editor. Only book of its sort on a truly elementary level, excellent introduction to advanced works. 82 figures. 251pp. 5⅜ x 8. T711 Paperbound **$1.35**

MATHEMATICS—INTERMEDIATE TO ADVANCED

General

INTRODUCTION TO APPLIED MATHEMATICS, Francis D. Murnaghan. A practical and thoroughly sound introduction to a number of advanced branches of higher mathematics. Among the selected topics covered in detail are: vector and matrix analysis, partial and differential equations, integral equations, calculus of variations, Laplace transform theory, the vector triple product, linear vector functions, quadratic and bilinear forms, Fourier series, spherical harmonics, Bessel functions, the Heaviside expansion formula, and many others. Extremely useful book for graduate students in physics, engineering, chemistry, and mathematics. Index. 111 study exercises with answers. 41 illustrations. ix + 389pp. 5⅜ x 8½.
S1042 Paperbound **$2.00**

OPERATIONAL METHODS IN APPLIED MATHEMATICS, H. S. Carslaw and J. C. Jaeger. Explanation of the application of the Laplace Transformation to differential equations, a simple and effective substitute for more difficult and obscure operational methods. Of great practical value to engineers and to all workers in applied mathematics. Chapters on: Ordinary Linear Differential Equations with Constant Coefficients;; Electric Circuit Theory; Dynamical Applications; The Inversion Theorem for the Laplace Transformation; Conduction of Heat; Vibrations of Continuous Mechanical Systems; Hydrodynamics; Impulsive Functions; Chains of Differential Equations; and other related matters. 3 appendices. 153 problems, many with answers. 22 figures. xvi + 359pp. 5⅜ x 8½.
S1011 Paperbound **$2.25**

APPLIED MATHEMATICS FOR RADIO AND COMMUNICATIONS ENGINEERS, C. E. Smith. No extraneous material here!—only the theories, equations, and operations essential and immediately useful for radio work. Can be used as refresher, as handbook of applications and tables, or as full home-study course. Ranges from simplest arithmetic through calculus, series, and wave forms, hyperbolic trigonometry, simultaneous equations in mesh circuits, etc. Supplies applications right along with each math topic discussed. 22 useful tables of functions, formulas, logs, etc. Index. 166 exercises, 140 examples, all with answers. 95 diagrams. Bibliography. x + 336pp. 5⅜ x 8.
S141 Paperbound **$1.75**

Algebra, group theory, determinants, sets, matrix theory

ALGEBRAS AND THEIR ARITHMETICS, L. E. Dickson. Provides the foundation and background necessary to any advanced undergraduate or graduate student studying abstract algebra. Begins with elementary introduction to linear transformations, matrices, field of complex numbers; proceeds to order, basal units, modulus, quaternions, etc.; develops calculus of linears sets, describes various examples of algebras including invariant, difference, nilpotent, semi-simple. "Makes the reader marvel at his genius for clear and profound analysis," Amer. Mathematical Monthly. Index. xii + 241pp. 5⅜ x 8.
S616 Paperbound **$1.50**

THE THEORY OF EQUATIONS WITH AN INTRODUCTION TO THE THEORY OF BINARY ALGEBRAIC FORMS, W. S. Burnside and A. W. Panton. Extremely thorough and concrete discussion of the theory of equations, with extensive detailed treatment of many topics curtailed in later texts. Covers theory of algebraic equations, properties of polynomials, symmetric functions, derived functions, Horner's process, complex numbers and the complex variable, determinants and methods of elimination, invariant theory (nearly 100 pages), transformations, introduction to Galois theory, Abelian equations, and much more. Invaluable supplementary work for modern students and teachers. 759 examples and exercises. Index in each volume. Two volume set. Total of xxiv + 604pp. 5⅜ x 8.
S714 Vol I Paperbound **$1.85**
S715 Vol II Paperbound **$1.85**
The set **$3.70**

COMPUTATIONAL METHODS OF LINEAR ALGEBRA, V. N. Faddeeva, translated by C. D. Benster. First English translation of a unique and valuable work, the only work in English presenting a systematic exposition of the most important methods of linear algebra—classical and contemporary. Shows in detail how to derive numerical solutions of problems in mathematical physics which are frequently connected with those of linear algebra. Theory as well as individual practice. Part I surveys the mathematical background that is indispensable to what follows. Parts II and III, the conclusion, set forth the most important methods of solution, for both exact and iterative groups. One of the most outstanding and valuable features of this work is the 23 tables, double and triple checked for accuracy. These tables will not be found elsewhere. Author's preface. Translator's note. New bibliography and index. x + 252pp. 5⅜ x 8.
S424 Paperbound **$1.95**

ALGEBRAIC EQUATIONS, E. Dehn. Careful and complete presentation of Galois' theory of algebraic equations; theories of Lagrange and Galois developed in logical rather than historical form, with a more thorough exposition than in most modern books. Many concrete applications and fully-worked-out examples. Discusses basic theory (very clear exposition of the symmetric group); isomorphic, transitive, and Abelian groups; applications of Lagrange's and Galois' theories; and much more. Newly revised by the author. Index. List of Theorems. xi + 208pp. 5⅜ x 8.
S697 Paperbound **$1.45**

Differential equations, ordinary and partial; integral equations

INTRODUCTION TO THE DIFFERENTIAL EQUATIONS OF PHYSICS, L. Hopf. Especially valuable to the engineer with no math beyond elementary calculus. Emphasizing intuitive rather than formal aspects of concepts, the author covers an extensive territory. Partial contents: Law of causality, energy theorem, damped oscillations, coupling by friction, cylindrical and spherical coordinates, heat source, etc. Index. 48 figures. 160pp. 5⅜ x 8.
S120 Paperbound **$1.25**

INTRODUCTION TO THE THEORY OF LINEAR DIFFERENTIAL EQUATIONS, E. G. Poole. Authoritative discussions of important topics, with methods of solution more detailed than usual, for students with background of elementary course in differential equations. Studies existence theorems, linearly independent solutions; equations with constant coefficients; with uniform analytic coefficients; regular singularities; the hypergeometric equation; conformal representation; etc. Exercises. Index. 210pp. 5⅜ x 8.
S629 Paperbound **$1.65**

DIFFERENTIAL EQUATIONS FOR ENGINEERS, P. Franklin. Outgrowth of a course given 10 years at M. I. T. Makes most useful branch of pure math accessible for practical work. Theoretical basis of D.E.'s; solution of ordinary D.E.'s and partial derivatives arising from heat flow, steady-state temperature of a plate, wave equations; analytic functions; convergence of Fourier Series. 400 problems on electricity, vibratory systems, other topics. Formerly "Differential Equations for Electrical Engineers." Index 41 illus. 307pp. 5⅜ x 8.
S601 Paperbound **$1.65**

DIFFERENTIAL EQUATIONS, F. R. Moulton. A detailed, rigorous exposition of all the nonelementary processes of solving ordinary differential equations. Several chapters devoted to the treatment of practical problems, especially those of a physical nature, which are far more advanced than problems usually given as illustrations. Includes analytic differential equations; variations of a parameter; integrals of differential equations; analytic implicit functions; problems of elliptic motion; sine-amplitude functions; deviation of formal bodies; Cauchy-Lipschitz process; linear differential equations with periodic coefficients; differential equations in infinitely many variations; much more. Historical notes. 10 figures. 222 problems. Index. xv + 395pp. 5⅜ x 8.
S451 Paperbound **$2.00**

DIFFERENTIAL AND INTEGRAL EQUATIONS OF MECHANICS AND PHYSICS (DIE DIFFERENTIAL-UND INTEGRALGLEICHUNGEN DER MECHANIK UND PHYSIK), edited by P. Frank and R. von Mises. Most comprehensive and authoritative work on the mathematics of mathematical physics available today in the United States: the standard, definitive reference for teachers, physicists, engineers, and mathematicians—now published (in the original German) at a relatively inexpensive price for the first time! Every chapter in this 2,000-page set is by an expert in his field: Carathéodory, Courant, Frank, Mises, and a dozen others. Vol I, on mathematics, gives concise but complete coverages of advanced calculus, differential equations, integral equations, and potential, and partial differential equations. Index. xxiii + 916pp. Vol. II (physics): classical mechanics, optics, continuous mechanics, heat conduction and diffusion, the stationary and quasi-stationary electromagnetic field, electromagnetic oscillations, and wave mechanics. Index. xxiv + 1106pp. Two volume set. Each volume available separately. 5⅝ x 8⅜.
S787 Vol I Clothbound **$7.50**
S788 Vol II Clothbound **$7.50**
The set **$15.00**

LECTURES ON CAUCHY'S PROBLEM, J. Hadamard. Based on lectures given at Columbia, Rome, this discusses work of Riemann, Kirchhoff, Volterra, and the author's own research on the hyperbolic case in linear partial differential equations. It extends spherical and cylindrical waves to apply to all (normal) hyperbolic equations. Partial contents: Cauchy's problem, fundamental formula, equations with odd number, with even number of independent variables; method of descent. 32 figures. Index. iii + 316pp. 5⅜ x 8. S105 Paperbound **$1.75**

THEORY OF DIFFERENTIAL EQUATIONS, A. R. Forsyth. Out of print for over a decade, the complete 6 volumes (now bound as 3) of this monumental work represent the most comprehensive treatment of differential equations ever written. Historical presentation includes in 2500 pages every substantial development. Vol. 1, 2: EXACT EQUATIONS, PFAFF'S PROBLEM; ORDINARY EQUATIONS, NOT LINEAR: methods of Grassmann, Clebsch, Lie, Darboux; Cauchy's theorem; branch points; etc. Vol. 3, 4: ORDINARY EQUATIONS, NOT LINEAR; ORDINARY LINEAR EQUATIONS: Zeta Fuchsian functions, general theorems on algebraic integrals, Brun's theorem, equations with uniform periodic coffiecients, etc. Vol. 4, 5: PARTIAL DIFFERENTIAL EQUATIONS: 2 existence-theorems, equations of theoretical dynamics, Laplace transformations, general transformation of equations of the 2nd order, much more. Indexes. Total of 2766pp. 5⅜ x 8. S576-7-8 Clothbound: the set **$15.00**

PARTIAL DIFFERENTIAL EQUATIONS OF MATHEMATICAL PHYSICS, A. G. Webster. A keystone work in the library of every mature physicist, engineer, researcher. Valuable sections on elasticity, compression theory, potential theory, theory of sound, heat conduction, wave propagation, vibration theory. Contents include: deduction of differential equations, vibrations, normal functions, Fourier's series, Cauchy's method, boundary problems, method of Riemann-Volterra. Spherical, cylindrical, ellipsoidal harmonics, applications, etc. 97 figures. vii + 440pp. 5⅜ x 8. S263 Paperbound **$2.00**

CATALOGUE OF DOVER BOOKS

ELEMENTARY CONCEPTS OF TOPOLOGY, P. Alexandroff. First English translation of the famous brief introduction to topology for the beginner or for the mathematician not undertaking extensive study. This unusually useful intuitive approach deals primarily with the concepts of complex, cycle, and homology, and is wholly consistent with current investigations. Ranges from basic concepts of set-theoretic topology to the concept of Betti groups. "Glowing example of harmony between intuition and thought," David Hilbert. Translated by A. E. Farley. Introduction by D. Hilbert. Index. 25 figures. 73pp. 5⅜ x 8. **S747 Paperbound $1.00**

Number theory

INTRODUCTION TO THE THEORY OF NUMBERS, L. E. Dickson. Thorough, comprehensive approach with adequate coverage of classical literature, an introductory volume beginners can follow. Chapters on divisibility, congruences, quadratic residues & reciprocity, Diophantine equations, etc. Full treatment of binary quadratic forms without usual restriction to integral coefficients. Covers infinitude of primes, least residues, Fermat's theorem, Euler's phi function, Legendre's symbol, Gauss's lemma, automorphs, reduced forms, recent theorems of Thue & Siegel, many more. Much material not readily available elsewhere. 239 problems. Index. 1 figure. viii + 183pp. 5⅜ x 8. **S342 Paperbound $1.65**

ELEMENTS OF NUMBER THEORY, I. M. Vinogradov. Detailed 1st course for persons without advanced mathematics; 95% of this book can be understood by readers who have gone no farther than high school algebra. Partial contents: divisibility theory, important number theoretical functions, congruences, primitive roots and indices, etc. Solutions to both problems and exercises. Tables of primes, indices, etc. Covers almost every essential formula in elementary number theory! Translated from Russian. 233 problems, 104 exercises. viii + 227pp. 5⅜ x 8. **S259 Paperbound $1.60**

THEORY OF NUMBERS and DIOPHANTINE ANALYSIS, R. D. Carmichael. These two complete works in one volume form one of the most lucid introductions to number theory, requiring only a firm foundation in high school mathematics. "Theory of Numbers," partial contents: Eratosthenes' sieve, Euclid's fundamental theorem, G.C.F. and L.C.M. of two or more integers, linear congruences, etc "Diophantine Analysis": rational triangles, Pythagorean triangles, equations of third, fourth, higher degrees, method of functional equations, much more. "Theory of Numbers": 76 problems. Index. 94pp. "Diophantine Analysis": 222 problems. Index. 118pp. 5⅜ x 8. **S529 Paperbound $1.35**

Numerical analysis, tables

MATHEMATICAL TABLES AND FORMULAS, Compiled by Robert D. Carmichael and Edwin R. Smith. Valuable collection for students, etc. Contains all tables necessary in college algebra and trigonometry, such as five-place common logarithms, logarithmic sines and tangents of small angles, logarithmic trigonometric functions, natural trigonometric functions, four-place antilogarithms, tables for changing from sexagesimal to circular and from circular to sexagesimal measure of angles, etc. Also many tables and formulas not ordinarily accessible, including powers, roots, and reciprocals, exponential and hyperbolic functions, ten-place logarithms of prime numbers, and formulas and theorems from analytical and elementary geometry and from calculus. Explanatory introduction. viii + 269pp. 5⅜ x 8½. **S111 Paperbound $1.00**

MATHEMATICAL TABLES, H. B. Dwight. Unique for its coverage in one volume of almost every function of importance in applied mathematics, engineering, and the physical sciences. Three extremely fine tables of the three trig functions and their inverse functions to thousandths of radians; natural and common logarithms; squares, cubes; hyperbolic functions and the inverse hyperbolic functions; $(a^2 + b^2)$ exp. $\frac{1}{2}a$; complete elliptic integrals of the 1st and 2nd kind; sine and cosine integrals; exponential integrals Ei(x) and Ei(−x); binomial coefficients; factorials to 250; surface zonal harmonics and first derivatives; Bernoulli and Euler numbers and their logs to base of 10; Gamma function; normal probability integral; over 60 pages of Bessel functions; the Riemann Zeta function. Each table with formulae generally used, sources of more extensive tables, interpolation data, etc. Over half have columns of differences, to facilitate interpolation. Introduction. Index. viii + 231pp. 5⅜ x 8. **S445 Paperbound $1.75**

TABLES OF FUNCTIONS WITH FORMULAE AND CURVES, E. Jahnke & F. Emde. The world's most comprehensive 1-volume English-text collection of tables, formulae, curves of transcendent functions. 4th corrected edition, new 76-page section giving tables, formulae for elementary functions—not in other English editions. Partial contents: sine, cosine, logarithmic integral; factorial function; error integral; theta functions; elliptic integrals, functions; Legendre, Bessel, Riemann, Mathieu, hypergeometric functions, etc. Supplementary books. Bibliography. Indexed. "Out of the way functions for which we know no other source," SCIENTIFIC COMPUTING SERVICE, Ltd. 212 figures. 400pp. 5⅜ x 8. **S133 Paperbound $2.00**

CHEMISTRY AND PHYSICAL CHEMISTRY

ORGANIC CHEMISTRY, F. C. Whitmore. The entire subject of organic chemistry for the practicing chemist and the advanced student. Storehouse of facts, theories, processes found elsewhere only in specialized journals. Covers aliphatic compounds (500 pages on the properties and synthetic preparation of hydrocarbons, halides, proteins, ketones, etc.), alicyclic compounds, aromatic compounds, heterocyclic compounds, organophosphorus and organometallic compounds. Methods of synthetic preparation analyzed critically throughout. Includes much of biochemical interest. "The scope of this volume is astonishing," INDUSTRIAL AND ENGINEERING CHEMISTRY. 12,000-reference index. 2387-item bibliography. Total of x + 1005pp. 5⅜ x 8. Two volume set.

S700 Vol I Paperbound **$2.25**
S701 Vol II Paperbound **$2.25**
The set **$4.50**

THE MODERN THEORY OF MOLECULAR STRUCTURE, Bernard Pullman. A reasonably popular account of recent developments in atomic and molecular theory. Contents: The Wave Function and Wave Equations (history and bases of present theories of molecular structure); The Electronic Structure of Atoms (Description and classification of atomic wave functions, etc.); Diatomic Molecules; Non-Conjugated Polyatomic Molecules; Conjugated Polyatomic Molecules; The Structure of Complexes. Minimum of mathematical background needed. New translation by David Antin of "La Structure Moleculaire." Index. Bibliography. vii + 87pp. 5⅜ x 8½.

S987 Paperbound **$1.00**

CATALYSIS AND CATALYSTS, Marcel Prettre, Director, Research Institute on Catalysis. This brief book, translated into English for the first time, is the finest summary of the principal modern concepts, methods, and results of catalysis. Ideal introduction for beginning chemistry and physics students. Chapters: Basic Definitions of Catalysis (true catalysis and generalization of the concept of catalysis); The Scientific Bases of Catalysis (Catalysis and chemical thermodynamics, catalysis and chemical kinetics); Homogeneous Catalysis (acid-base catalysis, etc.); Chain Reactions; Contact Masses; Heterogeneous Catalysis (Mechanisms of contact catalyses, etc.); and Industrial Applications (acids and fertilizers, petroleum and petroleum chemistry, rubber, plastics, synthetic resins, and fibers). Translated by David Antin. Index. vi + 88pp. 5⅜ x 8½.

S998 Paperbound **$1.00**

POLAR MOLECULES, Pieter Debye. This work by Nobel laureate Debye offers a complete guide to fundamental electrostatic field relations, polarizability, molecular structure. Partial contents: electric intensity, displacement and force, polarization by orientation, molar polarization and molar refraction, halogen-hydrides, polar liquids, ionic saturation, dielectric constant, etc. Special chapter considers quantum theory. Indexed. 172pp. 5⅜ x 8.

S64 Paperbound **$1.50**

THE ELECTRONIC THEORY OF ACIDS AND BASES, W. F. Luder and Saverio Zuffanti. The first full systematic presentation of the electronic theory of acids and bases—treating the theory and its ramifications in an uncomplicated manner. Chapters: Historical Background; Atomic Orbitals and Valence; The Electronic Theory of Acids and Bases; Electrophilic and Electrodotic Reagents; Acidic and Basic Radicals; Neutralization; Titrations with Indicators; Displacement; Catalysis; Acid Catalysis; Base Catalysis; Alkoxides and Catalysts; Conclusion. Required reading for all chemists. Second revised (1961) eidtion, with additional examples and references. 3 figures. 9 tables. Index. Bibliography xii + 165pp. 5⅜ x 8.

S201 Paperbound **$1.50**

KINETIC THEORY OF LIQUIDS, J. Frenkel. Regarding the kinetic theory of liquids as a generalization and extension of the theory of solid bodies, this volume covers all types of arrangements of solids, thermal displacements of atoms, interstitial atoms and ions, orientational and rotational motion of molecules, and transition between states of matter. Mathematical theory is developed close to the physical subject matter. 216 bibliographical footnotes. 55 figures. xi + 485pp. 5⅜ x 8.

S95 Paperbound **$2.55**

THE PRINCIPLES OF ELECTROCHEMISTRY, D. A. MacInnes. Basic equations for almost every subfield of electrochemistry from first principles, referring at all times to the soundest and most recent theories and results; unusually useful as text or as reference. Covers coulometers and Faraday's Law, electrolytic conductance, the Debye-Hueckel method for the theoretical calculation of activity coefficients, concentration cells, standard electrode potentials, thermodynamic ionization constants, pH, potentiometric titrations, irreversible phenomena, Planck's equation, and much more. "Excellent treatise," AMERICAN CHEMICAL SOCIETY JOURNAL. "Highly recommended," CHEMICAL AND METALLURGICAL ENGINEERING. 2 Indices. Appendix. 585-item bibliography. 137 figures. 94 tables. ii + 478pp. 5⅝ x 8⅜.

S52 Paperbound **$2.45**

THE PHASE RULE AND ITS APPLICATION, Alexander Findlay. Covering chemical phenomena of 1, 2, 3, 4, and multiple component systems, this "standard work on the subject" (NATURE, London), has been completely revised and brought up to date by A. N. Campbell and N. O. Smith. Brand new material has been added on such matters as binary, tertiary liquid equilibria, solid solutions in ternary systems, quinary systems of salts and water. Completely revised to triangular coordinates in ternary systems, clarified graphic representation, solid models, etc. 9th revised edition. Author, subject indexes. 236 figures. 505 footnotes, mostly bibliographic. xii + 494pp. 5⅜ x 8.

S91 Paperbound **$2.50**

PHYSICS

General physics

FOUNDATIONS OF PHYSICS, R. B. Lindsay & H. Margenau. Excellent bridge between semi-popular works & technical treatises. A discussion of methods of physical description, construction of theory; valuable for physicist with elementary calculus who is interested in ideas that give meaning to data, tools of modern physics. Contents include symbolism, mathematical equations; space & time foundations of mechanics; probability; physics & continua; electron theory; special & general relativity; quantum mechanics; causality. "Thorough and yet not overdetailed. Unreservedly recommended," NATURE (London). Unabridged, corrected edition. List of recommended readings. 35 illustrations. xi + 537pp. 5⅜ x 8.
S377 Paperbound **$2.75**

FUNDAMENTAL FORMULAS OF PHYSICS, ed. by D. H. Menzel. Highly useful, fully inexpensive reference and study text, ranging from simple to highly sophisticated operations. Mathematics integrated into text—each chapter stands as short textbook of field represented. Vol. 1: Statistics, Physical Constants, Special Theory of Relativity, Hydrodynamics, Aerodynamics, Boundary Value Problems in Math. Physics; Viscosity, Electromagnetic Theory, etc. Vol. 2: Sound, Acoustics, Geometrical Optics, Electron Optics, High-Energy Phenomena, Magnetism, Biophysics, much more. Index. Total of 800pp. 5⅜ x 8.
Vol. 1 S595 Paperbound **$2.00**
Vol. 2 S596 Paperbound **$2.00**

MATHEMATICAL PHYSICS, D. H. Menzel. Thorough one-volume treatment of the mathematical techniques vital for classic mechanics, electromagnetic theory, quantum theory, and relativity. Written by the Harvard Professor of Astrophysics for junior, senior, and graduate courses, it gives clear explanations of all those aspects of function theory, vectors, matrices, dyadics, tensors, partial differential equations, etc., necessary for the understanding of the various physical theories. Electron theory, relativity, and other topics seldom presented appear here in considerable detail. Scores of definitions, conversion factors, dimensional constants, etc. "More detailed than normal for an advanced text . . . excellent set of sections on Dyadics, Matrices, and Tensors," JOURNAL OF THE FRANKLIN INSTITUTE. Index. 193 problems, with answers. x + 412pp. 5⅜ x 8.
S56 Paperbound **$2.00**

THE SCIENTIFIC PAPERS OF J. WILLARD GIBBS. All the published papers of America's outstanding theoretical scientist (except for "Statistical Mechanics" and "Vector Analysis"). Vol I (thermodynamics) contains one of the most brilliant of all 19th-century scientific papers—the 300-page "On the Equilibrium of Heterogeneous Substances," which founded the science of physical chemistry, and clearly stated a number of highly important natural laws for the first time; 8 other papers complete the first volume. Vol II includes 2 papers on dynamics, 8 on vector analysis and multiple algebra, 5 on the electromagnetic theory of light, and 6 miscellaneous papers. Biographical sketch by H. A. Bumstead. Total of xxxvi + 718pp. 5⅝ x 8⅜.
S721 Vol I Paperbound **$2.50**
S722 Vol II Paperbound **$2.00**
The set **$4.50**

BASIC THEORIES OF PHYSICS, Peter Gabriel Bergmann. Two-volume set which presents a critical examination of important topics in the major subdivisions of classical and modern physics. The first volume is concerned with classical mechanics and electrodynamics: mechanics of mass points, analytical mechanics, matter in bulk, electrostatics and magnetostatics, electromagnetic interaction, the field waves, special relativity, and waves. The second volume (Heat and Quanta) contains discussions of the kinetic hypothesis, physics and statistics, stationary ensembles, laws of thermodynamics, early quantum theories, atomic spectra, probability waves, quantization in wave mechanics, approximation methods, and abstract quantum theory. A valuable supplement to any thorough course or text.
Heat and Quanta: Index. 8 figures. x + 300pp. 5⅜ x 8½.   S968 Paperbound **$1.75**
Mechanics and Electrodynamics: Index. 14 figures. vii + 280pp. 5⅜ x 8½.
S969 Paperbound **$1.75**

THEORETICAL PHYSICS, A. S. Kompaneyets. One of the very few thorough studies of the subject in this price range. Provides advanced students with a comprehensive theoretical background. Especially strong on recent experimentation and developments in quantum theory. Contents: Mechanics (Generalized Coordinates, Lagrange's Equation, Collision of Particles, etc.), Electrodynamics (Vector Analysis, Maxwell's equations, Transmission of Signals, Theory of Relativity, etc.), Quantum Mechanics (the Inadequacy of Classical Mechanics, the Wave Equation, Motion in a Central Field, Quantum Theory of Radiation, Quantum Theories of Dispersion and Scattering, etc.), and Statistical Physics (Equilibrium Distribution of Molecules in an Ideal Gas, Boltzmann statistics, Bose and Fermi Distribution, Thermodynamic Quantities, etc.). Revised to 1961. Translated by George Yankovsky, authorized by Kompaneyets. 137 exercises. 56 figures. 529pp. 5⅜ x 8½. S972 Paperbound **$2.50**

ANALYTICAL AND CANONICAL FORMALISM IN PHYSICS, André Mercier. A survey, in one volume, of the variational principles (the key principles—in mathematical form—from which the basic laws of any one branch of physics can be derived) of the several branches of physical theory, together with an examination of the relationships among them. Contents: the Lagrangian Formalism, Lagrangian Densities, Canonical Formalism, Canonical Form of Electrodynamics, Hamiltonian Densities, Transformations, and Canonical Form with Vanishing Jacobian Determinant. Numerous examples and exercises. For advanced students, teachers, etc. 6 figures. Index. viii + 222pp. 5⅜ x 8½.   S1077 Paperbound **$1.75**

MATHEMATICAL PUZZLES AND RECREATIONS

AMUSEMENTS IN MATHEMATICS, Henry Ernest Dudeney. The foremost British originator of mathematical puzzles is always intriguing, witty, and paradoxical in this classic, one of the largest collections of mathematical amusements. More than 430 puzzles, problems, and paradoxes. Mazes and games, problems on number manipulation, unicursal and other route problems, puzzles on measuring, weighing, packing, age, kinship, chessboards, joining, crossing river, plane figure dissection, and many others. Solutions. More than 450 illustrations. vii + 258pp. 5⅜ x 8.   T473 Paperbound **$1.25**

SYMBOLIC LOGIC and THE GAME OF LOGIC, Lewis Carroll. "Symbolic Logic" is not concerned with modern symbolic logic, but is instead a collection of over 380 problems posed with charm and imagination, using the syllogism, and a fascinating diagrammatic method of drawing conclusions. In "The Game of Logic," Carroll's whimsical imagination devises a logical game played with 2 diagrams and counters (included) to manipulate hundreds of tricky syllogisms. The final section, "Hit or Miss" is a lagniappe of 101 additional puzzles in the delightful Carroll manner. Until this reprint edition, both of these books were rarities costing up to $15 each. Symbolic Logic: Index, xxxi + 199pp. The Game of Logic: 96pp. Two vols. bound as one. 5⅜ x 8.   T492 Paperbound **$1.50**

MAZES AND LABYRINTHS: A BOOK OF PUZZLES, W. Shepherd. Mazes, formerly associated with mystery and ritual, are still among the most intriguing of intellectual puzzles. This is a novel and different collection of 50 amusements that embody the principle of the maze: mazes in the classical tradition; 3-dimensional, ribbon, and Möbius-strip mazes; hidden messages; spatial arrangements; etc.—almost all built on amusing story situations. 84 illustrations. Essay on maze psychology. Solutions. xv + 122pp. 5⅜ x 8.   T731 Paperbound **$1.00**

MATHEMATICAL RECREATIONS, M. Kraitchik. Some 250 puzzles, problems, demonstrations of recreational mathematics for beginners & advanced mathematicians. Unusual historical problems from Greek, Medieval, Arabic, Hindu sources; modern problems based on "mathematics without numbers," geometry, topology, arithmetic, etc. Pastimes derived from figurative numbers, Mersenne numbers, Fermat numbers; fairy chess, latruncles, reversi, many topics. Full solutions. Excellent for insights into special fields of math. 181 illustrations. 330pp. 5⅜ x 8.   T163 Paperbound **$1.75**

MATHEMATICAL PUZZLES OF SAM LOYD, Vol. I, selected and edited by M. Gardner. Puzzles by the greatest puzzle creator and innovator. Selected from his famous "Cyclopedia of Puzzles," they retain the unique style and historical flavor of the originals. There are posers based on arithmetic, algebra, probability, game theory, route tracing, topology, counter, sliding block, operations research, geometrical dissection. Includes his famous "14-15" puzzle which was a national craze, and his "Horse of a Different Color" which sold millions of copies. 117 of his most ingenious puzzles in all, 120 line drawings and diagrams. Solutions. Selected references. xx + 167pp. 5⅜ x 8.   T498 Paperbound **$1.00**

MY BEST PUZZLES IN MATHEMATICS, Hubert Phillips ("Caliban"). Caliban is generally considered the best of the modern problemists. Here are 100 of his best and wittiest puzzles, selected by the author himself from such publications as the London Daily Telegraph, and each puzzle is guaranteed to put even the sharpest puzzle detective through his paces. Perfect for the development of clear thinking and a logical mind. Complete solutions are provided for every puzzle. x + 107pp. 5⅜ x 8½.   T91 Paperbound **$1.00**

MY BEST PUZZLES IN LOGIC AND REASONING, H. Phillips ("Caliban"). 100 choice, hitherto unavailable puzzles by England's best-known problemist. No special knowledge needed to solve these logical or inferential problems, just an unclouded mind, nerves of steel, and fast reflexes. Data presented are both necessary and just sufficient to allow one unambiguous answer. More than 30 different types of puzzles, all ingenious and varied, many one of a kind, that will challenge the expert, please the beginner. Original publication. 100 puzzles, full solutions. x + 107pp. 5⅜ x 8½.   T119 Paperbound **$1.00**

MATHEMATICAL PUZZLES FOR BEGINNERS AND ENTHUSIASTS, G. Mott-Smith. 188 mathematical puzzles to test mental agility. Inference, interpretation, algebra, dissection of plane figures, geometry, properties of numbers, decimation, permutations, probability, all enter these delightful problems. Puzzles like the Odic Force, How to Draw an Ellipse, Spider's Cousin, more than 180 others. Detailed solutions. Appendix with square roots, triangular numbers, primes, etc. 135 illustrations. 2nd revised edition. 248pp. 5⅜ x 8.   T198 Paperbound **$1.00**

MATHEMATICS, MAGIC AND MYSTERY, Martin Gardner. Card tricks, feats of mental mathematics, stage mind-reading, other "magic" explained as applications of probability, sets, theory of numbers, topology, various branches of mathematics. Creative examination of laws and their applications with scores of new tricks and insights. 115 sections discuss tricks with cards, dice, coins; geometrical vanishing tricks, dozens of others. No sleight of hand needed; mathematics guarantees success. 115 illustrations. xii + 174pp. 5⅜ x 8.   T335 Paperbound **$1.00**

CATALOGUE OF DOVER BOOKS

RECREATIONS IN THE THEORY OF NUMBERS: THE QUEEN OF MATHEMATICS ENTERTAINS, Albert H. Beiler. The theory of numbers is often referred to as the "Queen of Mathematics." In this book Mr. Beiler has compiled the first English volume to deal exclusively with the recreational aspects of number theory, an inherently recreational branch of mathematics. The author's clear style makes for enjoyable reading as he deals with such topics as: perfect numbers, amicable numbers, Fermat's theorem, Wilson's theorem, interesting properties of digits, methods of factoring, primitive roots, Euler's function, polygonal and figurate numbers, Mersenne numbers, congruence, repeating decimals, etc. Countless puzzle problems, with full answers and explanations. For mathematicians and mathematically-inclined laymen, etc. New publication. 28 figures. 9 illustrations. 103 tables. Bibliography at chapter ends. vi + 247pp. 5⅜ x 8½.   T1096 Paperbound **$1.85**

PAPER FOLDING FOR BEGINNERS, W. D. Murray and F. J. Rigney. A delightful introduction to the varied and entertaining Japanese art of origami (paper folding), with a full crystal-clear text that anticipates every difficulty; over 275 clearly labeled diagrams of all important stages in creation. You get results at each stage, since complex figures are logically developed from simpler ones. 43 different pieces are explained: place mats, drinking cups, bonbon boxes, sailboats, frogs, roosters, etc. 6 photographic plates. 279 diagrams. 95pp. 5⅝ x 8⅜.
                                                                       T713 Paperbound **$1.00**

1800 RIDDLES, ENIGMAS AND CONUNDRUMS, Darwin A. Hindman. Entertaining collection ranging from hilarious gags to outrageous puns to sheer nonsense—a welcome respite from sophisticated humor. Children, toastmasters, and practically anyone with a funny bone will find these zany riddles tickling and eminently repeatable. Sample: "Why does Santa Claus always go down the chimney?" "Because it soots him." Some old, some new—covering a wide variety of subjects. New publication. iii + 154pp. 5⅜ x 8½. T1059 Paperbound **$1.00**

EASY-TO-DO ENTERTAINMENTS AND DIVERSIONS WITH CARDS, STRING, COINS, PAPER AND MATCHES, R. M. Abraham. Over 300 entertaining games, tricks, puzzles, and pastimes for children and adults. Invaluable to anyone in charge of groups of youngsters, for party givers, etc. Contains sections on card tricks and games, making things by paperfolding—toys, decorations, and the like; tricks with coins, matches, and pieces of string; descriptions of games; toys that can be made from common household objects; mathematical recreations; word games; and 50 miscellaneous entertainments. Formerly "Winter Nights Entertainments." Introduction by Lord Baden Powell. 329 illustrations. v + 186pp. 5⅜ x 8.
                                                                       T921 Paperbound **$1.00**

DIVERSIONS AND PASTIMES WITH CARDS, STRING, PAPER AND MATCHES, R. M. Abraham. Another collection of amusements and diversion for game and puzzle fans of all ages. Many new paperfolding ideas and tricks, an extensive section on amusements with knots and splices, two chapters of easy and not-so-easy problems, coin and match tricks, and lots of other parlor pastimes from the agile mind of the late British problemist and gamester. Corrected and revised version. Illustrations. 160pp. 5⅜ x 8½. T1127 Paperbound **$1.00**

STRING FIGURES AND HOW TO MAKE THEM: A STUDY OF CAT'S-CRADLE IN MANY LANDS, Caroline Furness Jayne. In a simple and easy-to-follow manner, this book describes how to make 107 different string figures. Not only is looping and crossing string between the fingers a common youthful diversion, but it is an ancient form of amusement practiced in all parts of the globe, especially popular among primitive tribes. These games are fun for all ages and offer an excellent means for developing manual dexterity and coordination. Much insight also for the anthropological observer on games and diversions in many different cultures. Index. Bibliography. Introduction by A. C. Haddon, Cambridge University. 17 full-page plates. 950 illustrations. xxiii + 407pp. 5⅜ x 8½.   T152 Paperbound **$2.00**

CRYPTANALYSIS, Helen F. Gaines. (Formerly ELEMENTARY CRYPTANALYSIS.) A standard elementary and intermediate text for serious students. It does not confine itself to old material, but contains much that is not generally known, except to experts. Concealment, Transposition, Substitution ciphers; Vigenere, Kasiski, Playfair, multafid, dozens of other techniques. Appendix with sequence charts, letter frequencies in English, 5 other languages, English word frequencies. Bibliography. 167 codes. New to this edition: solution to codes. vi + 230pp. 5⅜ x 8.   T97 Paperbound **$2.00**

MAGIC SQUARES AND CUBES, W. S. Andrews. Only book-length treatment in English, a thorough non-technical description and analysis. Here are nasik, overlapping, pandiagonal, serrated squares; magic circles, cubes, spheres, rhombuses. Try your hand at 4-dimensional magical figures! Much unusual folklore and tradition included. High school algebra is sufficient. 754 diagrams and illustrations. viii + 419pp. 5⅜ x 8.   T658 Paperbound **$1.85**

CALIBAN'S PROBLEM BOOK: MATHEMATICAL, INFERENTIAL, AND CRYPTOGRAPHIC PUZZLES, H. Phillips ("Caliban"), S. T. Shovelton, G. S. Marshall. 105 ingenious problems by the greatest living creator of puzzles based on logic and inference. Rigorous, modern, piquant, and reflecting their author's unusual personality, these intermediate and advanced puzzles all involve the ability to reason clearly through complex situations; some call for mathematical knowledge, ranging from algebra to number theory. Solutions. xi + 180pp. 5⅜ x 8.
                                                                       T736 Paperbound **$1.25**

FICTION

THE LAND THAT TIME FORGOT and THE MOON MAID, Edgar Rice Burroughs. In the opinion of many, Burroughs' best work. The first concerns a strange island where evolution is individual rather than phylogenetic. Speechless anthropoids develop into intelligent human beings within a single generation. The second projects the reader far into the future and describes the first voyage to the Moon (in the year 2025), the conquest of the Earth by the Moon, and years of violence and adventure as the enslaved Earthmen try to regain possession of their planet. "An imaginative tour de force that keeps the reader keyed up and expectant," NEW YORK TIMES. Complete, unabridged text of the original two novels (three parts in each). 5 illustrations by J. Allen St. John. vi + 552pp. 5⅜ x 8½.
T1020 Clothbound **$3.75**
T358 Paperbound **$2.00**

AT THE EARTH'S CORE, PELLUCIDAR, TANAR OF PELLUCIDAR: THREE SCIENCE FICTION NOVELS BY EDGAR RICE BURROUGHS. Complete, unabridged texts of the first three Pellucidar novels. Tales of derring-do by the famous master of science fiction. The locale for these three related stories is the inner surface of the hollow Earth where we discover the world of Pellucidar, complete with all types of bizarre, menacing creatures, strange peoples, and alluring maidens—guaranteed to delight all Burroughs fans and a wide circle of adventure lovers. Illustrated by J. Allen St. John and P. F. Berdanier. vi + 433pp. 5⅜ x 8½.
T1051 Paperbound **$2.00**

THE PIRATES OF VENUS and LOST ON VENUS: TWO VENUS NOVELS BY EDGAR RICE BURROUGHS. Two related novels, complete and unabridged. Exciting adventure on the planet Venus with Earthman Carson Napier broken-field running through one dangerous episode after another. All lovers of swashbuckling science fiction will enjoy these two stories set in a world of fascinating societies, fierce beasts, 5000-ft. trees, lush vegetation, and wide seas. Illustrations by Fortunino Matania. Total of vi + 340pp. 5⅜ x 8½.
T1053 Paperbound **$1.75**

A PRINCESS OF MARS and A FIGHTING MAN OF MARS: TWO MARTIAN NOVELS BY EDGAR RICE BURROUGHS. "Princess of Mars" is the very first of the great Martian novels written by Burroughs, and it is probably the best of them all; it set the pattern for all of his later fantasy novels and contains a thrilling cast of strange peoples and creatures and the formula of Olympian heroism amidst ever-fluctuating fortunes which Burroughs carries off so successfully. "Fighting Man" returns to the same scenes and cities—many years later. A mad scientist, a degenerate dictator, and an indomitable defender of the right clash—with the fate of the Red Planet at stake! Complete, unabridged reprinting of original editions. Illustrations by F. E. Schoonover and Hugh Hutton. v + 356pp. 5⅜ x 8½.
T1140 Paperbound **$1.75**

THREE MARTIAN NOVELS, Edgar Rice Burroughs. Contains: Thuvia, Maid of Mars; The Chessmen of Mars; and The Master Mind of Mars. High adventure set in an imaginative and intricate conception of the Red Planet. Mars is peopled with an intelligent, heroic human race which lives in densely populated cities and with fierce barbarians who inhabit dead sea bottoms. Other exciting creatures abound amidst an inventive framework of Martian history and geography. Complete unabridged reprintings of the first edition. 16 illustrations by J. Allen St. John. vi + 499pp. 5⅜ x 8½.
T39 Paperbound **$1.85**

THREE PROPHETIC NOVELS BY H. G. WELLS, edited by E. F. Bleiler. Complete texts of "When the Sleeper Wakes" (1st book printing in 50 years), "A Story of the Days to Come," "The Time Machine" (1st complete printing in book form). Exciting adventures in the future are as enjoyable today as 50 years ago when first printed. Predict TV, movies, intercontinental airplanes, prefabricated houses, air-conditioned cities, etc. First important author to foresee problems of mind control, technological dictatorships. "Absolute best of imaginative fiction," N. Y. Times. Introduction. 335pp. 5⅜ x 8.
T605 Paperbound **$1.50**

28 SCIENCE FICTION STORIES OF H. G. WELLS. Two full unabridged novels, MEN LIKE GODS and STAR BEGOTTEN, plus 26 short stories by the master science-fiction writer of all time. Stories of space, time, invention, exploration, future adventure—an indispensable part of the library of everyone interested in science and adventure. PARTIAL CONTENTS: Men Like Gods, The Country of the Blind, In the Abyss, The Crystal Egg, The Man Who Could Work Miracles, A Story of the Days to Come, The Valley of Spiders, and 21 more! 928pp. 5⅜ x 8.
T265 Clothbound **$4.50**

THE WAR IN THE AIR, IN THE DAYS OF THE COMET, THE FOOD OF THE GODS: THREE SCIENCE FICTION NOVELS BY H. G. WELLS. Three exciting Wells offerings bearing on vital social and philosophical issues of his and our own day. Here are tales of air power, strategic bombing, East vs. West, the potential miracles of science, the potential disasters from outer space, the relationship between scientific advancement and moral progress, etc. First reprinting of "War in the Air" in almost 50 years. An excellent sampling of Wells at his storytelling best. Complete, unabridged reprintings. 16 illustrations. 645pp. 5⅜ x 8½.
T1135 Paperbound **$2.00**

CATALOGUE OF DOVER BOOKS

SEVEN SCIENCE FICTION NOVELS, H. G. Wells. Full unabridged texts of 7 science-fiction novels of the master. Ranging from biology, physics, chemistry, astronomy to sociology and other studies, Mr. Wells extrapolates whole worlds of strange and intriguing character. "One will have to go far to match this for entertainment, excitement, and sheer pleasure . . . ," NEW YORK TIMES. Contents: The Time Machine, The Island of Dr. Moreau, First Men in the Moon, The Invisible Man, The War of the Worlds, The Food of the Gods, In the Days of the Comet. 1015pp. 5⅜ x 8. T264 Clothbound **$4.50**

BEST GHOST STORIES OF J. S. LE FANU, Selected and introduced by E. F. Bleiler. LeFanu is deemed the greatest name in Victorian supernatural fiction. Here are 16 of his best horror stories, including 2 nouvelles: "Carmilla," a classic vampire tale couched in a perverse eroticism, and "The Haunted Baronet." Also: "Sir Toby's Will," "Green Tea," "Schalken the Painter," "Ultor de Lacy," "The Familiar," etc. The first American publication of about half of this material: a long-overdue opportunity to get a choice sampling of LeFanu's work. New selection (1964). 8 illustrations. 5⅜ x 8⅜. T415 Paperbound **$1.85**

THE WONDERFUL WIZARD OF OZ, L. F. Baum. Only edition in print with all the original W. W. Denslow illustrations in full color—as much a part of "The Wizard" as Tenniel's drawings are for "Alice in Wonderland." "The Wizard" is still America's best-loved fairy tale, in which, as the author expresses it, "The wonderment and joy are retained and the heartaches and nightmares left out." Now today's young readers can enjoy every word and wonderful picture of the original book. New introduction by Martin Gardner. A Baum bibliography. 23 full-page color plates. viii + 268pp. 5⅜ x 8. T691 Paperbound **$1.50**

GHOST AND HORROR STORIES OF AMBROSE BIERCE, Selected and introduced by E. F. Bleiler. 24 morbid, eerie tales—the cream of Bierce's fiction output. Contains such memorable pieces as "The Moonlit Road," "The Damned Thing," "An Inhabitant of Carcosa," "The Eyes of the Panther," "The Famous Gilson Bequest," "The Middle Toe of the Right Foot," and other chilling stories, plus the essay, "Visions of the Night" in which Bierce gives us a kind of rationale for his aesthetic of horror. New collection (1964). xxii + 199pp. 5⅜ x 8⅜. T767 Paperbound **$1.00**

HUMOR

MR. DOOLEY ON IVRYTHING AND IVRYBODY, Finley Peter Dunne. Since the time of his appearance in 1893, "Mr. Dooley," the fictitious Chicago bartender, has been recognized as America's most humorous social and political commentator. Collected in this volume are 102 of the best Dooley pieces—all written around the turn of the century, the height of his popularity. Mr. Dooley's Irish brogue is employed wittily and penetratingly on subjects which are just as fresh and relevant today as they were then: corruption and hypocrisy of politicans, war preparations and chauvinism, automation, Latin American affairs, superbombs, etc. Other articles range from Rudyard Kipling to football. Selected with an introduction by Robert Hutchinson. xii + 244pp. 5⅜ x 8½. T626 Paperbound **$1.00**

RUTHLESS RHYMES FOR HEARTLESS HOMES and MORE RUTHLESS RHYMES FOR HEARTLESS HOMES, Harry Graham ("Col. D. Streamer"). A collection of Little Willy and 48 other poetic "disasters." Graham's funniest and most disrespectful verse, accompanied by original illustrations. Nonsensical, wry humor which employs stern parents, careless nurses, uninhibited children, practical jokers, single-minded golfers, Scottish lairds, etc. in the leading roles. A precursor of the "sick joke" school of today. This volume contains, bound together for the first time, two of the most perennially popular books of humor in England and America. Index. vi + 69pp. 5⅜ x 8. T930 Paperbound **75¢**

A WHIMSEY ANTHOLOGY, Collected by Carolyn Wells. 250 of the most amusing rhymes ever written. Acrostics, anagrams, palindromes, alphabetical jingles, tongue twisters, echo verses, alliterative verses, riddles, mnemonic rhymes, interior rhymes, over 40 limericks, etc. by Lewis Carroll, Edward Lear, Joseph Addison, W. S. Gilbert, Christina Rossetti, Chas. Lamb, James Boswell, Hood, Dickens, Swinburne, Leigh Hunt, Harry Graham, Poe, Eugene Field, and many others. xiv + 221pp. 5⅜ x 8½. T195 Paperbound **$1.25**

MY PIOUS FRIENDS AND DRUNKEN COMPANIONS and MORE PIOUS FRIENDS AND DRUNKEN COMPANIONS, Songs and ballads of Conviviality Collected by Frank Shay. Magnificently illuminated by John Held, Jr. 132 ballads, blues, vaudeville numbers, drinking songs, cowboy songs, sea chanties, comedy songs, etc. of the Naughty Nineties and early 20th century. Over a third are reprinted with music. Many perennial favorites such as: The Band Played On, Frankie and Johnnie, The Old Grey Mare, The Face on the Bar-room Floor, etc. Many others unlocatable elsewhere: The Dog-Catcher's Child, The Cannibal Maiden, Don't Go in the Lion's Cage Tonight, Mother, etc. Complete verses and introductions to songs. Unabridged republication of first editions, 2 Indexes (song titles and first lines and choruses). Introduction by Frank Shay. 2 volumes bounds as 1. Total of xvi + 235pp. 5⅜ x 8½. T946 Paperbound **$1.25**

CATALOGUE OF DOVER BOOKS

MAX AND MORITZ, Wilhelm Busch. Edited and annotated by H. Arthur Klein. Translated by H. Arthur Klein, M. C. Klein, and others. The mischievous high jinks of Max and Moritz, Peter and Paul, Ker and Plunk, etc. are delightfully captured in sketch and rhyme. (Companion volume to "Hypocritical Helena.") In addition to the title piece, it contians: Ker and Plunk; Two Dogs and Two Boys; The Egghead and the Two Cut-ups of Corinth; Deceitful Henry; The Boys and the Pipe; Cat and Mouse; and others. (Original German text with accompanying English translations.) Afterword by H. A. Klein. vi + 216pp. 5⅜ x 8½.
T181 Paperbound **$1.15**

THROUGH THE ALIMENTARY CANAL WITH GUN AND CAMERA: A FASCINATING TRIP TO THE INTERIOR, Personally Conducted by George S. Chappell. In mock-travelogue style, the amusing account of an imaginative journey down the alimentary canal. The "explorers" enter the esophagus, round the Adam's Apple, narrowly escape from a fierce Amoeba, struggle through the impenetrable Nerve Forests of the Lumbar Region, etc. Illustrated by the famous cartoonist, Otto Soglow, the book is as much a brilliant satire of academic pomposity and professional travel literature as it is a clever use of the facts of physiology for supremely comic purposes. Preface by Robert Benchley. Author's Foreword. 1 Photograph. 17 illustrations by O. Soglow. xii + 114pp. 5⅜ x 8½.
T376 Paperbound **$1.00**

THE BAD CHILD'S BOOK OF BEASTS, MORE BEASTS FOR WORSE CHILDREN, and A MORAL ALPHABET, H. Belloc. Hardly an anthology of humorous verse has appeared in the last 50 years without at least a couple of these famous nonsense verses. But one must see the entire volumes—with all the delightful original illustrations by Sir Basil Blackwood—to appreciate fully Belloc's charming and witty verses that play so subacidly on the platitudes of life and morals that beset his day—and ours. A great humor classic. Three books in one. Total of 157pp. 5⅜ x 8.
T749 Paperbound **$1.00**

THE DEVIL'S DICTIONARY, Ambrose Bierce. Sardonic and irreverent barbs puncturing the pomposities and absurdities of American politics, business, religion, literature, and arts, by the country's greatest satirist in the classic tradition. Epigrammatic as Shaw, piercing as Swift, American as Mark Twain, Will Rogers, and Fred Allen. Bierce will always remain the favorite of a small coterie of enthusiasts, and of writers and speakers whom he supplies with "some of the most gorgeous witticisms of the English language." (H. L. Mencken) Over 1000 entries in alphabetical order. 144pp. 5⅜ x 8.
T487 Paperbound **$1.00**

THE COMPLETE NONSENSE OF EDWARD LEAR. This is the only complete edition of this master of gentle madness available at a popular price. A BOOK OF NONSENSE, NONSENSE SONGS, MORE NONSENSE SONGS AND STORIES in their entirety with all the old favorites that have delighted children and adults for years. The Dong With A Luminous Nose, The Jumblies, The Owl and the Pussycat, and hundreds of other bits of wonderful nonsense. 214 limericks, 3 sets of Nonsense Botany, 5 Nonsense Alphabets. 546 drawings by Lear himself, and much more. 320pp. 5⅜ x 8.
T167 Paperbound **$1.00**

SINGULAR TRAVELS, CAMPAIGNS, AND ADVENTURES OF BARON MUNCHAUSEN, R. E. Raspe, with 90 illustrations by Gustave Doré. The first edition in over 150 years to reestablish the deeds of the Prince of Liars exactly as Raspe first recorded them in 1785—the genuine Baron Munchausen, one of the most popular personalities in English literature. Included also are the best of the many sequels, written by other hands. Introduction on Raspe by J. Carswell. Bibliography of early editions. xliv + 192pp. 5⅜ x 8. T698 Paperbound **$1.00**

HOW TO TELL THE BIRDS FROM THE FLOWERS, R. W. Wood. How not to confuse a carrot with a parrot, a grape with an ape, a puffin with nuffin. Delightful drawings, clever puns, absurd little poems point out farfetched resemblances in nature. The author was a leading physicist. Introduction by Margaret Wood White. 106 illus. 60pp. 5⅜ x 8.
T523 Paperbound **75¢**

JOE MILLER'S JESTS OR, THE WITS VADE-MECUM. The original Joe Miller jest book. Gives a keen and pungent impression of life in 18th-century England. Many are somewhat on the bawdy side and they are still capable of provoking amusement and good fun. This volume is a facsimile of the original "Joe Miller" first published in 1739. It remains the most popular and influential humor book of all time. New introduction by Robert Hutchinson. xxi + 70pp. 5⅜ x 8½.
T423 Paperbound **$1.00**

Prices subject to change without notice.

Dover publishes books on art, music, philosophy, literature, languages, history, social sciences, psychology, handcrafts, orientalia, puzzles and entertainments, chess, pets and gardens, books explaining science, intermediate and higher mathematics, mathematical physics, engineering, biological sciences, earth sciences, classics of science, etc. Write to:

Dept. catrr.
Dover Publications, Inc.
180 Varick Street, N.Y. 14, N.Y.

24884

DATE DUE

Henning			